Alternative Fuels

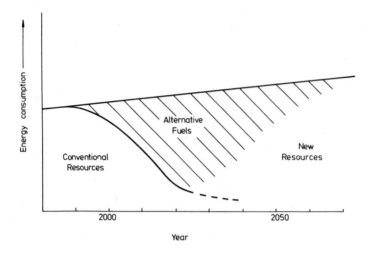

ALTERNATIVE FUELS
Chemical Energy Resources

E. M. GOODGER

Ph.D., M.Sc. (Eng.), C.Eng.,
M.I.Mech.E., M.I.E.Aust., M.R.Ae.S.,
F.Inst.E., F.Inst.Pet.

Cranfield Institute of Technology

*Sometime Professor of Mechanical Engineering,
The University of Newcastle, N.S.W., Australia*

First published 1980 by
THE MACMILLAN PRESS LTD
London and Basingstoke
Associated companies in Delhi Dublin
Hong Kong Johannesburg Lagos Melbourne
New York Singapore and Tokyo

Typeset in 10/12 Press Roman by
STYLESET LIMITED
Salisbury · Wiltshire
and printed in Hong Kong

British Library Cataloguing in Publication Data

Goodger, E M
    Alternative fuels.
    1. Fuel
    I. Title
    662'.6   TP318

    ISBN 0−333−25813−4

Contents

Preface

The whole concept of energy, its resources and consumption, was brought sharply into relief late in 1973 when the Western world was faced with massive increases in price and, on occasions, actual shortfalls in supplies. The end of the era of 'cheap energy' has been proclaimed frequently ever since, and predictions of future energy patterns and policies have featured in all forms of discussion, debate and dissemination. The vital nature of an assured supply of energy, at realistic costs, has now been recognised for the continuation, let alone development, of our lifestyles, and concern is felt by many over the impending gap which appears to be inevitable at the turn of this century between the eventual demise of some conventional fossil fuels, and the emergence of long-term replacements. Throughout the world, many active research programmes are directed towards the long-term harnessing of alternative sources of energy including wind, waves, tides, geothermal, direct solar radiation and nuclear fusion. From the viewpoint of fuel, as distinct from overall energy, this gap may well be postponed by the more logical conversion and use of the more enduring and available fossil-based fuels, and eventually filled to a large extent by means of fuels derived from alternative, replenishable sources. Both actions will help to provide a 'breathing period' for further development of alternative sources of energy.

This present work attempts to explore briefly the candidate alternative chemical fuels, in terms of their nature, availability, production, properties, combustion performance, emission characteristics, handling problems and, tentatively, possible future costs. It concerns fuels intended for oxidation only, either via combustion or by direct conversion in a fuel cell, and so excludes nuclear fuels and also the wider remit of alternative energy sources. In general, the fuels considered are by no means newcomers to the energy scene, but the incentive in the past has been to seek improved performance, whereas the present criterion is for continuing availability, with reasonable performance as an important but secondary issue.

For each geographical region at any given time, certain practices will be well established and classed as conventional, whereas others are either new or projected, and thus alternative. As these new practices themselves achieve wide acceptance, they also become conventional, and the projected, if successful, become new. The dividing lines between these classes are not always clearly definable, and some fuels considered here may well have become commonplace in some parts of the world by the time the printing ink is dry! However, since a background picture of conventional fuels is essential as a comparative base from which to assess the potential of the alternative fuels, a brief review of conventional fuels is given in the early part of the book, and the dividing line between these two main types of fuel can be imagined steadily working its way through the book with the passage of time as the alternatives graduate to the conventional.

Energy, economics and the environment are inseparably linked within a modern society, and must be considered together in future planning. Limitation in demand by energy thrift, and protection of the environment from combustion-generated pollutants, are equally necessary. However, it was decided at the outset of this project to concentrate on the technical potential of alternative fuels as a stop-gap prior to the emergence of some new and copious energy source, and to refer only occasionally to the other related topics, which are dealt with in detail elsewhere.

As shown by the chapter headings, the layout of the book consists essentially of an initial background survey of conventional fuels, followed by a suggested classification of the alternative fuels of interest. After reviewing the theoretical and likely practical combustion processes of these alternatives, a summary is made of their reported laboratory and field performance in various types of combustor. Complementary data on the handling characteristics of these fuels are then examined, and the work concludes with a summary of the techniques proposed for the future production of the most promising of the alternative fuels, together with some forecasts of possible fuel utilisation patterns in the major energy-consuming sectors, and fuel costs. For ease of reference, all the major chemical reactions are numbered consecutively. A more detailed treatment of the book layout is made the subject of the introductory chapter.

By illustrating the range and availability of the various types of alternative fuel, the book identifies a substantial ray of hope for the future in an energy-hungry world, provided the options are managed with wisdom and justice, in the absence of some colossal accident or act of folly. The author feels confident that the energy problem can be met, and even cautiously optimistic that it will be. But the fact remains that the lead time for most of the technological developments discussed bears a striking resemblance to the period when fossil fuel production will already be well in decline. It would seem imperative, therefore, for a balance to be struck without delay between the conflicting needs to maintain a flexible approach and yet make firm decisions. To quote John R. Kiely of the World Energy Conference, 'Long term programmes, resolutely pursued, are required: and they are required now.'

A prologue to such a policy is a detailed study of all the likely fuel options available; consequently this book is offered as one convenient format for the collation and analysis of much relevant data scattered about the literature. It is a contribution to the creation of, in the words of Jean Monet, 'a common language between those who know and those who decide'. It is intended to serve the fuel specialist and decision-maker alike. In the event, of course, the successful exploitation of nuclear fusion, outgassing methane from the Earth's surface, or some as yet undiscovered energy bonanza may render most of these materials superfluous. However, until the dawning of that happy day, the creation of an insurance policy in the form of alternative fuels would seem more than prudent.

Acknowledgement is made gratefully to colleagues and students at Cranfield Institute of Technology for the stimuli provided by discussion, questions and research, and also to J. Boddy of Mobil, J. M. Burnett of Merz & McLellan, N. French of A.P.V. Ltd, F. J. G. Griffiths of Woburn Chemicals, J. Masson of Davy Powergas, Dr A. Stratton of ICI, senior staff of DERD, Ministry of Defence, the energy industry generally, and the entire staff of the Cranfield Institute Library for providing helpful data so readily. While acknowledging an editorial interest, comment must be made on the invaluable aid provided by the Fuel and Energy Abstracts published on behalf of the Institute of Energy by IPC Science and Technology Press Ltd, Guildford. Once again, the untiring excellence of the Cranfield SME Drawing Office in preparing the illustrations, is greatly appreciated. Thanks are also due to my wife for her acceptance of yet another period of absent-minded responses to requests to mend the ironing-board or feed the cat! Finally, the encouragement received from Professor R. S. Fletcher, Head of the Cranfield School of Mechanical Engineering, is very much appreciated, and it is hoped that this study marks an early step in an essential and exciting long-term project.

Cranfield, 1979   E. M. GOODGER

Units

In any system of units, a number of quantities are defined as basic to the system, and all the remaining quantities derived from them. If the system is coherent, the products and quotients of any two or more unit quantities themselves become the units of the derived quantities, in the absence of any conversion factors or proportionality constants. The rationalised system of metric units known as SI (Système International d'Unités) is coherent in this way, and applies to all branches of science and engineering.

The quantities and units of interest in this study consist of the following.

	Quantity	Unit	Symbol
(Basic)	length	metre	m
	mass	kilogram	kg
	time	second	s
	electric current	ampere	A
	thermodynamic temperature	kelvin	K
	amount of substance	mole	mol
(Derived)	force	newton	$N (= kg\,m/s^2)$
	pressure	pascal	$Pa (= N/m^2)$
	energy	joule	$J (= N\,m)$
	power	watt	$W (= J/s)$

No change is made to any symbol to indicate the plural, and quantities are expressed in units which result in numerical values between 0.1 and 1000, with preferred single multiples and sub-multiples that differ in stages of 10 raised to a power which is a multiple of ±3, ranging normally from 10^{18}, exa, to 10^{-18}, atto. Those used most commonly in this study are as follows.

Factor	Prefix	Symbol
10^{18}	exa	E
10^9	giga	G
10^6	mega	M
10^3	kilo	k
10^{-3}	milli	m
10^{-6}	micro	μ

SI has been adopted by various industries (for example, *Recommended SI units*, Institute of Petroleum, London, 1970), some of which also use earlier metric units (litre, bar, centipoise, centistokes) together with non-metric units (atmosphere) which are considered acceptable. Since the adoption of SI is not yet worldwide, the following conversion factors and other metric relationships are given.

Length	1 in. = **25.4 mm**
	1 ft = **0.304 8 m**
	1 mile = 1.609 km
Volume	1 ft^3 = 0.028 32 m^3
	1 UK gal = 1.201 US gal = 4.546 l
	1 US gal = 0.832 7 UK gal = 3.785 l
	1 US barrel = 34.97 UK gal = **42 US gal** = 158.9 l
Mass	1 lb = 0.453 6 kg
	1 (long) ton = **2240 lb** = 1016 kg
	1 short ton = **2000 lb** = 907.6 kg
	1 tonne = 0.984 2 (long) ton = **1000 kg = 1 Mg**
Density	1 lb/ft^3 = 16.02 kg/m^3
Force	1 lbf = 4.448 N
Pressure	1 lbf/in.^{2} = 6.895 kPa
	1 mm Hg = 133.3 Pa
	1 atm = **1.013 25 bar** = **101.325 kPa**
	1 bar = **100 kPa = 10^5 Pa**
Energy	1 Btu = 1.055 kJ
	1 Chu = 1.899 kJ
	1 kcal (international table) = **4.186 8 kJ**
	1 kcal (thermochemical) = 4.184 kJ
	1 kW h = **3.6 MJ**
	1 hp h = 2.685 MJ
	1 therm = **10^5 Btu** = 105.5 MJ
Specific energy	1 Btu/lb = **2.326 kJ/kg**
	1 Chu/lb = **4.186 8 kJ/kg**
Specific	1 Btu/lb °R = **1 Chu/lb K = 4.186 8 kJ/kg K**
energy	1 Btu/ft^3 = 0.037 26 kJ/l (or MJ/m^3)
capacity	1 Chu/ft^3 = 0.067 07 kJ/l (or MJ/m^3)
	1 Btu/UK gal = 0.232 1 kJ/l (or MJ/m^3)
Power	1 hp = 745.7 W

(Figures in bold type are exact)

Approximate Fuel Energy Equivalents

	b.o.e.	t.o.e.	t.c.e.	c.m.n.g.e.
1 barrel oil equivalent (b.o.e.)	1	0.136	0.211	163
1 tonne oil equivalent (t.o.e.)	7.35	1	1.55	1200
1 tonne coal equivalent (t.c.e.)	4.74	0.645	1	775
1 cubic metre natural gas equivalent (c.m.n.g.e.)	0.006	83×10^{-3}	1.29×10^{-3}	1

Note: 100 ppm = 0.01%

Notation

(Customary units are given)

a	annually
A/F	air/fuel molar ratio
a/f	air/fuel mass ratio
API	American Petroleum Institute
BFG	blast furnace gas
bp	boiling point (°C)
BWG	blue water gas
CFR	Co-operative Fuel Research
CHP	combined heat and power
COG	coke oven gas
CPG	coke producer gas
CTF	coal tar fuel
CWG	carburetted water gas
daf	dry ash-free
dmmf	dry mineral-matter-free
E	electrical potential
E_{ign}	ignition energy (mJ)
EAD	equilibrium air distillation
fbp	final boiling point (°C)
FL	flash point (°C)
G	Gibbs free-energy molar function (kJ/mol)
(g)	gaseous phase
(gr)	graphite
H	molar enthalpy (kJ/mol)
H/C	hydrogen/carbon atomic (or molar) ratio
HTP	high test peroxide (concentrated H_2O_2)
I	specific impulse (N s/kg, or N s/l)
ibp	initial boiling point (°C)

imep	indicated mean effective pressure (kPa)
IP	Institute of Petroleum
K	equilibrium constant
k	rate constant
L	liquid volume
(l)	liquid phase
LNG	liquefied natural gas
LPG	liquefied petroleum gases
m	moles of oxygen per mole of fuel
MM	molar mass (g/mol)
mp	melting point ($^{\circ}$C)
n	moles of given product per mole of fuel
NASA	National Aeronautics and Space Administration
NCB	National Coal Board
n-f	non-flow
NG	natural gas
NO_x	mixed oxide products of nitrogen
p	pressure (kPa)
PI	performance index
P/R	products/reactants molar ratio
Q	calorific value (MJ/kg, MJ/l, or MJ/m^3)
Q	heat transfer
r	ratio
R, R$'$, etc.	radicals
R_0	universal gas constant (kJ/mol K)
rel d	relative density
RFNA	red fuming nitric acid
RFO	residual fuel oil
RON	research octane number
S	entropy
(s)	solid phase
s-f	steady-flow
sfc	specific fuel consumption
SIT	spontaneous ignition temperature ($^{\circ}$C)
SMW	solid municipal waste
SNG	supplemental natural gas
T	absolute thermodynamic temperature (K)
tdc	top dead centre
TEB	triethyl borane
TEL	tetraethyllead
TML	tetramethyllead
TVO	tractor vaporising oil
U	internal energy
UBF	unburnt fuel

UDMH	unsymmetrical dimethylhydrazine
UFL	upper flash point (°C)
UHC	unburnt hydrocarbons
V	volume
V	vapour volume
VP	vapour pressure
W	work transfer
Wo	Wobbe number (MJ/m^3)
x	carbon number
α	cut-off ratio in diesel cycle
γ	ratio of c_p/c_v for ideal gas
Δ	finite change in a quantity
η	efficiency
ϕ	equivalence ratio

Superscripts

0	standard state of 25 °C (298.15 K) and 1 atm
′	concentration basis
*	algebraic sum of sensible and standard formation values

Subscripts

a	atomisation
ad	adiabatic
F	forward
f	formation
gr	gross value
I	initial
i	any arbitrary reactant component
j	any arbitrary product component
max	maximum
min	minimum
net	net value
P	product
p	pressure or constant pressure
R	reactant
R	reverse
r	reaction
s	stoichiometric
sp	specific
T	total
v	volume or constant volume

1. Introduction

The prime task in a work of this kind is to determine the likelihood of need for the materials under discussion, and therefore for the work itself. For this reason, chapter 2 explores briefly the overall reserves and consumption rates of energy, seeking the probability or otherwise of a shortfall in the foreseeable future. The prediction of such an event is found to figure in the conclusions of so many energy studies that the relevance of the work appears to be established. The following firm statements lend support to this conclusion,

'Alternative fuels will be needed on an enormous scale'
(Workshop on Alternative Energy Strategies, *Chart. mech. Engr,*
    Sept. 1977, 27)
'Synthetic fuels generally are expected to become significant forms of
energy supply before the end of this century'
    (W. L. Lom and A. F. Williams, *Substitute Natural Gas,* Applied
        Science, London, 1976)

A world-wide basis is adopted for study, but on occasions the United Kingdom is used as an example of a country with substantial experience in fuel production and utilisation. In chapter 2 and subsequently, the terms 'source' and 'resource' are used in a general descriptive sense only, whereas 'reserve' represents an estimated finite quantity expressed on either a proved or ultimate basis. For a deeper study of this topic, the definitions given by Ion[1] are recommended. Chapter 2 also attempts to identify those fuels which are likely to be the first to reach exhaustion.

A concise survey of the properties and performance characteristics of conventional fuels is presented in chapter 3 to provide the necessary basis of comparison for the alternative fuels, and also permit an understanding of the uses of conventional fuels in alternative ways. The terms 'atomic weight' and 'molecular weight' are gradually being replaced by 'relative atomic mass' and 'relative molecular mass', but some confusion can still arise owing to the SI adoption of the mole in units of grams, and the mass in kilograms. The opportunity has been taken in chapter 3, therefore, to adopt the term 'molar mass' which is equal numerically to the previous terms but has the advantages of continually reminding that its units are in g/mol rather than kg/mol, and of being applicable to both atoms and molecules (Personal communication, Dr Y. R. Mayhew, University of Bristol, 1978). Again, in the interests of clarity, chapter 3 distinguishes between the reactions described as 'water-gas' and 'water-gas shift', in view of some inconsistencies in the literature.

Since this work is in the nature of a first attempt at a comprehensive over-view of the alternative fuel scene, the next important task is to establish a system of classification for the different fuel types, with definitions thought out in some depth on a comparative basis, and then tested for suitability by consistent use throughout the book. As a result of this exercise, some of the terms adopted in chapter 4 are submitted, with respect, as being more appropriate than certain other terms that are already creeping in to the jargon. For example, the frequent American reference to these fuels as 'alternate' is challenged since, in this part of the English-speaking world, *alternate* implies a continual interchange between the new and conventional fuels on a cyclic turn-by-turn basis, whereas the term *alternative* underscores the harsh reality of a once-and-for-all replacement, with permanent loss of the conventional fuels. Even this word may not appear entirely suitable, since some pocket dictionaries define alternative in terms of a choice between two mutually exclusive options only. However, the larger dictionaries add the rider that, from 1861, the word has been used sometimes to cover more than two options, as is the case in this present study.

It is the author's opinion also that the meaning of the term 'synthetic' has been blurred by over-use, and that its linking with the word 'natural', as in 'synthetic natural gas', is quite inappropriate. Synthesis concerns the aggregation of the parts, and no doubt occurs as the final stage of many a production process but, for clarity, this grouping is used here only when the parts are the individual elements rather than component molecules or radicals. For this reason, therefore, the rather unwieldy title of 'elemental synthesis fuels' is suggested for this particular group. Specific use is also recommended for the terms 'simulated', 'supplemental' and 'substitute', as indicated by the definitions and examples given in chapter 4. It is perhaps approaching the pedantic to quarrel with the widespread use of the term 'biomass' but, strictly, this suggests some specific quantity of material, involving units of mass, whereas the term 'biomatter' seems more appropriate for general descriptive purposes, and 'biofuels' when they are used as such, either directly or in some derived form.

The opportunity has been taken in chapter 5 to be selective among the many terms available for the energy released by combustion. For thermo-chemical calculations, the term 'enthalpy of reaction' is retained, but for engineering purposes the term 'calorific value' is used in the generic sense, with the more precise 'specific energy' when expressed on the basis of fuel mass, and 'energy density' on fuel volume. In thermochemistry, the sign convention is such that heat flowing outwards from a material system is classed as negative, whereas in engineering, combustion heat tends to be viewed in a positive sense, but the form of plotting adopted in chapter 5 is likely to dispel any confusion on this score.

In chapter 6, a broad attempt is made to identify the fuel characteristics most relevant to each stage of combustion and, on this basis, to predict to some extent the combustion performance of individual alternative fuels. The actual performance with these fuels applied to various types of combustor, as reported in the literature, is then outlined and summarised in chapter 7. The related topics involved in the handling of these fuels are covered in chapter 8. In chapter 9, possible future production techniques are outlined briefly for those alternative fuels showing greatest promise. Some reference is made to conversion efficiencies of the many processes proposed and/or under development, but the data are incomplete partly because of scarcity of information, but also because of differing bases of calculation, and the fact that some of the later processes have not yet reached their represent- ative levels of performance. The final chapter then concludes with an attempt to foreshadow possible fuel developments in the major sectors of application, together with their costs.

Much data already exist concerning the properties of the various fuels discussed, but tend to be diffused throughout the literature. One of the features of this study, therefore, is the collation of these data on a comparative basis, For ease of reference, the data in tabulated form appear as an appendix, and in plotted form at the ends of the appropriate chapters rather than in the body of the text.

References

1.   D. C. Ion, *Availability of World Energy Resources*, Graham & Trotman, London (1975).

2. World Energy Resources and Consumption

Throughout the thousands of years prior to the industrialisation of societies, mankind's requirements for energy have been met primarily by muscular effort, wind and water currents, fuel wood, direct solar warming and other 'renewable' sources, punctuated only occasionally by the use of minor outcrops of coal and oil for the high-temperature fires needed to make terracotta and similar materials. However, the tempo of industrialisation has reversed this pattern, with major withdrawals on the irreplaceable 'capital' resources of time-stored solar energy, in the form of fossil fuels derived from vegetable and animal organisms, and minor contributions only from the renewable energy 'income'. In the absence of some virtually inexhaustible capital resource, it would appear that the world will eventually have to return to an energy income basis, and that it would be wise to invest some of the present 'capital' for research in anticipation of this event. The immediate concern therefore centres on the time scale still available for all the necessary preparations to be made, the vital question being the likelihood or otherwise of some energy deficiency arising before the full exploitation of the income flow. This in turn depends on both the overall extent of the remaining fossil fuel reserves, and the rate at which they are being consumed.

2.1 The Energy Gap

Fossil fuel reserves are usually expressed on either a *proved* or an *ultimate* basis, as listed in table 2.1. The former refers to the production that can be expected from known sources using current extraction techniques, whereas the latter refers to complete exhaustion of all likely sources including those not yet proved. Estimates of annual rates of energy consumption are also shown in the table for the years 1979 and 2000, based on an overall demand growth of 2.9 per cent per annum during this period.

A preliminary, very approximate, yardstick of the possible lifetimes of fuel reserves is given by the ratio of proved reserve to the current annual

Table 2.1 Estimated world energy 'reserves, consumption and 'lifetimes' (derived from references 1 to 4)

Source	Reserves (EJ)		Annual Consumption (EJ)		Proved Reserves Consumption (years)
	Proved	Ultimate	1979 (%)	2000 (%)*	
Natural gas	3000	8000	50 (16)	80 (13)	60
Petroleum	4000	20 000	140 (43)	} 190 (31)	30 } 60
Oil shale	2000	23 000	–		
Tar sands	3000	10 000	–		
Coal	20 000	300 000	70 (22)	150 (25)	280
Uranium	11 000	3×10^8	10 (3)	100 (16)	1100
**	$>10^{12}$	$>10^{17}$			
Renewables	–	–	50 (16)	90 (15)	–
World Total	–	–	320 (100)	610 (100)	–

* Assumed demand growth to year 2000 = 2.9% per annum
** Breeder reactors

EJ = Exajoule = $J \times 10^{18}$

5

consumption, the error incurred by ignoring the expected growth in consumption being offset to some degree by ignoring also the likely proving of additional reserves, and of improved extraction yields. These simple ratios are included in the table, and show the relatively short expectation of the hydrocarbon fuels in contrast to coal, and particularly to the long-term availability of fission energy from uranium. The almost unlimited source of energy from as-yet undeveloped nuclear fusion has not been included in the table.

In the event, fuel lifetimes are likely to be far more indefinite, since the consumption rate of each fuel tends to rise to a maximum and then decay, as in the familiar bell-shaped curves of the Hubbert model, the final rate of consumption being very largely controlled by such factors as prevailing cost, energy policy and availability of alternatives. The annual world rates of consumption for various primary energy sources over recent years are shown in figure 2.1, and compared (on a different time scale) with projections to year 2020. The three items of note are as follows.

1. The current rise in oil consumption which has now returned to its earlier rate after the hesitation immediately following the oil embargo of 1973.

2. The consumption peaks for both oil and natural gas predicted early in the next century.

3. The rapid rise in future consumption of both solid and nuclear fuels, with a steady increase in 'renewables' (hydro, solar, wood, etc.).

Overall, these curves indicate the long-term first stages of the recommended transfer in energy consumption from 'capital' to 'income' which, provided a balance can be struck between availability and demand, could ensure continuing adequate supplies for the long-term future. However, major problems could arise during a critical transition between the capital and income systems, particularly if the demise of the former precedes the full development of the latter. This possibility is strengthened by the gap beginning to appear between the world total demand and availability curves within the first few years of the next century, as shown in figure 2.2. This underlines the needs during this critical transitional period for energy conservation and the more rational use of the fuels still available, together with the development of fuels from alternative sources. It also highlights the fact that the time available before the appearance of this embarrassing disparity between supply and demand is of the same order as the lead time required to select and develop the production processes for the alternative energy schemes needed to close the gap. Energy stored within alternative types of fuel — which form the *raison d'être* of this present study — therefore appear to represent one very important group of alternative sources of energy.

Clearly, the long-term availability of any one fuel, such as coal, will be a very welcome factor, with the market adjusting itself accordingly to attempt to use the remaining current, and emerging alternative, fuels in the most

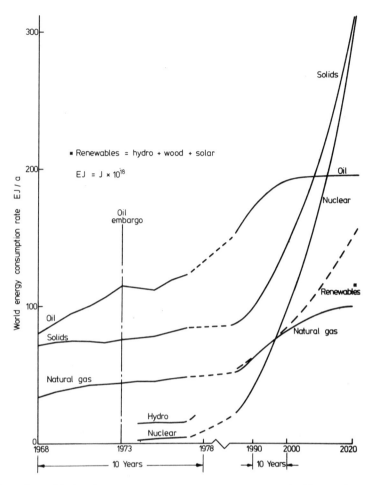

Figure 2.1   World primary energy consumption, by source (derived from references 1 and 3)

rational manner. In order to give some background to the differing energy requirements in the various consuming sectors, predictions of the percentage consumptions by the major sectors in several geographical areas are shown in figure 2.3 for the years 1980 and 2020. It must be emphasised here that the straight lines drawn through these 40-year periods are schematic only, and not intended to suggest constant rates of change — the likely variations between these years are indicated by Bloodworth[3] and others. The broad overall conclusions arising from these curves are those of modest reductions in *relative* proportions of energy assigned to transport and industry, and substantial increases to energy conversion (chemical and/or nuclear to electrical).

7

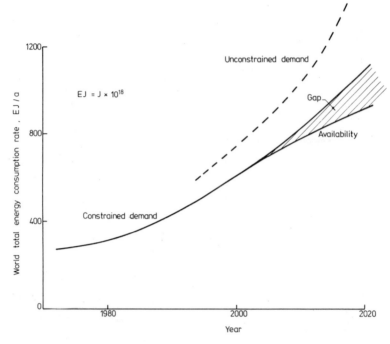

Figure 2.2   World total primary energy consumption (derived from reference 3)

2.2 Hydrocarbon Fuels

In view of the overall convenience of winning, processing and utilisation of
the products, crude oil and natural gas have emerged as particularly attractive
sources of finished fuels for the industrial, commercial, domestic and
transport sectors. For this very reason, these two resources are likely to be
the first to show signs of local shortages, and eventually total exhaustion;
consequently their reserves, production and consumption are examined here
in rather more detail.

In figure 2.4, the lower full curve (**A**) indicates the steady growth in
proved world oil reserves up to year 1972. In 1973, the year of the oil
embargo, the first reduction in reserves appeared. Although this was offset by
additional finds the following year, further reductions have appeared since,
and these may indicate that the 'peak' of reserves has been reached, to be
followed by a progressive reduction. Curve B shows the world annual
consumption of crude oil, drawn to the same scale. Redrawing this curve to
10 x scale (**C**) shows the steady rise in consumption up to 1973, followed by
two years of reduction. However, the former rate of increase is now evident

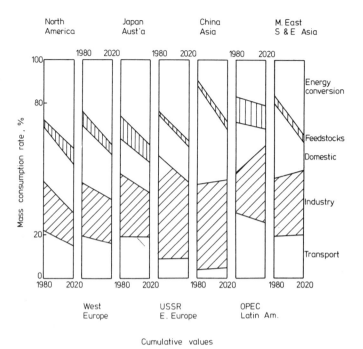

Figure 2.3 World primary energy consumption, by sector and by region (derived from reference 3)

again. These facts are brought together effectively in terms of the (reserves/consumption) ratio of curve D. Here, the marked fall from 1970 to 1973 is seen to have been reversed following the oil embargo but, once again, to be falling at a significant rate. Clearly, the days of crude oil are beginning to appear numbered!

Some comparable data are included in the diagram for natural gas — expressed in terms of equivalent tonnes of oil. Over the three-year period shown, its (reserves/consumption) ratio is also seen to have reached a peak.

These same data are shown by region for year 1978 in table 2.2. Comparison of reserve values shows the majority of crude oil to be located in the Middle East, and most gas in the Sino/Soviet/East European region. Comparison of production and consumption values identifies the major oil importers as Western Europe, the United States and the Far East, and the exporters as the Middle East and Africa. For natural gas, the major consumers are the United States and the Sino/Soviet/East European region, followed by Western Europe. Although the solid fuel deposits are extensive, the consumption figures have been included in the table for comparison, and show the major consumers to be the Sino/Soviet/East European region, followed by

9

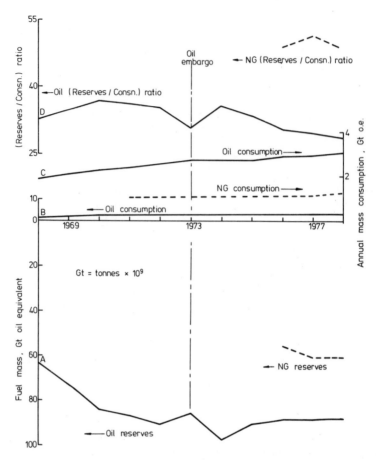

Figure 2.4   World crude oil reserves and consumption variations with year (derived from reference 1)

the United States, Western Europe and the Far East. From the annual consumption rates for the major petroleum products in figure 2.5, the overall post-1973 trends show steady increases for the gasolines and middle distillates, and a reduction for fuel oil.

In conclusion, a more detailed analysis of petroleum product demand is shown for the United Kingdom alone in table 2.3. The three years chosen for comparison are 1973 and 1974, the years immediately before and after the oil embargo, together with a recent year, 1978. Whereas the consumption of aviation fuels, motor gasolines and gas oil/diesel fuels (all the transport fuels) showed immediate reductions in 1974 but subsequent gains, all the other products, together with the totals, show the reductions to be continuing.

10

Table 2.2 World reserves, annual production and consumption of fossil fuels, 1978 (derived from reference 1)

Region	Crude Oil						Natural Gas				Coal	
	Proved reserves		Production		Consumption		Proved reserves		Consumption		Consumption	
	Gt	(%)	Mt	(%)	Mt	(%)	Gtoe	(%)	Mtoe	(%)	Mtoe	(%)
U.S.A.	4.4	(5.2)	487.8	(15.8)	887.9	(28.9)	4.8	(7.9)	504.2	(40.7)	355.0	(19.6)
Canada	1.1	(1.3)	74.4	(2.4)	86.9	(2.8)	2.0	(3.2)	47.3	(3.8)	19.2	(1.1)
Latin America	5.8	(6.4)	251.5	(8.1)	202.0	(6.6)	2.7	(4.5)	42.3	(3.4)	15.2	(0.8)
Western Europe including U.K.	3.3	(3.7)	89.7	(2.9)	714.6	(23.1)	3.4	(5.7)	178.9	(14.4)	198.4	(11.0)
U.K.	–		53.4	(1.7)	94.0	(3.1)	–		37.9	(3.1)	70.4	(3.9)
Middle East	50.3	(56.9)	1054.1	(34.1)	83.3	(2.7)	17.5	(29.0)	30.1	(2.4)	–	
Africa	7.7	(8.9)	297.1	(9.8)	60.3	(2.0)	4.5	(7.4)	8.3	(0.7)	49.2	(2.7)
Sino/Soviet/E. Europe	12.8	(14.5)	689.0	(22.4)	597.9	(19.6)	22.7	(37.5)	387.0	(31.2)	985.0	(54.4)
Far East/Japan/Australia	2.7	(3.1)	140.4	(4.5)	443.0	(14.3)	2.9	(4.8)	42.4	(3.4)	189.3	(10.4)
Totals	88.1	(100.0)	3084.0	(100.0)	3075.9	(100.0)	60.5	(100.0)	1240.5	(100.0)	1811.3	(100.0)

Differences between production and consumption due to stock changes and unknown military liftings.

Gtoe = gigatonnes oil equivalent; Mtoe = megatonnes oil equivalent

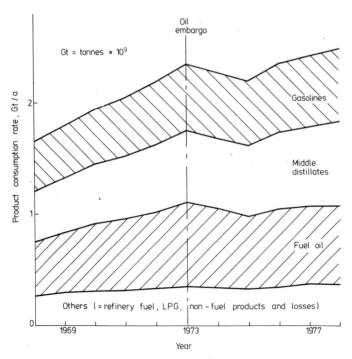

Figure 2.5   Annual consumption of main oil products — world excluding USSR, Eastern Europe and China (derived from reference 1)

Table 2.3   *UK petroleum product consumption, megatonnes* (derived from reference 5)

Product	1973	(%)	1974	(%)	1978	(%)
Aviation fuels	4.337	(4.1)	3.806	(3.8)	4.557	(5.0)
Motor gasolines	16.926	(15.9)	16.483	(16.5)	18.349	(20.3)
Industrial kerosines	3.454	(3.2)	3.015	(3.0)	2.855	(3.1)
Gas oils/Diesel fuels	20.758	(19.5)	19.099	(19.1)	19.475	(21.5)
Fuel oils	39.447	(37.1)	37.323	(37.4)	28.233	(31.2)
Refinery consumption	7.052	(6.6)	6.945	(7.0)	6.423	(7.1)
Other products	14.423	(13.6)	13.127	(13.2)	10.673	(11.8)
Totals	106.397	(100.0)	99.798	(100.0)	90.565	(100.0)
Change from 1973	—	—	−6.599	(−6.2)	−15.832	(−14.9)

12

These conclusions foreshadow the emphasis to be placed on the need for liquid fuels in the transport sector, to be discussed in later sections.

References

1. *BP Statistical Review of the World Oil Industry*, The British Petroleum Co. Ltd, London (1978).
2. I. Fells (ed), *Energy for the Future*, Institute of Fuel, London (1973).
3. I. J. Bloodworth, E. Bossanyi, D. S. Bowers, E. A. C. Crouch, R. J. Eden C. W. Hope, W. S. Humphrey, J. V. Mitchell, D. J. Pullin and J. A. Stanislaw, *World Energy Demand to 2020*, World Energy Conference/ IPC Science & Technology Press, Guildford (1978).
4. I. G. C. Dryden (ed), *The Efficient Use of Energy*, Institute of Fuel and IPC Science & Technology Press, Guildford (1975).
5. *U.K. Petroleum Industry Statistics – Consumption and Refinery Production, 1977 and 1978*, Institute of Petroleum, London (1979).

3. Conventional Combustion Reactants

With the exception of a small group of monopropellant and tripropellant reactant systems used in rocketry, combustion is generally understood to entail the chemical reaction between two materials, namely fuel and oxidant. As a basic frame of reference, therefore, this chapter classifies and describes briefly the more conventional members of both groups of reactant: in general, these are dealt with in ascending order of density. Also for reference purposes, the chemical elements and their oxides of interest in this study are listed in table 3.1 and, for simplicity, the approximate values of molar mass have been used throughout this work.

3.1 Individual Hydrocarbons

Since commercial fuels consist almost exclusively of mixtures of various types of hydrocarbon, logical first steps are to identify the main hydrocarbons individually, and to classify them into related groups. As the name implies, these compounds are carbon hydrides, and each may be represented by a formula of the $C_x H_y$ type, where x and y and integers, and x is known as the *carbon number*. Although many thousands of hydrocarbon structures are possible, most fall into a few major groups or 'series', each member of a particular series differing slightly from its adjacent fellow members but having a general formula and structural characteristics in common. The main series, with their lighter members illustrated, are shown in table 3.2, arranged in reducing content of hydrogen. In each series, the density of the members increases with carbon number, the members themselves passing progressively from gases to liquids and eventually to solids. Parts of incomplete molecules are termed *radicals*, for example, methyl CH_3, and ethyl C_2H_5, and represented generally by the symbols R, R', and so on.

Although the two-dimensional representation of these molecules is satisfactory for most purposes, it is occasionally necessary to recall that the structures are, in fact, three dimensional.[1] In the case of methane, for

14

Table 3.1 *Molar masses* (C^{12} = 12 g/mol)

Element	Symbol	MM	Approx. MM	Compound	Symbol	MM	Approx. MM
Argon	Ar	39.948	40	Carbon dioxide	CO_2	44.00995	44
Carbon	C	12.01115	12	Carbon monoxide	CO	28.01055	28
Hydrogen	H	1.00797	1	Hydrogen	H_2	2.01594	2
Nitrogen	N	14.0067	14	Nitrogen	N_2	28.0134	28
Oxygen	O	15.9994	16	Oxygen	O_2	31.9988	32
Boron	B	10.81	10.8	Boron oxide	B_2O_3	69.6182	69.6
Sulphur	S	32.064	32	Sulphur dioxide	SO_2	64.0628	64
				Water	H_2O	18.01534	18

Table 3.2   Structure of lighter members of the major hydrocarbon series

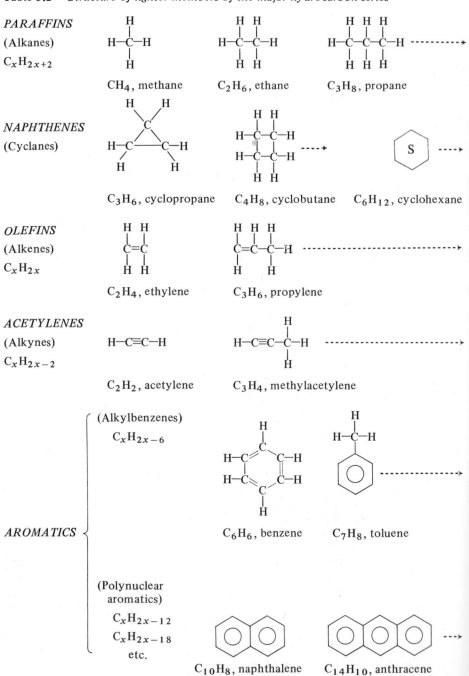

PARAFFINS
(Alkanes)
C_xH_{2x+2}

CH_4, methane

C_2H_6, ethane

C_3H_8, propane

NAPHTHENES
(Cyclanes)

C_3H_6, cyclopropane

C_4H_8, cyclobutane

C_6H_{12}, cyclohexane

OLEFINS
(Alkenes)
C_xH_{2x}

C_2H_4, ethylene

C_3H_6, propylene

ACETYLENES
(Alkynes)
C_xH_{2x-2}

C_2H_2, acetylene

C_3H_4, methylacetylene

AROMATICS

(Alkylbenzenes)
C_xH_{2x-6}

C_6H_6, benzene

C_7H_8, toluene

(Polynuclear aromatics)
C_xH_{2x-12}
C_xH_{2x-18}
etc.

$C_{10}H_8$, naphthalene

$C_{14}H_{10}$, anthracene

example, the identical electrostatic nature of the four C–H bonds provides a repulsion which forces them to take up a tetrahedral form, resulting in bond angles of $109.47°$ rather than the $90°$ shown. This gives a particularly compact structure for the methane molecule. In general, the 'saturated' single bonding between carbon atoms, C–C, represents molecular stability, whereas the 'unsaturated' C=C bonds tend to instability and the C≡C bonds more so. There are two exceptions to this general ruling, as follows.

1. The first three members of the naphthene series, although saturated, experience some ring strain due to the disparity between the bond angles required by the two-dimensional ring geometry and the three-dimensional $109.47°$. Since the C–C bonds are axially rotatable, the C_6H_{12} cyclohexane ring is able to shed such internal strain by crinkling.

2. It is common practice to represent the ring structure of benzene, C_6H_6, with three C–C and three C=C bonds in order to meet the requirements of valency, since there is one hydrogen atom only at each carbon atom, as shown in table 3.2. However, this is schematic only, and does not imply that the benzene ring is unstable. On the contrary, the ring is stable to such an extent that heavier members can be constructed only by the substitution of the external hydrogen atoms with methyl or other radicals (hence, alkylbenzenes).

The aromatics can take an additional form by the combination of benzene rings to give the polynuclear, or fused ring, aromatics naphthalene $C_{10}H_8$ (C_xH_{x-2} or C_xH_{2x-12}), anthracene $C_{14}H_{10}$ (C_xH_{x-4} or C_xH_{2x-18}), and so on (see section 4.4.2).

For an individual hydrocarbon, it follows that

$$\text{molar mass} = MM = 12x + y \quad \text{g/mol}$$

and its relative quantities of hydrogen and carbon can be expressed as

$$\text{hydrogen/carbon atomic (or molar) ratio} = y/x$$

This ratio is also equal to the equivalent value of hydrogen atoms when x is reduced to unity, that is, when the formula is wirtten as $CH_{(y/x)}$. A plot of the H/C atomic ratio y/x is shown against the carbon number x in figure 3.1 for the individual hydrocarbons up to $x = 14$. Clearly, as the value of x increases, the differences between the paraffins C_xH_{2x+2} and the alkyl-benzenes C_xH_{2x-6} tend to vanish and, with the exception of the polynuclear aromatics, most of the curves tend to the unique value of 2. An isomer of a hydrocarbon molecule is one in which the geometry of the molecular structure has been rearranged, but with no change in the total numbers of hydrogen and carbon atoms. This has no effect on molar mass, H/C ratio or stoichiometry (chapter 5), but it can have a profound effect on ignitability (chapter 6), together with a mild influence on density, melting and freezing.

In practice, individual hydrocarbons are rarely used as such, naturally

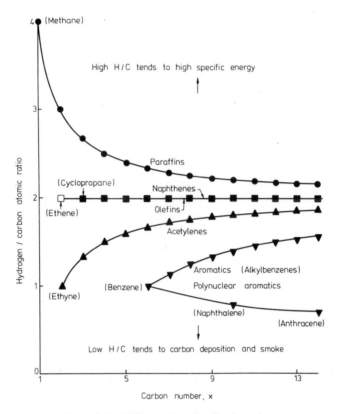

Figure 3.1   H/C atomic ratio of hydrocarbons

occurring or commercially manufactured fuels generally consisting of many hydrocarbon and/or other materials blended or compounded together in gaseous, liquid or solid form. These are considered in turn in the following sections.

3.2 Conventional Gaseous Fuels

This section reviews briefly the following two main groups of conventional gaseous fuel

1. Hydrocarbon gases, requiring minor processing only and storable in liquefied form.

2. Manufactured fuel gas mixtures, including industrial by-products derived from solid and/or liquid sources, and also mixtures of relatively low energy density due to the presence of inert compounds and/or hydrogen.

18

3.2.1 Hydrocarbon Gases

Comparative properties of some representative individual hydrocarbon gases
are given in table A4.1. Natural gas deposits exist either as free gas or in
association with crude oil. Useful quantities are also derived from the de-
gassing of coal mines. Natural gas consists mainly of methane but, having
evolved from organic deposits, invariably contains some higher hydrocarbons
together with traces of inert nitrogen, carbon dioxide and/or hydrogen
sulphide, depending on the geological location and history. Natural gases from
different fields within the North Sea, for example, also differ from each other
but, on average, show the following composition, in volume percent

CH_4	93.3
Higher hydrocarbons	4.6
N_2	1.8
CO_2	0.3
H_2S	0

The relatively small proportion of higher hydrocarbons, and the absence of
hydrogen sulphide, together categorise this gas as dry and sweet. In comparison with methane itself, the presence of these additional components
gives the gas about an 8 per cent increase in density, 4 per cent reduction in
specific energy, and 4 per cent increase in energy density. Other natural gases
range in composition from almost pure methane (99.5 per cent CH_4, Ravenna,
Italy), through the wet gases containing the higher hydrocarbon condensate
(27.8 per cent C_xH_y, Kuwait), the high nitrogen content gases with correspondingly low energy density (14.3 per cent N_2 and 29 MJ/m^3 net, Groningen,
Netherlands), and the high carbon dioxide content gases (44 per cent CO_2,
Kapuri, New Zealand) to the sour gases containing hydrogen sulphide
(15 per cent H_2S, Lacq, France). The treatment of natural gas comprises the
separation of the higher hydrocarbon condensates and water, first at the well
head and subsequently by refrigeration treatment or desiccants to give
appropriate dewpoints. Removal of carbon dioxide and/or hydrogen sulphide
is by alkaline scrubbing or adsorption, or the latter may be sweetened to
innocuous disulphide, whereas the nitrogen content is usually left untreated.
Natural gas has now become the standard commercially supplied gas for
industrial and domestic space heating, hot water supplies and cooking, and
also some applications to boilers, furnaces and kilns.

The condensate gases extracted from wet natural gas, as with the
petroleum gases from crude oil, consist mainly of propane and butane,
together with some corresponding unsaturateds, isomers, and traces of ethane,
ethene and paraffins C_5 to C_{12}. The commercial grade of propane and butane
each contain a minimum of 95 per cent by volume of the named gas, limits on
the concentrations of other materials being set by BS 4250.[2] Since these
other materials lie on either side of the named hydrocarbon, the overall

properties are closely similar to those of the pure hydrocarbon, differing usually by about 1 per cent only. In some cases, commercial mixtures of propane and butane are available under the name of petroleum gases. The principal treatment of petroleum gases comprises the removal or sweetening of mercaptans in order to eliminate both obnoxious odour and corrosive potential. Petroleum gases are used for industrial and agricultural heating and drying.

The standard industrial method of producing acetylene gas by the action of water on calcium carbide, which is itself derived from the high-temperature reaction of coke and limestone, has tended to be replaced by the controlled high-temperature decomposition and/or partial oxidation of methane. Like methane and natural gas, acetylene is lighter than air but, in comparison with the other paraffinic gases, it has a high vaporisation enthalpy, a wide range of flammability, a high flame speed and a particularly high flame temperature. It is, however, unstable due to its high degree of unsaturation, and is necessarily stored in solution with acetone. The main industrial use of acetylene fuel is for gas welding and cutting, and for the production of acetic acid.

3.2.2 Manufactured Fuel Gases

In comparison with solid fuels, gaseous fuels offer the very significant advantages of ease of handling, mixing and ignition, together with flexibility in combustion control, far less requirement for excess air, and freedom from smoke, ash and contaminants. Consequently, many manufacturing processes have evolved for the derivation of gaseous fuel from coal and coke, and recently from the heavier liquid fuels. It is important, however, that the above advantages should not be nullified by loss of heat following exothermic conversion reactions. In some cases, fuel gases evolved as by-products of other manufacturing processes represent sources of energy. The main processes of gaseous fuel manufacture subdivide into carbonisation, gasification and catalytic synthesis, and are considered in turn below.

Carbonisation of a bituminous coal involves heating to about 1000 °C in the absence of air for purposes of devolatilisation and partial thermal cracking of the heavy molecules, leading to *coal* (or *town*) *gas*, tar liquids, and solid char in the form of gas coke. In the gas industry, reaction conditions would be optimised for gas output, whereas in the coking industry the yield of hard crush-resistant metallurgical coke is optimised, with an incidental by-product of *coke oven gas* (COG) very similar to coal gas. The constituents of a representative COG are shown in table A4.2. The yield of gas is augmented by steaming the incandescent coal bed prior to its discharge, giving rise to the *water-gas reaction*

$$C(gr) + H_2O(g) \longrightarrow CO(g) + H_2(g) \qquad \Delta H_r^0 = 131.30 \text{ kJ/mol} \quad (1)$$

Being endothermic (see chapter 5), this technique also controls the bed temperature by converting some of the sensible heat of the hot coke into chemical energy of the additional gases. Steaming also improves the combustion reactivity and porosity of the coke. On the other hand, carbonisation of the heavier liquid petroleum products leads to a comparable fuel gas mixture known as *oil gas*, with the advantages of higher gasification efficiency and convenience of fluid handling. The levels of contamination are also lower, and the costs of purification correspondingly less. Town gas and COG were formerly used for general heating and lighting, and still have value for certain process and metallurgical furnaces.

Gasification of coal, on the other hand, represents a technique for the complete conversion of fuel solids into liquids and gases, and is achieved by partial oxidation on a 'dry blast' basis using air alone (or on a 'wet blast' basis using air and steam — see later). The passage of air through a bed of incandescent carbon (as coal or, more frequently, coke) up to a thickness of about 100 mm results in complete oxidation of the carbon to carbon dioxide. With an increasing thickness of bed, the carbon dioxide is reduced progressively to carbon monoxide. Ideally, the bed thickness, temperature of operation and residence time would be optimised for this reduction to be complete but, in practice, the resulting *coke producer gas* (CPG) contains some carbon dioxide, as well as atmospheric nitrogen, and is classed as a low-energy gas. The producer gas reactions appear as follows

$$C(gr) + (O_2 + 3.76N_2)(g) \longrightarrow CO_2(g) + 3.76N_2(g) \qquad (2)$$

$$\Delta H_r^0 = -393.52 \text{ kJ/mol}$$

$$C(gr) + CO_2(g) \longrightarrow 2CO(g) \qquad \Delta H_r^0 = 172.46 \text{ kJ/mol} \quad (3)$$

Overall, these reactions can be written as

$$C(gr) + \tfrac{1}{2}(O_2 + 3.76N_2)(g) \longrightarrow CO(g) + 1.88N_2(g) \qquad (4)$$

$$\Delta H_r^0 = -110.53 \text{ kJ/mol}$$

A rather poorer quality of CPG is produced during the smelting of iron ore using air with coke in a blast furnace. The resulting *blast furnace gas* (BFG) has a slightly higher content of nitrogen, and a correspondingly lower energy density. It is used for a variety of purposes within the steel industry.

When steam is used in place of air for blast furnaces, further quantities of carbon monoxide and hydrogen are generated by the water-gas reaction (1), together with

$$C(gr) + 2H_2O(g) \longrightarrow CO_2(g) + 2H_2(g) \quad \Delta H_r^0 = 90.13 \text{ kJ/mol} \quad (5)$$

The concentration of nitrogen is also low in the absence of blast air. The characteristic blue coloration of the flame resulting from the high carbon monoxide content leads to the nomenclature *blue water gas* (BWG). Although still classed as a low-energy gas, since hydrogen is of particularly low energy density, it is superior to CPG.

The producer and water-gas reactions may be combined to give overall advantages. Since the former reaction (4) is exothermic, the resulting sensible heat is lost unless it can be transferred by heat exchange, or the producer gas itself used immediately. Reactions 1 and 5 from steam blasting, on the other hand, are both endothermic. The generation of producer gas on a 'wet blast' basis basis incorporating both air and steam permits part of the sensible heat to be retained chemically, as discussed earlier with COG. It also improves the gas conversion efficiency, and counteracts the clinkering action of the molten ash by cooling the hot oxidation region. Excess steam is to be avoided in the upper region of the reactor otherwise further sensible heat will be released by the exothermic *water-gas shift* reaction

$$CO(g) + H_2O(g) \longrightarrow CO_2(g) + H_2(g) \quad \Delta H_r^0 = -41.17 \text{ kJ/mol} \quad (6)$$

It is customary to use alternate blasts of air and steam, and sometimes the producer gas arising from the air blast is used to raise the steam for subsequent generation of BWG. The main attraction of BWG is its suitability for rapid furnace heating in intermittent processes.

Since BWG still lies within the low-energy classification, enrichment with the hydrocarbon gases from cracked petroleum oils can be used to increase the methane concentration, giving *carburetted water gas* (CWG), also shown in table A4.2, with an energy level comparable with COG and coal gases generally. For this reason, CWG was generally used as a component of town gas.

In order to accept lower grade coals, and to improve the quality and conversion efficiency of the producer gas, more recent processes involve nitrogen-free and other gases for blast purposes, higher pressures, fluidised solid beds and/or ash removal in the form of slag. In the Lurgi process, for example, oxygen and steam are used for blasting, an excess of the latter counteracting the tendency for additional clinker formation at the higher temperature, and the moderately high pressure permitting the water wash-out of the additional carbon dioxide and hydrogen sulphide. Some fuel enrichment occurs, possibly due to the following methanation reactions

$$C(gr) + 2H_2(g) \longrightarrow CH_4(g) \quad \Delta H_r^0 = -74.90 \text{ kJ/mol} \quad (7)$$

$$CO(g) + 3H_2(g) \longrightarrow CH_4(g) + H_2O(g) \quad \Delta H_r^0 = -206.20 \text{ kJ/mol} \quad (8)$$

$$CO_2(g) + 4H_2(g) \longrightarrow CH_4(g) + 2H_2O(g) \quad (9)$$

$$\Delta H_r^0 = -165.03 \text{ kJ/mol}$$

but more likely due to the hydrogenation of the volatile matter liberated from the upper layers of the coal. Similar overall reactions occur in the Winkler and

Koppers–Totzec fluidised processes, designed to permit continuous removal of slag.

Enriched forms of BWG are produced by using hydrogen or coal gas with steam for gas blasting. Fuel gas mixtures rich in carbon monoxide and hydrogen are generally produced by such methods, and are examples of *synthesis gas*. After thorough removal of sulphur, such gases may be made to react exothermically in the presence of a metal catalyst, with conditions optimised for the production of methane or of hydrogen–carbon–oxygen compounds.

Catalytic methods of coal-to-gas conversion are also possible by the direct hydrogenation of coal under high pressure and temperature, or by the donor solvent method involving the dehydrogenation of a polynuclear hydroaromatic, as shown in section 4.4.2, together with further hydrogenation in the presence of a catalyst. In each case, methanation occurs by reaction (7).

A combination of carbonisation and gasification may be used to convert completely a solid fuel to a mixture of coal gas and water gas. However, as in carbonisation, the petroleum oils themselves can be used as feedstock for gasification with steam and oxygen, and these latter methods are more efficient. The following reactions occur

$$C_x H_y + \frac{x}{2} O_2 \longrightarrow xCO + \frac{y}{2} H_2 \tag{10}$$

$$C_x H_y + xH_2O \longrightarrow xCO + \left(x + \frac{y}{2}\right) H_2 \tag{11}$$

In summary, due to the wide variation in the composition and corresponding properties of fuel gases, it is common practice to classify such gases within families, sometimes containing sub-groups, based on the level of gross Wobbe number, as shown typically in table 3.3. Many of these gases can, of course, be used as chemical feedstocks for other fuels and, in some cases, for the manufacture of such constructional materials as plastics.

Table 3.3   Families of fuel gases (derived from reference 3)

Family	Gross Wobbe No. (MJ/m³)	Examples
Low Energy	Up to 16	BFG, CPG, CO, BWG
1	24.4 to 28.8	CWG, COG (Town gas)
2	48.2 to 53.2	NG
3	72.6 to 87.8	PG

3.3 Conventional Liquid Fuels

The lighter members of the hydrocarbon series have been seen to exist either as gases or vapours at ambient conditions, and it follows that very large volumes are required for purposes of storage. These requirements can be reduced substantially by storage in the liquid phase. Since the critical temperature of methane is low ($-82.6\,°C$), liquefaction of natural gas is not possible by compression at ambient temperature. However, the gas can be liquefied and stored (as LNG) by cooling; in normal practice either to about $-118\,°C$ at a pressure of 13.5 atm, or down to the boiling point of $-161.5\,°C$ at a pressure of 1 atm. The vapour/liquid volume ratio for natural gas at $15\,°C$ is 624/1.

Commercial grades of propane and butane, on the other hand, may be liquefied at ambient temperature at pressures of about 7 and 2 atm respectively, with corresponding vapour/liquid ratios at $15\,°C$ of 273/1 and 236/1. These materials, and their mixtures, are generally classified as liquefied petroleum gases (LPG), and used as portable fuels for industrial and agricultural sites, domestic dwellings and the leisure trades generally.

Crude petroleum (rock oil) is a naturally occuring, yellowish-brown to black, relatively free-flowing liquid of relative density ranging from about 0.78 to 1.00, consisting essentially of saturated hydrocarbon compounds, largely of unknown composition. Each crude is an individual, unique, mixture with composition and properties depending on the location, age and nature of the organic source material, and the ultimate analyses, in mass percentages, range as follows

C	80 to 90
H	10 to 15
S	0.1 to 3.5 (sometimes up to 7)
O	0.1 to 3
N	0.1 to 2

Also present may be a concentration of up to 0.1 per cent of mineral ash, incorporating a number of metals, commonly as hydrocarbon derivatives in concentrations of parts per million, due to the constitution of the original marine environment, and to intimate contact with the source and reservoir rocks.

Since knowledge of the wide variety of the individual hydrocarbon components is limited to the lighter members up to about C_9, boiling at about $150\,°C$, crude oils may be classified only on a semi-empirical basis, for example, as generally paraffinic, asphaltic or mixed, based entirely on the nature of the residue, that is, on *one* characteristic of distillation. More effectively, they may be compared on the basis of the relative densities of *two* key fractions of distillation. Increases in relative density give varying classes from paraffinic through intermediate to naphthenic.

The commercial liquid products derived from crude petroleum also consist of fractions of different hydrocarbons boiling within certain predetermined ranges of temperature. The primary step in fractionation of a petroleum feedstock is distillation, entailing thermal separation into streams of products ranging from gasolines through kerosines, gas oils and diesel fuels, to the various grades of distillate and residual fuel oils. Since this step is basically a physical separation only, the resulting 'straight run' yield represents the proportions of these fractions initially present in the parent crude oil. Inevitably, these proportions do not tally with the current pattern of demand for petroleum products, consequently several methods of chemical inter-conversion of fractions (polymerisation, cracking, reforming, alkylation, isomerisation, and so on) are then used so that the straight run yield can be suitably tailored. Finally, petroleum products are subjected to blending, stabilisation, cleansing, deodorising, inhibition and other forms of finishing treatment ready for the energy market.

The gasolines are colourless blends of volatile hydrocarbons with components ranging from about C_5 to C_{12}, but average properties roughly equivalent to those of octane, C_8H_{18}. These fuel blends boil within the temperature range of about 30 to 200 °C, and have relative densities of about 0.72 (aviation gasoline, or Avgas)[4] and 0.74 (motor gasoline, or Mogas),[5] as shown in table A4.3. The well-known major application of gasoline is the spark-ignition reciprocating-piston engine widely used for powered transport, and for certain portable or static equipment where modest power is required from small lightweight units. Being volatile, gasoline can be metered through a relatively inexpensive carburettor, and its natural resistance to spontaneous ignition renders it suitable for reasonably high compression ratios, which assist economy. One minor application is as fuel for flameless heaters of the catalytic type. 'Wide-cut gasoline' (Avtag)[6] is the name given to the blend of gasoline and kerosine boiling between about 60 and 240 °C which was developed to ensure strategic supplies of fuel suitable for gas-turbine-powered aircraft. Its relative density is about 0.77, and overall average properties roughly equivalent to decane, $C_{10}H_{22}$.

The kerosines are colourless blends of relatively involatile petroleum fractions which boil between about 150 and 300 °C, and have a relative density in the region of 0.8. This fuel was formerly used as 'lamp kerosine' for wick-fed illumination, and more recently for domestic heating systems. Aviation gas-turbine kerosine (Avtur)[7] is similar in many respects but with particular care taken over the properties controlling atomisation, combustion efficiency, smoke, freezing, and so on. On overall average properties, kerosine equates approximately to $C_{13}H_{25.5}$.

The gas oils are brownish-coloured petroleum fractions comprising distillates boiling between about 180 and 360 °C (which overlaps to some extent with kerosine) and with a relative density of about 0.84. Their main uses are in high-speed diesel engines used in transport and relatively small static installations, and as a fuel in domestic and industrial central heating. They comprise the lighter members of a group known as the industrial fuel oils, and equate roughly to $C_{15}H_{28}$. They are sometimes dyed for brand identification.

The diesel fuels are darkish-brown petroleum fractions comprising distillate and/or residual components, with a relative density of about 0.87. They are used in the heavier, larger diesel engine used in marine and stationary electricity-generating installations, which operate at relatively low rotational speeds and are less critical of fuel quality.

The fuel oils are brownish-black petroleum fractions consisting largely of the distillation residues from asphaltic-type crude oils, with relative densities from about 0.95 to 0.97. Their most important property is viscosity, and the fuels classed as F, G and H in BS 2869[8] have maximum viscosities at 82.2 °C (180 °F) specified as 30, 70 and 115 cSt respectively. The lighter members of the group are residues with sufficient blended gas oil or other distillate 'cutter stock' to meet the viscosity requirements, whereas the heavier members are entirely residual in origin but with viscosities reduced where necessary by means of a mild form of molecular cracking known as 'visbreaking'. Being of a residual nature, the fuel oils generally retain any heavy inorganic contaminants present in the parent crude, as shown in figure 3.2. Fuel oils are used for heating and steam-raising in ships and in industry generally.

Liquid fuels may be derived from the distillation of coal tar, which is itself produced by high temperature carbonisation of coal. Progressive distillation leads from light oils through carbolic oil, creosote oil and anthracene oil to pitch as the residual product, and the range of coal tar fuels (CTF) is prepared by re-blending these fractions. The resulting heavy aromatic-rich blends are classified according to the temperature (in °F) at which the viscosity falls to 24.1 cSt (100 Redwood I seconds) which is suitable for atomisation, and range from CTF 50, 100, 200, 250 and 300 to 400.[9] The first two fuels are blends of the light oil fractions, whereas the following three are blends of the liquids with CTF 400 which is the pitch residue in 'medium soft' form, with a softening point of 75 to 85 °C. Their relative densities range from about 0.95 to 1.31. They are not compatible with petroleum fuels since admixture leads to unmanageable deposits of pitch from solution, but for use in oil burners, the following pairs of fuels may be regarded as roughly equivalent

CTF 100 — light fuel oil, Class E

CTF 200 — medium fuel oil, Class F

CTF 250 — heavy fuel oil, Class G

The ultimate analysis in mass percentages of a typical CTF 200 (a 50/50

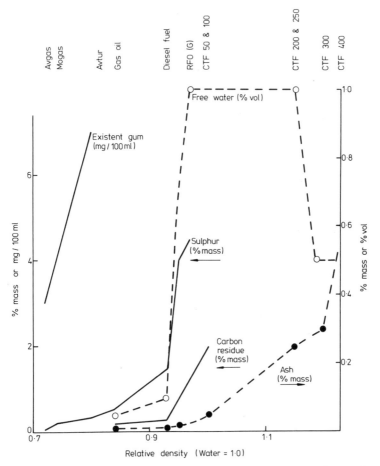

Figure 3.2   Maximum specified concentrations of contaminants in petroleum and coal tar fuels

blend of pitch/creosote) is as follows

C	89.0
H	6.4
S	0.5
O	3.0
N	1.0
Ash	0.1

giving a hydrogen/carbon atomic ratio of about 0.857.

Although the CTFs have lower specific energies, and are more difficult to atomise than their petroleum counterparts, they have been used to advantage for open-hearth furnaces in steelmaking due to their relative freedom from contamination with sulphur and vanadium, and their high luminosity. They are also suitable for the manufacture of cement and glass.

3.4 Conventional Solid Fuels

The majority of solid fuels are derived from vegetable matter, consequently the first conventional fuel to be considered in this group is the vegetable matter itself, in the form of wood. In view of its wide availability, rapid reproduction, free burning quality and relative lack of ash, fuel wood has served as a general-purpose fuel for many centuries, and still represents a major source of domestic heating and cooking in some areas where other fuels are not readily available. The major component of wood is cellulose, $(C_6H_{10}O_5)_n$, and a modified form, lignin, comprises the combustible portion together with any resin present. The water content ranges from about 50 per cent by mass in the freshly cut 'green' condition, to about 10 per cent when air-dried. The inorganic ash content does not exceed about 0.6 per cent, but the oxygen content is high, and the specific energy correspondingly low. Woods range in combustion quality from ash to fir, graded excellent and poor respectively, whether in the green or dry state, and a representative ultimate analysis is shown in table A4.4. The carbonisation or incomplete combustion of wood drives off most of the combined oxygen, the residual charcoal, although only about 20 per cent of the initial mass of the wood, having a higher specific energy.

The density of any solid material which tends to exist in discrete particles can be expressed in two ways

1. Lump density = mass per unit volume of a single lump
2. Bulk density = mass per unit volume containing many lumps with air voids between them

This excludes the complications of porosity which would need to be taken into account for more accurate combustion work. For comparative purposes here, the more precise lump density has been adopted, and the lump based relative densities for wood range from about 0.5 to 1.1.

The range of solid fuels from peat to anthracite derived from vegetable matter deposited in water arises through a process of coalification initiated by anaerobic bacteria, and continued under the action of temperature and pressure within the Earth's crust over a period of several million years. The first stage in this natural conversion of vegetable matter is peat, a partly decomposed material originating from either aquatic plants (bog peat) or tree growths (forest peat) under temperate marshy conditions, with a growth rate of about 1 mm per year. The composition and properties depend on the location, nature of the original vegetable matter, and the processes of decay, but a representative ultimate analysis is included in table A4.4. Raw peat is associated with over 90 per cent of water, and so requires draining before recovery by hand cutting or by dredging machines. Alternatively, thin layers of peat may be milled from the surface of the bog for drying and briquetting or, in awkwardly timbered bogs, 'hydropeat' recovery practised by displacing the peat with water jets, and spreading it over cambered surfaces for drying. Air drying reduces the moisture content to about 25 per cent, but spontaneous ignition of the drying stocks presents a problem. The relative density of air-dried peat is about 0.5, but is increased to about 0.8 by maceration, and to 1.25 by briquetting.

The carbon dioxide produced during coalification is neutralised by the alkalinity of the clay overburden, the nature of which may be an important factor in the type of coal eventually formed. As the coal material matures, there is a progressive loss in the volatile matter containing the hydrogen and oxygen, and an increase in the relative proportion of carbon. The content of water also reduces, but this depends on previous conditions of storage, consequently coal samples are usually air-dried under specified conditions (typically, 60 per cent relative humidity at 15.5 °C) before testing. Since solid fuels also tend to contain inorganic ash, analysis and performance are frequently assessed on a dry ash-free (daf) basis or, more accurately, on a dry mineral-matter-free (dmmf) basis. The structure of the remaining coal substance, when examined by low angle X-rays, is found to be in the form of platelets, each comprising 3 to 30 fused benzene rings, interconnected by carbon chains of 2 to 5 atoms in length. The main members of the peat-to-anthracite series are discussed briefly below, and details of their ultimate analyses included in table A4.4.

The second member of this series is lignite, or brown coal, which is dark brown in colour, with a pronounced earthy or woody texture. The moisture content ranges from about 60 per cent as mined, to about 20 per cent when air dried. The brown coals tend to shrink and disintegrate on drying, and are therefore briquetted for handling convenience. Spontaneous ignition is a problem due to the ready absorption of oxygen. The third member is black lignite, or high-volatility sub-bituminous coal, which is pitch-like, being sufficiently mature to show no obvious signs of fibrous structure.

Medium-volatility bituminous coal is black, hard and usually banded parallel to the bedding plane. Its good heating and handling qualities render it the general-purpose solid fuel for domestic and industrial purposes. Two significant properties of the coal fuels are their ability for individual particles to adhere to one another on heating (caking), and to soften, swell and resolidify with shrinkage to form coke (coking), rather than remaining as a soft easily crushed charred residue. All coking coals are therefore caking, but only some caking coals are able to form hard coke of sufficient strength to maintain a cellular structure on the furnace bed, permitting gaseous through-flow. Caking power can be determined by the Gray–King assay test, and the swelling necessary for coking by the crucible test. The ability to cake increases with carbon content up to a maximum at about 90 per cent carbon.

Low-volatility semi-bituminous coal, or semi-anthracite, represents a hard intermediate stage between bituminous coal and true anthracite, as shown in table A4.4. Anthracite itself is the ultimate form of metamorphosis of the original vegetable matter, and thus the member of highest rank in the series. It has a sub-metallic lustre, approaching the appearance of graphite, together with zero caking power. The main uses of anthracite are in industrial boilers, metallurgical furnaces and domestic stoves.

More precise methods are available for identifying and classifying the various types of coal. In Seyler's coal chart, percentage carbon is plotted against percentage hydrogen, and the location of the point within a broad band for the types of coal in the coalfield concerned is related to many other properties. More recent systems include the Coal Rank Numbers of the National Coal Board, based jointly on the percentage content of volatile matter and the caking quality. An international system derived for classifying the hard coals in Europe is an elaboration of the NCB scheme, based on volatile matter together with specific energy, and sub-divided according to the caking properties, and then to the type of coke produced on carbonisation.

Some coals exist outside the peat-to-anthracite series owing to their derivation from spores, algae and other small types of plant life. Cannel coal

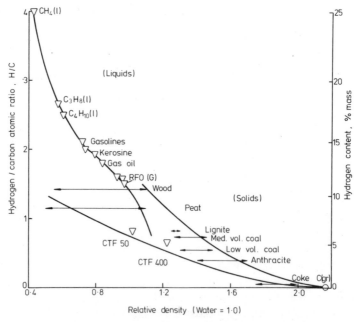

Figure 3.3   Estimated H/C atomic ratio of commercial fuels

is one such, containing a relatively higher propertion of hydrogen and volatile matter generally, and is so named in view of the candle-like nature of its flame. It is hard and tough with a dull black lustre, whereas one of its variants, boghead coal or torbanite, appears dull brownish. The H/C atomic ratio of all the commercial fuel types from methane to solids are shown in figure 3,3.

3.5 Oxidants

Atmospheric air is the most common oxidant used for all types of fuel and, for the handling of combustion calculations, its oxygen concentration is indicated in table A4.7. Allowance is made for the presence of traces of argon and carbon dioxide with the nitrogen to give 'atmospheric' nitrogen, with the following quantities

$$\text{'Atmospheric' } N_2/O_2 \quad \text{ratio} = 3.76 \text{ by volume (molar)}$$
$$= 3.31 \text{ by mass}$$

$$\text{Molar mass of air} = MM \text{ air} = (28.150 \times 0.790) + (31.9988 \times 0.210)$$
$$= 28.960 \text{ approximately, g/mol}$$

$$\text{Density of air} = \frac{\text{molar mass}}{\text{molar volume}}$$
$$= 28.960/22.414$$
$$= 1.292 \text{ kg/m}^3 \text{ at 1 atm and } 0\,^{\circ}\text{C}$$
$$(= 1.225 \text{ kg/m}^3 \text{ at 1 atm and } 15\,^{\circ}\text{C})$$

A number of concentrated oxidants are used in applications where very rapid reaction rates and high temperatures are paramount, as in rocketry and some aspects of steelmaking and other chemical processes. Oxygen itself is frequently preferred, and has been available on a 'tonnage' basis for some time. Its storage volume is reduced markedly by liquefaction, but it is then cryogenic, consequently such other oxidants as hydrogen peroxide (as concentrated 'high-test' peroxide, HTP), nitric acid and nitrogen tetroxide are considered as alternatives, particularly for rocketry. Since fuels react with fluorine by a comparable oxidation-type process, these alternative oxidants also include fluorine, chlorine trifluoride and oxygen difluoride (see table A4.7). As already suggested in the literature, some future applications of alternative fuels may also incur the use of such alternative oxidants.

References

1. E. M. Goodger, *Hydrocarbon Fuels*, Macmillan, London and Basingstoke (1975).

2. BS 4250:1968 Specifications for commercial butane and propane.
3. BS 4947:1973 Specifications for test gases and gas appliances.
4. DERD 2485, Issue 8, December 1978 Aviation gasolines, AVGAS.
5. BS 4040:1971 Specifications for petrol (gasoline) for motor vehicles.
6. DERD 2486, Issue 9, December 1978 Aviation turbine fuel, AVTAG.
7. DERD 2494, Issue 8, October 1978 Aviation turbine fuel, AVTUR.
8. BS 2869:1970 Specifications for petroleum fuels for oil engines and burners.
9. BS 1469:1962 Specifications for coal tar fuels.

4. Candidate Alternative Fuels

Faced with the impending decline of fossil fuel reserves, first reactions are to exercise greater economy over existing uses of energy, as exemplified by the 'Save it' campaign in the United Kingdom. It is no longer locally acceptable, for example, to flare off excess quantities of petroleum gases, or of low-grade industrial by-product gases, which are now expected to be consumed usefully either as energy sources or as feedstock for other products. Equally important are attempts at more logical and integrated usage patterns of existing resources, with better matching of large-scale availability to large-scale consumption, and of special-quality fuels to special-requirement applications. The wider interpretation of the term 'alternative fuels', therefore, starts with those cases in which conventional fuels are utilised either in some alternative form, or in some alternative application (somewhat analogous to the zeroth law located before the three main laws in thermodynamics). Their purpose is to permit the use of the more-available less-expensive fuels, particularly for large-scale operation, and/or to improve combustion. Although, in fact, some of these forms and applications are now becoming so commonplace as to approach the conventional, they are included early in the following sections in the sense of 'alternatives' to long-established practices, and therefore precursors of the alternative options of the future.

Of the alternative fuels proper, the first group considered here comprises those in which conventional fuels are 'simulated' by means of mixtures of fuels which are generally similar in type but identical in a few key properties only, and need to be used under prescribed conditions in order to match the performance of the conventional fuels they replace. They represent a temporary replacement only, since their origins also are fossil based, and they are more likely to be used locally.

In view of the massive investment represented by present-day fuel distribution and combustion equipment, and given further time for development, the next group of alternative fuels considered are those which are virtually identical with conventional fuels, and therefore compatible with

33

them and their associated equipment, in admixture or alone. Fuels of this kind may be termed 'supplemental' since they supplement existing supplies by being derived from alternative sources. These fuels also tend to be fossil-based, and therefore temporary sources only.

The chemical definition of synthesis is the formation of a compound by the combination of its components. These may be the elements themselves, consequently hydrocarbon fuels, for example, could be produced synthetically from elemental hydrogen and carbon, and be designed to meet the required properties. They could be produced indefinitely subject to the availability of the two elements, but an overall energy deficit is unavoidable from the formation and subsequent combustion.

With continuing depletion of conventional fuel stocks, simulation and supplementation will be progressive, and lead eventually to permanent 'substitution' by fuels which may be distinctly different in type, properties and performance, as well as in origin. The above considerations therefore lead to the following classification of alternative fuels.

1. Alternative forms of conventional fuel:
less expensive fuels usable, and/or combustion improved
(examples: pulverised or pelletised coal, and slurry, homogenised or emulsified liquid fuels).

2. Alternative applications of conventional fuel:
less expensive fuels usable, and/or combustion improved
(examples: liquefied hydrocarbon gases in piston engines, and heavy fuels in gas turbines).

3. Simulated fuels:
temporary replacements from alternative origins, matching key properties only of conventional fuels
(example: mixtures of petroleum gas with air simulating natural gas).

4. Supplemental fuels:
temporary compatible sources from alternative origins, virtually identical with conventional fuels
(examples: supplemental natural gas, and coal liquefaction products).

5. Elemental synthesis fuels:
permanent compatible sources from alternative origins, virtually identical with conventional fuels
(example: hydrocarbons derived from water and calcium carbonate using nuclear power for initial isolation of elements).

6. Substitute fuels:
permanent replacements, with properties and origins unrelated to those of conventional fuels
(examples: hydrogen, alcohols, nitrogen hydrides, nitrohydrocarbons, solid municipal waste, biofuels).

Although not classified here among the alternatives, fuels of particularly high levels of energy content have been of practical interest for many years as reactants for such applications as high-speed flight and rocket propulsion. These high-energy fuels are frequently the result of replacing the carbon in the hydrocarbons with some element contributing more calorific value to the resultant liquid hydride. However, since their future use could possibly be based on the conservation of more conventional fuels rather than on their performance potential, they are included here for completeness in the following additional group.

7. High-energy fuels:
permanent sources of superior energy content, and of alternative origins (examples: hydrides of boron, beryllium, lithium, magnesium, aluminium or titanium, and compounds of hydrogen, carbon and boron).

In all cases, practices which permit the use of wider-range or multifuels in any given application are attractive since they provide flexibility and optimisation of fuel selection, with extension of fossil fuel life, and a longer 'breathing period' available for development of alternative sources of energy.

4.1 Alternative Forms of Conventional Fuels

The earlier conventional concept of the combustion of coal is that of a fixed, or latterly a moving, grate on which a bed of relatively large particles of coal undergoes combustion due to the supply of primary, and subsequently secondary, air permitting the evolution of hot product gases and the retention on the bed of a protective layer of product ash. Too fine a size of coal particulate renders difficult the passage of air through the bed, and effectively chokes combustion, consequently minimal particle sizing is important. However, coal in pulverised form has a substantially increased area of surface, and can be burnt rapidly while maintained airborne in furnaces which provide long residence times, as in water-tube boilers and cement kilns. This permits a long flame and therefore virtually complete combustion with a minimum of excess air, together with high efficiency and little smoke. This system of combustion also offers good control flexibility, acceptance of a wide variety of fuel grades, and a strongly radiating flame. The coal is pulverised to an extent that about 75 per cent passes through a 75 μm sieve, which entails relatively high costs of milling, and also of gas cleaning plant for the removal of product fines carried over from the furnace. As an established fuel, therefore, pulverised coal represents an early example of a conventional fuel used to advantage in an alternative form. Pelletising or briquetting also permits the free flow of air through the fuel bed, and other examples follow.

The suspension of pulverised coal in liquid fuel to form a slurry offers the dual advantages of more convenient handling and of flexibility in the choice of both liquid fuel properties and coal–liquid proportions, up to about 60 per cent by mass of coal, depending on relative prices. Fuels of this type became attractive following the rise in price of coke for blast furnace use, and it was found that both coal size distribution and moisture content were far less critical than with pulverised fuel alone. Slurry fuels are also of interest in cases where fuel bulk presents problems of aerodynamic drag, as in high-speed flight, and slurries of solid carbon, boron, aluminium, etc., in petroleum-based liquids have been proposed for ramjet use in view of their relatively high levels of energy density (see section 5.4).

The heavier residual fuel oils contain asphaltic bitumen and tar components together with solid sediment to the extent of about 0.5 per cent by mass. All these materials are organic, with combustion energy potential, but are of particularly high viscosity, and therefore difficult to atomise using conventional equipment. Their removal and disposal by filtration or centrifugal separation represents both a handling cost and a loss of useful energy, and an attractive alternative is to break them down to a particulate size of 1 to 5 μm and distribute them thoroughly throughout the fuel so that they can be atomised and burnt in the usual way Both these requirements can be met by a process of homogenisation in which the fuel oil is subjected either to a grinding action within a cylinder,[1] or to passage under pressure through a small annulus.[2] Such low grade materials as colliery washings, sewage sludge, pulverised waste and sawdust may also be prepared and burnt in this manner, and the technique permits the uniform distribution of additives.

The dispersion of a liquid of relatively high vapour pressure throughout a residual type base fuel provides a very effective secondary stage of atomisation. This arises because the spray emerges primarily in the form of small droplets of the volatile additive liquid enveloped by shells of fuel oil. The fall in pressure in passing through the atomiser, coupled with the rise in temperature due to the proximity of the flame, leads to micro explosions as the small liquid droplets flash distil, which shatter the fuel oil shells and provide secondary atomisation into much finer droplets. The high vapour-pressure liquid may be water rather than some other fuel and, in practice, a volumetric concentration of about 6 per cent is found optimal, with a droplet size between about 1 to 5 μm. This infers that the water or other added liquid must be very thoroughly admixed, that is, emulsified with the base fuel, and these types of fuel are therefore described either as dispersion or emulsified. The emulsification can be effected by mechanical (as in homogenising), ultrasonic or chemical means, but subsequent physical stability can be retained only in the presence of emulsifying agents. With residual fuel oils, the natural content of tars, sludges and bitumens provides sufficient quantities of such agents, but artificial agents are required in the lighter petroleum-based fuels. Useful increases in combustion efficiency and outlet temperature traverse quality are claimed, with generally lower emissions. In essence, therefore, valuable improvements in combustion performance are possible by the pre-treatment of fuels into alternative forms.

36

4.2 Alternative Applications of Conventional Fuels

On the basis that gasoline is the conventional fuel for the spark-ignition reciprocating-piston engine, a mixture of liquefied hydrocarbon gases, which are themselves conventional fuels with wide ranges of established use, represents an alternative fuel in this particular application. These hydrocarbon gases offer several significant advantages in piston engine combustion since they exhibit high resistance to both spark knock and surface ignition, and so permit higher compression ratios with corresponding improvements in thermal efficiency. Their lack of contaminants also results in good thermal stability, low flame radiation and clean burning. For transport, the high specific energies of these fuels result in improved range. Secondary advantages arise from the availability of heat capacity when stored as cryogenic liquids in refrigerated trucks. Their disadvantages include low flame speed, and the low density and temperature requirements for large tanks with cryogenic insulation.

At the other end of the scale, the growth in industrial applications of the gas turbine suggests a corresponding adaptation to fuels which arise as by-products from other processes. The gas turbine was developed initially on kerosine for aero use, and subsequently on gas oil/diesel fuel for industry. Satisfactory performance with residual fuel oils, and subsequently coal or coal-oil slurries, would match more closely the existing availability pattern of these less-expensive fossil-based fuels, and promote flexibility. Also, despite the intrinsic value of crude oil due to its wide variety of components, adaptation to the direct use of crude oil at the wellhead or in pipeline pumping stations would be invaluable for such remote locations as the desert or offshore. However, early attempts with fuels containing appreciable quantities of metallic and other inorganic ash components invariably showed problems of turbine-blade fouling and corrosion and, until recently, practical interest in heavy-fuelled gas turbines waned after a peak of activity in 1954. The problems arise because, although solid ash particles pass through the turbine disc, liquid droplets tend to deposit on the blades by either impact or eddy motion. Turbine blade problems thus depend largely on the relative levels of ash melting point and blade metal temperature, and are exacerbated by the steady rise in level of operating temperature, and by the ample time for deposit build up resulting from the industrial engine life requirement of some 40 000 hours. The two principal contaminants of heavy fuels are sodium and vanadium, the products of which attack the protective oxide layer and/or base metal of the turbine blades.

4.3 Simulated Fuels

With regard to the gaseous fuels, the first key parameter used in simulating the combustion performance of conventional natural gas is the Wobbe number, *Wo*. As described more fully in chapter 5, gases of matched values of

Wo will each pass the same rate of energy through a given burner orifice under the same conditions. For equal levels of operating gas pressure, Wobbe number is defined as

$$Wo = \frac{\text{energy density}}{(\text{relative density})^{\frac{1}{2}}}$$

Figure 4.1 shows that blends of volume ratio 61/39 propane–air, and of 49/51 butane–air, both simulate natural gas in view of their common values of *Wo*. In no case does the calorific value or the relative density of the matching gas alone, or its admixture with air, equal the corresponding property of natural gas.

The stability of a flame established at a gas burner located in air is determined by the ability of the flame speed to equal the gas flow speed at some surface within the reasonably close vicinity of the burner orifice. If the speed of gas flow is reduced progressively, the flame approaches the burner orifice, and eventually 'flashes back' into it. Conversely, if the flow speed is increased, the flame lengthens, and eventually 'lifts off' from the rim of the orifice. Interchangeability of simulated and any other fuel gases therefore depends also on reasonably comparable flame speeds. One early method of comparison is the Weaver flame speed factor, expressed on an arbitrary scale based on a factor of 100 for hydrogen. In the Gilbert–Prigg system, as used in

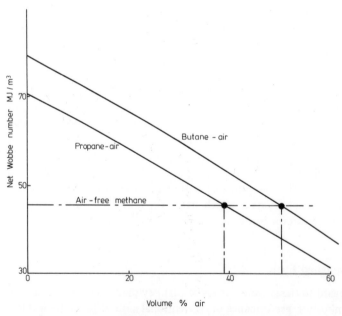

Figure 4.1   Use of Wobbe number to simulate natural gas

38

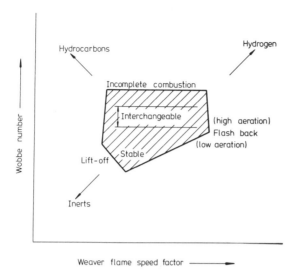

Figure 4.2   Gaseous fuel interchangeability diagram – Gilbert–Prigg system

the United Kingdom, the limits of flash back, lift off and incomplete combustion (giving a yellow-tipped flame due to fuel-cracked carbon) are plotted on a diagram with Wobbe number as ordinate and the Weaver flame speed factor as abscissa (figure 4.2). Fuel gases are then considered interchangeable if their plotted points lie inside the prescribed area and within acceptable displacement from each other. In a recent approach,[3] better prediction is claimed by means of a three-dimensional tetrahedral representation, based on the four major groups of constituents: hydrogen, methane, other hydrocarbons (expressed as equivalent propane) and inerts (expressed as equivalent carbon dioxide).

4.4 Supplemental Fuels

The fossil fuels first requiring supplementation are likely to be those which offer attractive performance and handling characteristics, and are therefore already in widespread use. These include natural gas (NG) which was seen in section 3.2 to have emerged as the conventional gaseous fuel because of its direct availability with minimal treatment, together with its attractive calorific value, clean burning capability and wide flammability range. For these same reasons, it has also become the quality standard of comparison for the gaseous fuels generally. Another popular fuel is gasoline for the automobile market, and processes are being investigated for its production from non-petroleum sources. Both these areas of supplementation are discussed briefly in the following sections, and considered in more detail in chapter 9.

4.4.1 Supplemental Natural Gas (SNG)

High-quality fuel gases of mainly methane composition are obtainable from a wide variety of feedstocks including the fossil range from petroleum gases to bituminous coal. Production costs are limited if the source molecules are light and simple, with high hydrogen content and low contaminants, but competitive demands, availabilities and price levels have directed attention to the heavier petroleum products, to crude oils themselves, and to coals.

The general requirements for a SNG feedstock may be summarised as follows.

1. Low carbon content, to minimise the necessary increase in hydrogen/carbon ratio using expensive hydrogen.

2. Low aromatic content to meet requirement 1, and to avoid liquid aromatic by-products.

3. Low content of olefins and other unsaturateds, to meet requirement 1.

4. Minimal content of contaminants which may poison conversion catalysts.

The processes of gasification of the heavier hydrocarbons of relatively low volatility and high contamination involve a rise in hydrogen/carbon atomic ratio from about 1.5 to 4, and can be achieved by hydrogen addition, carbon subtraction or a combination of both. With increasing complexity of feedstock, typical gasification processes appear as follows.

1. *Catalytic steam reforming of light hydrocarbons.* At relatively low temperatures between about 450 and 500 °C, and in the presence of very active catalysts, light hydrocarbons may be partially converted by a process of hydrolysis into methane and carbon dioxide, together with hydrogen which can then help to convert the carbon dioxide to additional methane. At appropriate conditions where the proportions of methane and carbon dioxide are equal, the reaction equation for a paraffinic feedstock is represented as follows

$$C_xH_{2x+2} + xH_2O \longrightarrow \frac{x}{2}CH_4 + \frac{x}{2}CO_2 + (x+1)H_2 \tag{12}$$

Methanation of carbon oxides with hydrogen is shown as

$$CO_2 + 4H_2 \longrightarrow CH_4 + 2H_2O \tag{9}$$

$$CO + 3H_2 \longrightarrow CH_4 + H_2O \tag{8}$$

and these subsequent steps may be undertaken separately. The overall process is carried out at a relatively high pressure of about 20 bar, and careful control needs to be exercised over operating conditions and fuel contaminant concentrations. Suitable feedstocks for this method include LPG, virgin naphtha and NG condensates which are generally free from catalyst-poisoning sulphur, unreactive aromatics and the unsaturated hydrocarbons.

2. *Hydrogasification of middle distillates and light residues*. The direct
bonding of hydrocarbons with hydrogen may be effected by hydrogenolysis
at high pressure and low temperature, represented for the heavier $C_x H_{2x}$
feedstocks as follows

$$C_x H_{2x} + xH_2 \longrightarrow xCH_4 \tag{13}$$

A catalyst is not normally necessary, but some carbon is formed due to
molecular cracking, particularly with the heavier feedstocks.

Suitable feedstocks include gas oils, diesel fuels and light fuel oils which
are generally free of sulphur, avoiding expensive removal of hydrogen
sulphide, and of aromatics which lower the gasification efficiency.

3. *Partial oxidation of residual oils and coal.* In this method, carbon is
removed from the heavy hydrocarbon feedstock by oxygenolysis at high
temperature to give methane and carbon monoxide, the latter being converted
subsequently by methanation. The overall reaction for the heavier $C_x H_{2x}$
feedstock may be represented as follows

$$C_x H_{2x} + \frac{x}{2} O_2 \longrightarrow \frac{x}{2} CH_4 + \frac{x}{2} CO_2 \tag{14}$$

A catalyst is not normally necessary. Suitable feedstocks include medium and
heavy fuel oils, and steam coals, preferably low in ash, sulphur, nitrogen and
moisture. Limited supplies of methane may also be forthcoming as
unavoidable by-products of cracking and other processes in the oil refinery.

A large number of individual carbon—hydrogen—oxygen reactions are
involved overall, and gasification efficiency and economy demand that the
endothermic and exothermic reaction energies be balanced as far as possible
in order to minimise the input of external energy and the loss of released heat.
Of the feedstocks outlined above, the straight-run liquids, low in aromatics,
are preferred to the cracked or reformed stocks, but only coal is likely to
meet the joint requirements of stable price and continuing long-term
availability.

4.4.2 Supplemental Liquid Fuels

Conventional liquid fuels of non-petroleum origin are obtainable from such
fossil resources as shale oil, tar (in sands) and coal. Oil shale contains resinous
remains of vegetation which, on heating, decompose to a complex oily liquid
(kerogen) containing a relatively high proportion of compounds of sulphur,
nitrogen and oxygen, from which a synthetic crude oil (syncrude) may be
derived. Oil shales are usually mined by conventional methods and then
treated in vertical distillation retorts over the temperature range 500 to
700 °C. *In situ* distillation has been attempted by means of electrical heating
underground. Shale syncrude is usually rich in aromatics (35 per cent), with

relatively high concentrations of wax, sulphur and oil-bound nitrogen. Although its octane rating is high, it tends to smoky combustion, high pour point (35 °C), corrosive emissions and thermal instability. Hydrogenation improves most of these factors, but is an expensive process.

Tars (asphalts, pitches, bitumens, etc.) are generally difficult to handle due to cohesion with their reservoir rock or sand, although some tars can be separated by hot water. Liquid fuels can be derived by solvent extraction giving yields comparable with those from oil shale.

In the liquefaction of coal, as with the supplementation of natural gas, one of the main objectives is to increase the hydrogen/carbon ratio. A relatively small increase in this ratio produces a fairly heavy liquid similar to a petroleum-based residual fuel oil. This type of fuel is suited to electrical power generation, replacing the high sulphur coal found in such areas as the eastern United States. The higher, more expensive, degree of hydrogenation, on the other hand, produces hydrocarbon fractions comparable to gasoline, and these are the liquids expected to be required eventually from United Kingdom coals, following depletion of North Sea oil. The three main routes to the liquefaction of coal are as follows

1. *Hydrocarbonisation.* Carbonisation (heating in the absence of air) breaks down the structure of the polymerised benzene-like coal molecules through thermal agitation (pyrolysis) resulting in coal gas and coke, giving as by-products the carbon-rich fluids coal tar and crude benzole. Although the coal tars themselves are classed as conventional fuels for furnaces and boilers, they can also be treated to yield conventional types of fuel oil, whereas motor benzole (an aromatic blend of approximately 70 per cent benzene, 18 per cent toluene, 8 per cent xylenes and 4 per cent other hydrocarbons) has long been of interest as a high anti-knock blending component of gasoline. However, the initial costs of coke-oven plant are too high for the production of such liquids to be economical, and current improvements include both the adoption of a fluidised bed of coal and carbonisation in the presence of hydrogen gas at moderate pressure. The hot unreacted coke may be used as the vehicle to extract the necessary hydrogen from a supply of steam and oxygen.

2. *Indirect Hydrogenation.* The coal is first gasified to syngas (carbon monoxide and hydrogen) as in the Lurgi system, followed by a Fischer–Tropsch conversion to liquid hydrocarbons using a catalyst. Such impurities as carbon dioxide and hydrogen sulphide are removed between the two stages. Plants of this type exist in the Federal Republic of Germany, Australia, South Africa and Scotland.

3. *Direct Hydrogenation.* More efficient methods of liquefaction are carried out directly either with or without a catalyst. For example, the stream of pulverised coal, usually in the form of 'slurry oil' or 'pasting oil' using recycled liquid products, is reacted with hydrogen gas at high pressure within a reaction vessel, usually containing a catalyst which is either fixed or

42

fluidised. Alternatively, in the extraction process the coal slurry is depolymer-
ised by means of a solvent, in some cases the solvent donating hydrogen to the
dissolved carbon compounds. Materials suitable as donor solvents include the
hydroaromatics tetralin (tetrahydronaphthalene) and hydrogenated anthracene,
which dehydrogenate to the normal polynuclear or fused ring form, as shown.

Tetralin , $C_{10}H_{12}$ Naphthalene , $C_{10}H_8$

Hydrogenated anthracene , $C_{14}H_{14}$ Anthracene , $C_{14}H_{10}$

4.5 Elemental Synthesis Fuels

A synthetic material is one which is produced by the combination of its
components, which may themselves be compounds of smaller components.
Synthesis is no doubt included with many other reactions in a wide variety of
production processes, but it is not necessarily dominant. In this study, most
of these types of fuel are found to segregate naturally into one or other of
the different groupings, with the exception of those derived by direct
synthesis of the parent elements, which are considered here.

It is technically feasible to prepare hydrocarbon blends, for example, with
properties approaching those of conventional fuels by the synthesis of
inorganic-based elemental hydrogen and carbon provided substantial energy
resources are available for the initial isolation of the elements and their
subsequent combination. Hydrogen has an inexhaustible source in water,
whereas carbon could be derived from calcium carbonate in limestone form,
atmospheric carbon-dioxide, or biomatter. The overall energy requirement
would probably be met from solar or off-peak nuclear sources.

When the elemental feedstock is also the oxide product, as is the case with
hydrogen from water, the reaction energy is being recycled by being supplied
during elemental isolation, and released on subsequent combustion. Since
some inefficiency is unavoidably associated with both processes, the overall
result must be an energy deficit. Fuel synthesis therefore implies an energy-
expensive approach which can be considered for special cases only. With
suitable control and blending, synthesis has the merit that the resulting fuels

43

could be so similar to the conventional that no radically new systems of distribution, or design of combustor, are required. Furthermore, fuel types can be changed by synthesis adjustment to suit combustor developments.

4.6 Substitute Fuels

The main feature of a substitute for a conventional fuel is that it should be relatively freely available, and its interchangeability, although highly desirable, is secondary since some further development of combustor and fuel systems to give compatibility with the substitute is almost inevitable. However, any fuel, by its very nature, is an energy store, consequently the level of energy stored is of immediate interest. Furthermore, since the fuel must have material substance in which to store the energy, two major requirements arise for any substitute fuel

1. it should comprise matter which is either available in abundance or, preferably, can be replenished in adequate quantities

2. it should possess an adequate level of chemical bond energy which can be relatively easily reduced to promote an outflow in the form of heat and/or work.

The fossil fuels have been seen to possess very useful quantities of energy, but their material supplies are not being replenished in view of the geological time scale required for formation, consequently they, and their stored energies, are depleting. In the following discussion, it will be seen that some substitute fuels are likely to be relatively freely available both in material and energy terms, whereas others can be made available plentifully as materials, but will have to be charged with energy during their formation, resulting in an overall energy deficit. With these concepts in mind, several candidate substitute fuels are considered below, arranged broadly in ascending order of molecular complexity.

4.6.1 Hydrogen

Diatomic hydrogen represents the simplest molecular structure of a fuel, and is attractive for its abundance (ninth in terms of mass, and third in terms of numbers of atoms) throughout the biosphere, and also its very high level of specific energy. Currently, industrial quantities of hydrogen gas are most economically derived from fossil sources, and production methods include the following.

1. Low temperature removal of non-hydrogen constitutents (for example, methane) from refinery tail gases or coke oven gas.

2. Water-gas shift reaction (6) either by cyclic steam/water gas over iron

oxide bed, or by continuous catalysis, with carbon dioxide removal by washing or absorption.

3. Production of synthesis gas by steam reforming of natural gas or of other hydrocarbon feedstock

$$CH_4 + H_2O \longrightarrow CO + 3H_2 \qquad\qquad (15)$$

followed by water-gas shift reaction (6) and carbon dioxide removal.

4. Production of synthesis gas by direct conversion of coal with oxygen and steam

$$3C + O_2 + H_2O \longrightarrow 3CO + H_2 \qquad\qquad (16)$$

followed by water-gas shift reaction (6) and carbon dioxide removal.

5. Production of synthesis gas by partial oxidation of hydrocarbons

$$CH_4 + \tfrac{1}{2}O_2 \longrightarrow CO + H_2 \qquad\qquad (17)$$

followed by water-gas shift reaction (6) and carbon dioxide removal.

The future of hydrogen as an alternative fuel, of course, requires other than fossil sources, and possible routes are through the large-scale dissociation of water via electrical or thermochemical processes, as discussed in chapter 9.

4.6.2 Alcohol Fuels

The monohydric alcohol molecule consists of a hydrocarbon in which one atom of hydrogen has been substituted by a hydroxyl group, thus it is represented by the formula ROH, where R is the remaining hydrocarbon group. Of main interest as alternative fuels are the first four normal members of the alkyl alcohols, of which symbol R indicates one of the alkyl groups CH_3 methyl to C_4H_9 butyl. Details of molecular structure and systems of nomenclature are outlined in appendix 1.

Methanol (CH_3OH) was formerly derived from the destructive distillation of wood (hence 'wood alcohol'), but synthetic processes were introduced in 1923 and production now stems from feedstocks of methane, carbon dioxide and water derived from naphtha, residual fuel oil, vacuum residue, or from coal. The ICI low-pressure process introduced in 1966, operating at about 50 bar and using a highly active copper-based catalyst, led to large increases in plant capacity to the 'jumbo' level of over 5000 tonne/day. High pressure (300 bar) processes are also used, with zinc–chromium as catalysts.

The next member, ethanol (C_2H_5OH), is currently made from ethylene derived from petroleum, but can be produced in bulk using yeasts at controlled temperature, by fermentation of the carbohydrates from a variety of vegetable sources. These include the starches from artichokes, potatoes, cassava and cereal grains (hence 'grain alcohol'), the sugars from sugar cane and beet, fruit juices and molasses, the cellulosic materials from wood, tropical grasses, straw

45

and the waste sulphite liquor from the production of wood pulp for paper mills. Propanol (C_3H_7OH), butanol (C_4H_9OH) and other higher alcohols (jointly termed 'fusel oil') are derived either from fermentation of corn, maize or molasses, or from synthetic processes using lower alcohols, acetone, aldehydes, and so on. A mixture of methanol and higher alcohols has been named 'Methyl fuel' by the former Vulcan–Cincinnatti organisation.

4.6.3 Nitrogen Hydrides

The two major members of this group are ammonia (NH_3) and hydrazine (N_2H_4) which are gaseous and liquid respectively at normal ambient temperatures. Since the parent elements are present in air and water, synthesis from these abundant natural materials is feasible, provided energy is available for the purpose, possibly from a nuclear power unit under off-peak conditions. Industrially, ammonia is manufactured by the Haber process of direct reaction of nitrogen and hydrogen

$$N_2 + 3H_2 \longrightarrow 2NH_3 \tag{18}$$

at about 500 °C and between 200 and 1000 bar using catalysts, and small-scale production is already under way using electrolytically generated hydrogen. Hydrazine is produced by partial oxidation of ammonia by hypochlorite, as in the endothermic Raschig process, represented overall as follows

$$2NH_3 \longrightarrow N_2H_4 + H_2 \tag{19}$$

Although nitrogen is inert, and therefore cannot contribute greatly to the energy content of its compounds, nitrogen hydrides are worthy of consideration as alternative fuels. Apart from their availability, under some conditions of combustion the quantity of energy actually usable in service is more important than that released during an idealised laboratory test for calorific value, and the nitrogen hydrides can be effective on this basis.

4.6.4 Nitrohydrocarbons

The nitroparaffins are produced by nitration of the paraffin vapours, giving nitromethane, CH_3NO_2, nitroethane, $C_2H_5NO_2$, 1- and 2-nitropropane, $C_3H_7NO_2$, and so on. Being based on hydrocarbons, they are not strong contenders as alternative fuels in the long term, unless they can be formed from otherwise unusable carbon–hydrogen materials, and/or have some particular performance advantages over other fuels.

4.6.5 Solid Municipal Wastes

From the earliest times of human society, the most direct method for disposing of communal waste products has been by dumping on or under the ground to await natural decomposition, and the locations of such aggregations have progressed from the floors of cave homes to remote distances from residential areas limited mainly by the range of transport of the period. In most developed countries, the majority of waste disposal is still by controlled landfill at sites which are intended to be both technically and environmentally acceptable. This method consists of tipping in about 2 m thick layers, topped by 150 mm layers of inert 'blinding' material. It generally involves least capital and operating costs, and can be utilised to restore derelict land. However, suitable sites become more difficult to find, making long-distance transport necessary, and some problems of odour, vermin and water contamination may arise.

Representative mass percentage components of dry municipal refuse in the United Kingdom are as follows[4]

Combustible rubbish	40
Putrescible rubbish	20
Metals	7
Glass	8
Ash	25

but the initially wet refuse can contain from 10 to 75 per cent of moisture.

The quantities of refuse handled annually in the United Kingdom and the United States total about 20 and 150 million tonnes respectively. The overall quantities generated by society are tending to rise with the increase in population, urbanisation and standards of living, together with the growing use of packaging materials and the acceptance of disposable short-life goods. One of the biggest problems in handling refuse is the bulk, since the relative bulk density is low, at about 0.15, and continues to fall due to the rising proportions of paper and plastics. Bulk can be reduced by shredding and/or compacting (baling), but the density cannot be increased above about half that of coal. An alternative scheme is to permit bacterial degradation by composting to produce a soil conditioner and fertiliser. However, the very effective method of incineration, introduced by the United Kingdom about a century ago, reduces the volume by as much as 90 per cent. Furthermore, the residue is both sterile and odourless, with a putrescible content of less than 0.3 per cent, and is thus more acceptable for final disposal by tipping, or even for use as a building infill. Wet refuse will burn without auxiliary fuel when its three major components meet the following mass limitations: combustibles 25 per cent minimum, non-combustibles 55 per cent maximum, and water

50 per cent maximum. In the United Kingdom, approximately 80 per cent of waste is tipped, 10 per cent incinerated and 4 per cent composted.

Initially, incineration was conducted merely for the reduction in bulk, and therefore without heat recovery. A minimum gas temperature of about 750 °C is necessary to ensure complete odour destruction, whereas the fuel bed temperature is limited to about 1000 °C, the softening point of the ash, to prevent ash fusion and slag removal difficulties. Temperature limitation is achieved by the use of excess air (over 100 per cent) or water spray, but the former represents even larger-scale precipitation plant for dust extraction, and the latter gives rise to objectionable vapour plumes from the chimney stack. Some designers therefore include boilers and air-cooled condensers in order solely to limit the size of the precipitators, even though the resulting steam is not used. Corrosion can be a problem, especially under reducing conditions, due to the presence of sulphur and chlorine derived from the content of plastics and winter road sweepings.

With the development of incineration towards the useful application of combustion heat, solid municipal waste becomes classified as a fuel, and knowledge of its calorific value becomes important. The overall specific energy has been determined by separation of a sample of waste into the various combustible components, and the weighting of each mass proportion with its appropriate specific energy, followed by summation. This method has given net values of about 9 MJ/kg in the United Kingdom, and 11 MJ/kg in the United States. However, due to problems of securing a truly representative sample, the incinerator itself has since been used as a calorimeter, resulting in revised values of about 7.5 and 8 MJ/kg respectively. Thus the 20 million tonnes of wastes handled each year in the United Kingdom are equivalent to about 4 million tonnes of coal (cf. 110 million tonnes of coal consumed annually), but much of this would be so widely dispersed as to make collection uneconomic.

When incineration can be used to advantage, the design of the incinerator is optimised for maximum heat output. Due to the low density of refuse, the fuel bed thickness approaches 2 m in comparison with the 200 mm when burning coal. Vigorous agitation is necessary to increase the combustion rate. Pulverised refuse may be burned directly to raise steam for the generation of electrical power, but the scale of a power station of about 50 MW sustained by the waste from a large community is not economic compared with the more efficient 4000 MW station fired by pulverised coal. As a variant, the refuse may be used in conjunction with the coal, particularly as its acidic ash can counteract the alkaline ash from the coal, but some 10 times more ash results from refuse, and severe problems of erosion and handling have arisen in attempts to date. More success has been achieved in applications to small industrial boilers, with the steam utilised for space heating in high-density housing areas, process work in industry or for private electricity generation. Up to 10 per cent of refuse has been added to the pulverised coal used in cement manufacture, since the residuals from refuse are similar to the constituents of cement, and the long flame geometry is appropriate.

The refuse itself may be processed physically or by fermentation to provide solid fuels with improved characteristics of handling and combustion, and so limit the costs of adapting existing equipment. These refuse-derived fuels generally require upgrading, or beneficiation, to about 15 MJ/kg, either by the removal of some impurities, or by the addition of such other organic materials as refinery wastes or sewage sludge. A combustible residue may be obtained as a result of shredding and automatic sorting of raw refuse (including glass by colour!), followed by enrichment and pelletising to a convenient size, but the potential of such methods is adversely affected by salvage schemes for paper and other combustibles. Alternatively, the combustible components of waste may be extracted chemically by conversion to storable gases, liquid distillates and char by means of anaerobic pyrolysis, that is, heating to about 1000 °C to break the molecular bonds, but in the absence of air to prevent oxidation. About 40 per cent of the mass results as low-grade ($20 \ MJ/m^3$) gas which can be used for process heating, whereas the 15 per cent of oil tar fluid (40 MJ/kg) and the 45 per cent of solid char (20 MJ/kg) can be sold commercially. Of the initial energy content of the waste, approximately 20 per cent is required for drying purposes, and only about 35 per cent appears in the finished fuels due to the endothermic nature of pyrolysis. This disadvantage must be offset against the sterility and storability of the resulting fuels.

If higher pressures are available, treatment of solid wastes with carbon monoxide and water tends to de-oxygenate the carbohydrate and cellulosic materials in paper, wood, straw and vegetable matter, and to convert most of the carbon content of the wastes into a heavy fuel-oil like fluid containing up to 10 per cent oxygen. If the wastes are treated with hydrogen, on the other hand, gas mixtures rich in hydrogen and methane result, together with some liquids. As before, high temperatures and pressures are required, and catalysts are generally used. In practice, the main problems appear to be concerned with economics, deterioration of the oil products, and the explosion risk arising from dust carry-over. However, incineration is stated to be more energy efficient, and interest in the pyrolysis route is largely restricted to used tyres as feedstock.

Biochemical processes represent further possibilities of the useful application of refuse energy, and these comprise anaerobic digestion to methane, and fermentation to ethanol. Digestion requires a wet waste of relatively high nitrogen content for the methane-forming bacteria to operate, and the nitrogen/carbon ratio of about 0.03 is increased to about 0.07 by the addition of sewage sludge, animal manure or other nitrogen-rich waste. Only about 60 per cent of the waste is converted to a gaseous mixture containing methane. One American proposal involves the sealing of a deep refuse tip in a steep-sided valley, with an offtake pipework system leading to some suitable furnace. The gas evolved is expected to comprise 55 per cent methane and 43 per cent

49

carbon dioxide, with an energy density of about 20 MJ/m^3, and to generate at the rate of about 65 million cubic metres per year for several years.

Since the elemental mass composition of the carbon—hydrogen—oxygen compounds in solid municipal waste approaches that of cellulose, yeast fermentation processes to ethanol are possible following acid hydrolysis to sugar, as shown in section 9.2.

4.6.6 Biofuels

Biomatter comprises all natural material associated with living organisms, including terrestrial and marine vegetable matter of all kinds from algae to trees, together with animal tissue and manure. The industrial source areas are therefore silviculture (forestry), agriculture, animal husbandry and sewage treatment. (To a certain extent, this topic overlaps that in the previous section since biomatter is one component of SMW, and since some methods of processing are common.) On a global basis, it is estimated that over 150 gigatonnes of vegetable biomatter are generated annually, much of it in the wild state, by the conversion of diffused solar energy via photosynthesis to stored chemical energy. The total mass of vegetable biomatter existing per unit area at any instant is termed 'biomass', usually expressed in units of tonnes per hectare (t/ha), and the total biomass harvested per annum is the 'biomass yield', in t/ha a. This ranges from about 13 t/ha a for water hyacinth (Mississippi) to 120 t/ha a for napier grass (Puerto Rico), with an average dry value of about 23 t/ha a.[5]

Exploitation of the biomass yield ranges from the relatively small-scale collection of agricultural wastes, through the direct harvesting of naturally seeded vegetation, to the purposeful cultivation of energy crops, known as energy farming. Because of the relatively extensive growth period of trees, other energy crops of interest include sugar cane, sugar beet, cassava, sorghum, corn, wheat, giant kelp and blue-green algae. Integration with food crops is essential, with irrigation, rotation, crop spacing, fertilisation and other agronomic practices optimised for the production of both food and energy rather than either alone. Using the energy content of food residues, for example, would improve the production economics of food crops. Although production costs on a wet basis vary widely between these crops, less variation occurs on a dry basis, as shown below in units of US $ per tonne

Grain sorghum	92
Sugar beet	87
Wheat	84
Corn	80
Sugar cane	71
Bagasse	20

In view of its energy content, biomatter represents a source of biofuels, and the associated energy can be released or stored by the following methods

1. Direct combustion
2. Conversion to SNG through pyrolysis, hydrogasification or anaerobic digestion.
3. Conversion to ethanol by fermentation
4. Conversion to syngas thermochemically, then to methanol or ammonia
5. Conversion to liquid hydrocarbons by hydrogenation, or by the syngas/ Fischer–Tropsch route.

For direct combustion, the main criterion is calorific value on a dry basis. The energy conversion efficiency in the growth of vegetation is very low, not exceeding about 2 per cent, but the specific energy of dried biomatter averages approximately 14 MJ/kg. For timbers, these values range from about 12 MJ/kg for hardwoods to 19 MJ/kg for pine. Fuel wood, of course, has been used as a source of heat for centuries, but its continuing uncontrolled use could lead to deforestation and shortages of fertiliser. Localised interest centres on the use of bark and wood waste for drying stock in sawmills. Various types of furnace are usable, either grateless or using a fixed, moving or inclined grate, with the wood waste reduced to appropriately sized particles by milling, giving heat release rates up to 350 kW/m^3, and the energy released can cut the drying time of the timber stocks by over 80 per cent.

Surplus cereal straw is also of interest as an energy source since it is commonly burnt to waste in the fields, with attendant smoke pollution and possible long-term effects on wildlife and the soil. With a specific energy of about 12 to 15 MJ/kg, the 3.5 million tonnes of straw burnt each year in the United Kingdom, for example, represent about 1.5 million tonnes of coal, which is about 1 per cent of the country's total coal consumption. Bulk is a vexed problem in handling straw, but experiments at Cranfield have raised the relative bulk density of wheat straw from about 0.11 to 0.35 by compression and baling, and up to 1.10 by additional heating to 85 °C to enable the waxes in the straw to melt and bind.[6]

In a similar manner, cotton gin wastes can be burnt for purposes of drying the seed cotton. The waste has a specific energy of about 18.5 MJ/kg dry, and 16 MJ/kg wet, and over 30 per cent of the released heat can be utilised. In the United States, the annual crop creates over 2 million tonnes of waste material, and the usable heat is sufficient to dry the entire crop.[7] In India, agricultural wastes used as fuels include rice husks, jute stick, coconut sheels, dry leaves, twigs and, perhaps regrettably, cattle dung which might be more valuable as a soil fertiliser. In times of crisis, coffee has been burnt as fuel in Brazil, and wheat in Argentina. An energy farming scheme based on direct combustion is proposed by the University of Bath, in which naturally confined free-floating seaweed is harvested, dried and processed to yield a flake fuel at an energy cost of about half that of coal.[8]

As an alternative to combustion, pyrolysis of biomatter at the relatively low temperature of about 430 °C tends to optimise the resultant gas mixture (sometimes called pyrogas) for methane, the remainder being carbon dioxide and some hydrogen, the mixture having a gross energy density of about 26 MJ/m^3. Higher processing temperatures optimise for hydrogen and carbon monoxide, with lower energy densities. Pyrolysis also yields char containing the fixed carbon and mineral ash, together with complex mixtures of organic liquids known as pyrolysis oil. Gasification is similar to pyrolysis except that the heat input is supplied internally by burning part of the feedstock with a limited amount of air. Some countries use the gasification of wood chips, logs, etc., to produce an inexpensive 'wood gas' consisting of hydrogen, carbon dioxide and carbon monoxide plus some methane and traces of nitrogen, with a relative density of about 0.6, and dry energy density of about 14 MJ/m^3. In the presence of hydrogen, the gasified biomatter converts to methane-rich gas. As in the conversion of refuse, anaerobic digestion of biomatter to methane can be achieved through bacterial action, and is well suited to organic wastes of high (above 45 per cent) moisture content. This method is utilised in the treatment of sewage sludge, which yields a biogas rich in methane (about 67 per cent) together with carbon dioxide and traces of nitrogen, hydrogen and oxygen, the mixture having a relative density of about 0.8, and a dry energy density of about 23 MJ/m^3. It is generally used for generating heat and power within the sewage works. Typically, about 0.1 kg of solids per capita per day are separated out as sewage sludge, generating approximately 10 to 30 l of gas. The remaining sludge is dried to give an innocuous odour-free fertiliser.

When bacterial digestion is applied to vegetation, paper studies show that intensive systems of energy farming are energy expensive, whereas less intensive systems demand very large areas of land. On the other hand, such countries as China, India and South Korea have very many domestic gas producers who convert manure and crop residues into methane-rich biogas, leaving a nitrogen-rich sludge which is used as a fertiliser.

Again, as with refuse, the cellulose of wet biomatter can be hydrolysed to sugar, followed by fermentation with yeast to ethanol, as shown in section 9.2. In 1975, Brazil started a National Alcohol Program to produce 3 million m^3 of anhydrous ethanol per annum by the early 1980s from sugar cane and cassava (manioc, or tapioca) for use in blending with motor gasoline.[9] In the case of sugar cane, the bagasse (cane fibre) is used as the fuel in the sugar factory, or sold for paper making.

Thermochemical processes involving oxygen exist for the production of synthesis gas from SMW, and could no doubt be adapted for fibrous agricultural matter, which has less ash than SMW but contains more moisture. Conversion to either methanol or ammonia could then follow, in the latter case using the nitrogen from the air-to-oxygen plant. Economic studies suggest that these routes would be best suited to the production of methanol and

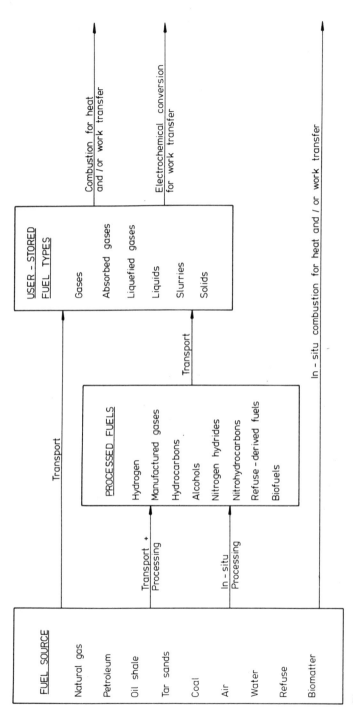

Figure 4.3　The overall fuel source-utilisation system (developed from an original diagram by Professor R. F. Sawyer, University of California, Berkeley)

53

ammonia for non-fuel uses, replacing the conventional fuel sources currently consumed for this purpose.

Hydrogenation of biomatter to liquid biofuels can take place either by the chemical addition of hydrogen, or by the removal of carbon and oxygen as carbon dioxide. The resultant oil, which still contains about 8 per cent oxygen, has a hydrogen/carbon atomic ratio of about unity, and a specific energy of about 35 MJ/kg. Some types of vegetation extend the carbon dioxide-to-cellulose process to produce hydrocarbons in the form of a latex sap, and further development may permit a useful oil yield by tapping the main stems, as in the harvesting of rubber.

4.7 Special 'High-energy' Hydrides

With the realisation that the specific energy of elemental carbon is only 27 per cent of that of elemental hydrogen, it is logical to attempt to replace carbon in the hydrocarbons with some other element to give hydrides of greater energy content. Boron, with a specific energy nearly twice that of carbon, is one case in point, and several other elements are also attractive on an energy basis. Gaseous diborane, B_2H_6, for example, will be expected to have a higher stock of energy than its counterpart, ethane, C_2H_6, as discussed in section 5.4.

Diborane is represented as a hydrogenation product of boron oxide

$$B_2O_3 + 3H_2 \longrightarrow B_2H_6 + 1.5H_2 \tag{20}$$

and the higher boranes (boron hydrides) are prepared by the thermal decomposition of diborane and subsequent re-combination of the radicals.

An overview of the conventional and alternative fuel source and utilisation system is shown in figure 4.3

References

1. J. H. Aubrey, Homogenising gives greater utilisation of low grade fuels, Energy for Industry Symposium Paper, Cranfield Institute of Technology, Pergamon, Oxford (1979).
2. Literature from APV Co. Ltd, P.O. Box No. 4, Manor Royal, Crawley, West Sussex RH10 2QB.
3. B. C. Dutton, Interchangeability prediction — the framework of a new approach, *J. Inst. Fuel*, **LI** (1978) 225—9.
4. J. M. Burnett, Waste materials as fuels, Energy for Industry Symposium Paper, Cranfield Institute of Technology, Pergamon, Oxford (1979).
5. K. Goddard, Liquid fuels from biomass, *Chart. mech. Engr*, **26** (1979) 33—5.

6. R. E. Stokes, The briquetting of cereal straw, Cranfield Institute of Technology, unpublished MSc thesis (1975).
7. Energy from cotton gin waste, *Agric. Res., Wash.,* **24** (1977) 3—5.
8. R. D. Pearson, *Energy Farms in Oceanic Gyres*, University of Bath (1977).
9. E. A. Jackson, Brazil's national alcohol programme, *Process Biochem.,* **11** (1976) 29—30.

5. Alternative-fuel Combustion Quantities

For the simpler fuels of known individual molecular structures, the stoichiometry, kinetics and thermochemistry of combustion can be derived from first principles, as shown briefly in the following sections. This in turn permits a broad extrapolation towards the unknown and relatively complex mixtures and blends of a wide variety of commercial and other combustible compounds.

5.1 Stoichiometry

The individual compound fuels considered here consist of various proportions of carbon, hydrogen, oxygen, nitrogen and boron, consequently complete combustion with air is represented by the stoichiometric equation of the following general form, expressed in molar quantities

$$1C_xH_yO_zN_aB_b + m_s(O_2 + 3.76\,N_2)$$
$$= n_1CO_2 + n_2H_2O + n_6N_2 + n_7B_2O_3$$

where m_s = stoichiometric moles of O_2 per mole of fuel, and n_j = moles of product j per mole of fuel. (The reason for the apparently inconsistent numbering of the 'n' subscripts appears at the end of the following section.)

The stoichiometric values of n_j are found by simple molar balances of all the elements concerned. In the case of hydrogen fuel, for example, for which $x = z = a = b = 0$, and $y = 2$, inspection of these balances gives the following values

$$n_1 = n_7 = 0, \text{ whereas } n_2 = 1, m_s = 0.5 \text{ and } n_6 = 1.88$$

Hence

$$\text{stoichiometric oxygen/fuel mass ratio} = m_s\left(\frac{MM\ O_2}{MM\ \text{fuel}}\right)$$

$$= 0.5\,(32/2)$$

$$= 8$$

Also

stoichiometric air/fuel molar ratio = $(A/F)_s$

$$= 4.76m_s$$
$$= 2.38$$

and

stoichiometric air/fuel mass ratio = $(a/f)_s$

$$= 2.38 \ (28.96/2)$$
$$= 34.46$$

For the general hydrocarbon fuel C_xH_y

C balance gives, $n_1 = x$

H_2 balance gives, $n_2 = 0.5y$

O_2 balance gives, $n_1 + 0.5n_2 = m_s = x + 0.25y$

N_2 balance gives, $n_6 = 3.76x + 0.94y$

B balance gives, $n_7 = 0$

It follows that

$$(A/F)_s = 4.76x + 1.19y$$

and

$$(a/f)_s = (A/F)_s \frac{28.96}{MM \text{ fuel}}$$

$$= \frac{137.9x + 34.46y}{12x + y}$$

Corresponding relationships hold for the other individual fuel types, all of which are shown in table 5.1 (at end of chapter) as general equations in terms of the carbon number x, the nitrogen number a, or the boron number b, as appropriate and, in the case of the hydrocarbons, also in terms of y. The individual values of $(a/f)_s$ are shown in figure 5.1. For the hydrocarbons generally, with the exception of the fused-ring aromatics, these are seen to approach the common value of about 14.7, with a corresponding $(f/a)_s$ value of 0.068, as the size of the molecule increases. The boron hydrides (boranes) show a similar relationship tending towards a common $(a/f)_s$ value of about 12.2. The values of $(a/f)_s$ for the alcohols and nitroparaffins are all low, but rise with increase in molecular size, whereas those for the nitrogen hydrides fall. In each case, the influence of the parent elements in these compounds can be seen clearly.

57

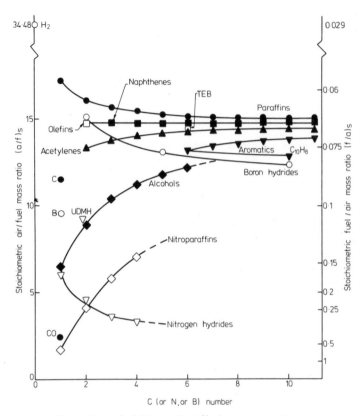

Figure 5.1   Stoichiometric air/fuel mass proportions

One feature contributing to the overall combustion performance of a fuel
is the gaseous molar ratio of the products to the reactants, since this helps to
determine the resulting pressure or velocity of the products, depending on the
mode of combustion. For the above hydrocarbon fuel

(product/reactant) molar ratio = P/R

$$= \frac{\Sigma n_j}{4.76m_s + 1}$$

$$= \frac{x + 0.5y + (3.76x + 0.94y)}{4.76(x + 0.25y) + 1}$$

$$= \frac{4.76x + 1.44y}{4.76(x + 0.25y) + 1}$$

The general equations for the P/R molar ratios of all the fuel groups
considered here are included in table 5.1, and the individual values plotted in

58

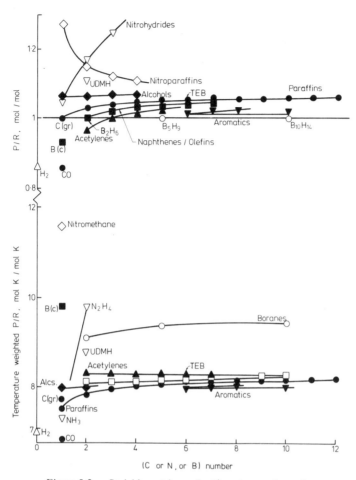

Figure 5.2 Stoichiometric product/reactant molar ratios

the upper part of figure 5.2. These values show the nitroparaffins and nitrogen hydrides to be particularly attractive, whereas the ratios for hydrogen, carbon monoxide, carbon and boron are less so. Most of the hydrocarbons lie just above unity with little to distinguish between them, whereas the alcohols are slightly more attractive. Since the factors affected by the molar ratio are also influenced in a similar manner by the level of flame temperature, each P/R ratio has been multiplied by the corresponding value of $T_{p\,ad}$ (the constant-pressure adiabatic flame temperature), and divided by the standard reactant temperature of 298.15 K. These temperature-weighted values plotted in the lower part of figure 5.2 show the relatively greater attraction of nitromethane, hydrazine and the boranes. They also show the alcohols and ammonia to be slightly less attractive than before. It should be noted that

59

the presence of the fuel in the liquid or solid phase, and the dissociation of the products, both tend to increase the level of the gaseous P/R ratio.

Since all fuels can burn in various proportions with air ranging over both sides of stoichiometric (up to weak and rich limits of flammability, as discussed in chapter 6), it is convenient to express the mixture proportions in terms of the percentage of fuel weakness or richness, the actual air/fuel ratio, fuel/air ratio, or the equivalence ratio given by

$$\text{equivalence ratio} = \phi = \frac{f/a}{(f/a)_s}$$

$$= \frac{(a/f)_s}{a/f}$$

$$= \frac{(A/F)_s}{A/F}$$

$$= m_s/m$$

where m = actual moles of oxygen per mole of fuel. In dealing with limits of flammability, the usual form of expression is in terms of percentage volume of fuel vapour in the mixture with air, given by

$$\% \text{ volume fuel} = 100\left(\frac{\text{fuel mol}}{\text{fuel mol} + 4.76m}\right)$$

$$= \frac{100}{1 + A/F}$$

5.2 Dissociation

For a hydrocarbon fuel, the two combustion equations expected are as follows.
Fuel weak, ϕ less than 1

$$C_xH_y + m(O_2 + 3.76N_2) = n_1CO_2 + n_2H_2O + n_5O_2 + n_6N_2 \qquad (21)$$

Fuel rich, ϕ greater than 1

$$C_xH_y + m(O_2 + 3.76N_2) = n_1CO_2 + n_2H_2O + n_3CO + n_4H_2 + n_6N_2$$
$$(22)$$

These equations show, first, the excess of oxygen appearing with the fully oxidised products and, second, the unburnt carbon monoxide and hydrogen present due to the insufficiency of oxygen. However, at high temperatures (above about 1800 K for the hydrocarbons), products become so energetic that they dissociate by reverse reactions to give carbon monoxide, hydrogen and oxygen plus traces of atomic hydrogen and oxygen and hydroxyl radicals, together with various oxides of nitrogen represented by NO_x and, in practice,

60

some unburnt fuel. At the maximum flame temperature, therefore, all these fully, and partially, burnt products co-exist at a condition of dynamic equilibrium in which the rates of combustion are exactly equal to the rates of dissociation. Each rate can be expressed in terms of a rate constant, together with the concentrations (raised to some power determined from the experiment) of the reactants involved. Hence the quantity of each product can be derived from a knowledge of the equilibrium constants for the reactions concerned, each equilibrium constant being derived from the ratio of the rate constants.

The two reversible combustion–dissociation reactions relevant to the hydrocarbons at high temperature appear as follows

$$CO + 0.5O_2 \rightleftharpoons CO_2$$

and

$$H_2 + 0.5O_2 \rightleftharpoons H_2O$$

Equilibrium constants are usually evaluated in terms of partial pressures, and then related to concentrations using the Avogadro–Dalton concepts, thus

$$K_{CO_2} = \frac{P_{CO_2}}{P_{CO}(P_{O_2})^{0.5}} = \frac{n_1}{n_3(Pn_5/n_T)^{0.5}}$$

and

$$K_{H_2O} = \frac{P_{H_2O}}{P_{H_2}(P_{O_2})^{0.5}} = \frac{n_2}{n_4(Pn_5/n_T)^{0.5}}$$

where P_x = partial pressure of material x, P = total pressure, n_T = total number of moles of products. Values of K, the partial pressure equilibrium constant, are tabulated in the literature[1,2] for different levels of temperature, as shown in table 5.2.

The general combustion equation for the high temperature conditions of combustion contain both 'weak' and 'rich' types of product simultaneously irrespective of the level of equivalence ratio. In order to keep the following treatment within reasonable bounds, dissociation to the major products of carbon monoxide and molecular hydrogen and oxygen only has been considered, since any further degree of dissociation would require computation. Hence, for the hydrocarbons at any mixture strength

$$C_xH_y + m(O_2 + 3.76N_2)$$

$$= n_1CO_2 + n_2H_2O + n_3CO + n_4H_2 + n_5O_2 + n_6N_2 \qquad (23)$$

The first step in determining the all-important flame temperature, therefore, is to solve this general equation. Assuming that the initial proportions of fuel and air, and thus m, are known, this gives six unknown values of n, requiring six equations for solution. The first four equations are derived from the molar balances of carbon, hydrogen, oxygen and nitrogen, as before. The remaining

Table 5.2 Equilibrium constants and algebraic total enthalpy changes for gases (derived from JANAF tables[1])

TEMP. (K)	Partial-pressure equilibrium constants atm$^{-0.5}$		$\Delta H^* = (\Delta H_T + \Delta H_f^0)$ for compounds (kJ/mol)			$\Delta H^* = \Delta H_T$ for elements (kJ/mol)			TEMP. (K)
	K_{CO_2}	K_{H_2O}	CO_2	H_2O	CO	H_2	O_2	N_2	
298.15	1.1641×10^{45}	11.169×10^{39}	-393.52	-241.83	-110.53	0	0	0	298.15
300	575.44×10^{42}	6.1094×10^{39}	-393.46	-241.76	-110.47	0.054	0.054	0.054	300
500	10.593×10^{24}	76.913×10^{21}	-385.21	-234.91	-104.60	5.883	6.088	5.912	500
1000	16.634×10^{9}	11.535×10^{9}	-360.12	-215.85	-88.843	20.686	22.707	21.460	1000
1500	207.01×10^{3}	530.88×10^{3}	-331.81	-193.73	-71.680	36.267	40.610	38.405	1500
2000	765.60	3.4670×10^{3}	-302.07	-169.14	-53.790	52.932	59.199	56.141	2000
2100	345.94	1.6866×10^{3}	-296.02	-164.00	-50.154	56.379	62.986	59.748	2100
2200	168.27	874.98	-289.95	-158.79	-46.509	59.860	66.802	63.371	2200
2300	87.097	480.84	-283.85	-153.53	-42.853	63.371	70.634	67.007	2300
2400	47.753	277.43	-277.73	-148.22	-39.183	66.915	74.492	70.651	2400
2500	27.543	167.49	-271.60	-142.86	-35.505	70.492	78.375	74.312	2500
2700	10.351	68.077	-259.27	-132.01	-28.121	77.718	86.199	81.659	2700
3000	3.0549	22.029	-240.66	-115.47	-16.987	88.743	98.098	92.738	3000

Note 1: At 298.15 K, ΔH^* for compounds $= \Delta H_f^0$

Note 2: $\Delta H_f^0\ H_2O(l) = -285.70$ kJ/mol

Note 3: In the water-gas shift reaction (6), $K_{WGS} = K_{H_2O}/K_{CO_2}$

two equations are then derived from the values of the equilibrium constants K_{CO_2} and K_{H_2O} at some assumed level of flame temperature. Solution is then possible by iteration using an energy balance, as discussed in section 5.5.

As the products leave the combustion zone, they cool progressively by the transfer of heat and/or work so that, below about 1800 K, dissociation would be expected to cease, and the products to assume the proportions shown in equations 21 and 22. Invariably, however, owing to local chilling through mixing imperfections, traces of dissociated products are unable to re-oxidise, and so remain trapped as such in the products, again irrespective of the level of equivalence ratio. Consequently, the combustion equation of type 23 still applies even when the products are cooled to ambient temperature although, of course, the individual molar values of n will differ from those within the flame. The data from the equilibrium constants are no longer valid here, but the two equations (additional to the carbon, hydrogen, oxygen and nitrogen balances) required for solution can be found relatively easily by means of gas analysis for carbon dioxide, carbon monoxide and oxygen. Although such analyses *do not* give the absolute molar values of n_1, n_3 and n_5 directly, they *do* give ratios of the volumetric proportions of these gases which are, of course, equal to the molar ratios, for example n_1/n_3 and n_1/n_5, and so provide the two additional equations.

The same principles apply to the other fuel molecules discussed above, the reactivity of boron being so high that dissociation of B_2O_3 is negligible, consequently the most general combustion equation can be written here as

$$C_x H_y O_z N_a B_b + m(O_2 + 3.76N_2)$$
$$= n_1 CO_2 + n_2 H_2O + n_3 CO + n_4 H_2 + n_5 O_2 + n_6 N_2 + n_7 B_2O_3 \quad (24)$$

This explains the adoption of the 'n' subscript numbers at the beginning of the previous section.

5.3 Fuel Thermochemistry

Thermodynamically, a body of fuel vapour in equilibrium can be classed as a system, since it is 'a fixed quantity of matter enclosed by a boundary defining a region in space', and the fact that it exists stably indicates that it lies within an energy trough, being unable to react until it can surmount some surrounding energy peak to find some other trough. The level of chemical energy of a fuel in its condition of stability is determined by the energies involved in the formation of the fuel molecule from the parent elemental molecules as they surmounted the energy peaks around their own troughs. Thus, stable molecules of elemental carbon (as graphite) and hydrogen (as H_2 gas), for example, can be energised to the tops of the surrounding peaks when their bonds are broken and they become gaseous atoms of carbon and hydrogen, after which they can create new bonds with each other to form a stable molecule of hydrocarbon compound, descending into another trough in the process. The difference in energy absorbed in atomising the parent elemental molecules, and that released subsequently in forming the molecule of hydrocarbon, is termed the energy of formation of the hydrocarbon. Exactly the same argument holds for any other elements forming alternative fuel molecules.

Energy can transfer across the boundary of a thermodynamic system in the forms of work W and/or heat Q, and the sign convention is such that work flow outwards and heat flow inwards are both classed as positive. Hence the total outwards flow of energy equals $(W - Q)$, and this takes place at the expense of the total stock of energy of the system. Thermodynamics also provides expressions for the energy flows under particular conditions for systems that are stationary, and for those that are flowing, including the 'reduced' cases with negligible changes in potential (height) or kinetic (velocity) energies.

From the non-flow energy equation

$$W - Q = -\Delta U$$

$$= \text{loss of internal energy}$$

From the reduced steady-flow energy equation

$$W - Q = -\Delta H$$

$$= \text{loss of enthalpy}$$

In the two special cases shown below where the work term is zero, the above expressions may be simplified to

non-flow heat transfer *at constant volume* = n-fQ_v

$$= \Delta U$$

$$= \text{internal energy of combustion}$$

and

steady-flow heat transfer *at constant pressure* = s-fQ_p

$$= \Delta H$$

$$= \text{enthalpy of combustion}$$

In view of the above sign convention, both these quantities will be *negative* since the combustion heat flows outwards.

This aspect of the subject, concerned with transfer of reaction energy in the form of heat only, is known as thermochemistry, and processes involving inward and outward transfers of heat are known as endothermic and exothermic respectively. Although thermochemistry is concerned with *changes* in energy, a condition of 25 °C (298.15 K) and 1 atm is selected as datum, and all values related to this are described as standard, and indicated by the superscript ^{0}. In view of the many applications of steady-flow reaction at constant pressure in furnaces, gas turbines, ramjets, rockets and a wide variety of chemical and industrial processes, the following treatment is based largely on enthalpy, but corresponding arguments apply to internal energy in non-flow. In terms of enthalpy, therefore, and with initial and final conditions as standard, the isobaric flow case gives

$$\text{standard enthalpy of formation} = \Delta H_f^0$$

$$= \Sigma \Delta H_a - \Sigma D(X{-}Y)$$

where

ΔH_a = enthalpy of chemical atomisation

= enthalpy required to dissociate the molecular bonds of a parent element

and

$D(X{-}Y)$ = bond dissociation enthalpy

= enthalpy required to dissociate an $X{-}Y$ bond within the resulting compound

These enthalpy relationships are illustrated in figure 5.3, and values of ΔH_f^0

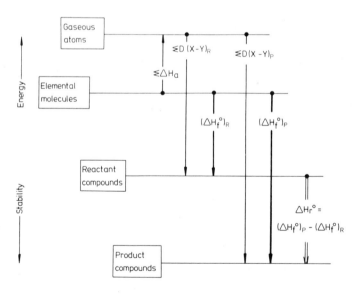

Each material at 298·15 K and 1 atm

Figure 5.3   Schematic of standard enthalpies of formation (ΔH_f^0) and reaction (ΔH_r^0)

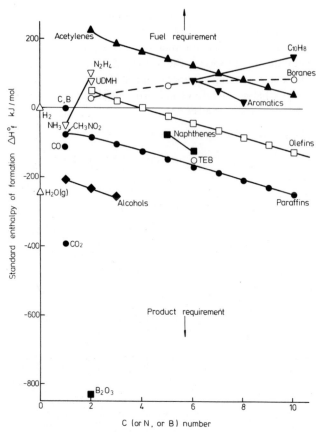

Figure 5.4   Standard molar enthalpies of formation of individual fuels in gaseous phase (derived from references 1 and 6)

plotted in figure 5.4 and listed in table 5.3. A fuller account is given in reference 2.

When oxygen molecules are included with the parent molecules of carbon and hydrogen, it is equally possible for the overall atomisation to be followed by bonding to promote oxide products rather than mixed reactants of hydrocarbon fuel and oxygen, with descent into an even lower trough. This event is also illustrated in figure 5.3, which shows the subsequent enthalpy of reaction as the net result of the enthalpies of formation. Consequently, values of ΔH_a and $D(X-Y)$ can generally be dispensed with, and all further derivation based on published values of ΔH_f^0 alone, thus

$$\text{standard enthalpy of reaction} = \Delta H_r^0$$

$$= (\Delta H_f^0)_P - (\Delta H_f^0)_R$$

$$= \Sigma n_j (\Delta H_f^0)_j - \Sigma m_i (\Delta H_f^0)_i$$

66

where n_j = moles of product j, m_i = moles of reactant i and subscripts P and R refer to products and reactants respectively.

The molar values of ΔH_r^0 have been plotted in figure 5.5 on a negative basis in order to relate directly with the data presented in the following section.

5.4 Calorific Value

For engineering purposes, mass and stored volume are adopted in preference to the molar basis for expressing energy quantities, and heat release is viewed in the positive sense. As discussed in chapter 1, this quantity is referred to generally as the calorific value, but on a mass basis, the term 'specific energy' in units of MJ/kg is being used here, and on a volume basis, the term 'energy density' (being the energy, rather than the mass, per unit volume) adopted in units of MJ/l for liquid and solid fuels, and MJ/m^3 for gaseous fuels at standard conditions of 1.013 25 bar pressure and 25 °C.

Although calorific values are defined for a variety of conditions (see appendix 3 and reference 3), the two special cases adopted for purposes of experimental determination are those of non-flow constant volume, and steady-flow constant pressure, as discussed in the previous section. The fact that, in both cases, the energy is released in the form of heat only has led to the alternative name of heat of combustion, and the symbol Q. Furthermore, measurement of the temperature rise is all that is required to determine the quantity of heat absorbed by a known mass of water coolant. With allowance for any losses, this value then provides the quantity of heat released by combustion of the fuel sample, and division by mass (or volume) of the sample then gives the appropriate calorific value.

In the laboratory, values of the specific energy of a liquid or solid fuel are determined in a calorimeter on the basis of non-flow constant volume, and of the energy density of a gaseous fuel at steady-flow constant pressure. Although some finite rise in coolant temperature is essential to permit measurement of heat absorption, use of plentiful cooling water keeps this rise down to a few degrees only, and the resulting calorific values differ only marginally from the corresponding theoretical standard values of ΔU_r^0 and ΔH_r^0 respectively. Furthermore, since the temperature of the combustion products is reduced to near ambient level in each case, the water resulting from the combustion of the hydrogen in the fuel (the *combustion* water) together with any water present in the original fuel sample (the *fuel* water) condense almost completely, and their latent heat of vaporisation is included in the heat absorbed by the calorimeter cooling water. The resultant calorific value is thus known as the *gross* value, Q_{gr}. In practical applications, products are invariably still hot when they leave the combustion zone, carrying with them the latent heat of the total (combustion + fuel) water, together with the sensible heat of all the

67

Table 5.3 Standard enthalpies of formation and reaction, kJ/mol (drived from reference 1, 6, 7 and 8)

Compound		ΔH_f^0	ΔH_r^0		T_p ad (K)
			Gross $H_2O(l)$, $B_2O_3(c)$	Net $H_2O(g)$, $B_2O_3(g)$	
Hydrogen	$H_2(g)$	0	−285.82	−241.83	2431
	(l)	−0.90	−284.92	−240.93	2425
Carbon (graphite)	C(gr)	0	−393.52	−393.52	2313
Carbon monoxide	$CO(g)$	−110.52	−283.00	−283.00	2399
Methane	$CH_4(g)$	−74.848	−890.31	−802.33	2247
Propane	$C_3H_8(g)$	−103.85	−2220.0	−2044.0	2291
Butane	$C_4H_{10}(g)$	−124.73	−2878.5	−2658.5	2293
Octane	$C_8H_{18}(g)$	−208.45	−5512.1	−5116.2	2300
	(l)	−243.06	−5477.5	−5081.6	2290
Benzene	$C_6H_6(g)$	82.927	−3301.5	−3169.5	2366
	(l)	52.152	−3270.7	−3138.8	2353
Acetylene	$C_2H_2(g)$	226.75	−1299.6	−1255.6	2591
Methanol	$CH_3OH(g)$	−201.17	−763.99	−676.01	2243
	(l)	−238.57	−726.59	−638.61	2229
Ethanol	$C_2H_5OH(g)$	−235.31	−1409.2	−1277.2	2258
	(l)	−277.63	−1366.9	−1234.9	2214

1-Propanol	C$_3$H$_7$OH(g)	−255.94	−2067.9	−1891.9	2273
	(l)	−297.29	−2026.6	−1850.6	2243
Ammonia	NH$_3$(g)	−46.191	−382.64	−316.56	2084
Hydrazine	N$_2$H$_4$(g)	95.186	−666.83	−578.85	2492
	(l)	50.417	−622.06	−534.08	2431
UDMH	(CH$_3$)$_2$N$_2$H$_2$(g)	88.157	−2018.5	−1842.5	2382
	(l)	53.137	−1983.5	−1807.5	2355
Nitromethane	CH$_3$NO$_2$(g)	−74.726	−747.52	−681.54	2709
	(l)	−89.036	−733.21	−667.23	2677
Boron (crystalline)	B(c)	0	−635.22	−416.60	3139
Diborane	B$_2$H$_6$(g)	31.380	−2159.3	−1590.1	2716
Pentaborane	B$_5$H$_9$(g)	73.22	−4535.5	−3244.5	2797
	(l)	42.84	−4505.1	−3214.0	2780
Decaborane	B$_{10}$H$_{14}$(g)	47.279	−8400.2	−5906.1	2809
	(c)	−28.87	−8324.0	−5829.9	2785
Triethylborane	(C$_2$H$_5$)$_3$B(g)	−158.99	−4981.1	−4432.4	2341
	(l)	−195.81	−4944.2	−4395.6	2330

Note: Values of T_p ad are for dissociation to CO, H$_2$ and O$_2$ only
(c) = crystalline

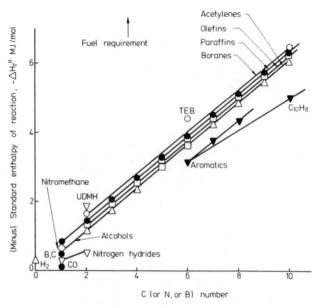

Figure 5.5 Standard molar enthalpies of reaction of individual fuels in gaseous phase with gaseous products

product components. A more appropriate indication of the realisable calorific value is generally given by the *net* value, Q_{net}, determined by subtracting from the gross value the latent heat contained in the mass of total water, m_w. Strictly, these relationships should be expressed as follows

Non-flow $\qquad Q_{net\ v} = Q_{gr\ v} - m_w u_{fg}$

Steady-flow $\qquad Q_{net\ p} = Q_{gr\ p} - m_w h_{fg}$

where

$\qquad u_{fg}$ = specific internal energy of steam vaporisation

$\qquad$ = 2.31 MJ/kg at 25 °C

$\qquad h_{fg}$ = specific enthalpy of steam vaporisation

$\qquad$ = 2.44 MJ/kg at 25 °C

However, it has been found convenient to adopt different conversion factors for particular types of fuel, as outlined briefly in appendix 3. Furthermore, since the laboratory tests themselves require skilled staff and expensive equipment, and can be time-consuming, frequent use is made of empirical formulae based on more simply determined properties of a fuel (for example, relative density, aniline point, mass content of water, ash, sulphur, oxygen, and so on). These equations are also referred to briefly in appendix 3.

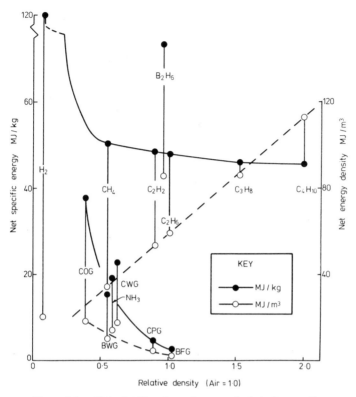

Figure 5.6   Net calorific values of gaseous fuels (reference 4)

Figure 5.6 shows a plot of net calorific values against relative density for the gaseous fuels, both hydrocarbon and manufactured. The following conclusions can be drawn regarding the specific energies.[4]

1. Hydrocarbons from methane to butane show a slight reduction with increase in relative density.
2. Diborane lies significantly higher than the hydrocarbons.
3. Hydrogen exhibits a maximum value of about 2.4 times that of methane.
4. Ammonia reaches a value of only about 0.4 that of methane.
5. Manufactured gases show a steep reduction with increase in relative density, from coke oven gas to blast furnace gas.

With regard to net energy densities

6. Hydrogen shows a very low value indeed, with hydrocarbons increasing steeply with relative density in a linear fashion.
7. Ammonia shows little increase over hydrogen.
8. Manufactured gases also show low values, reducing with increase in relative density.

71

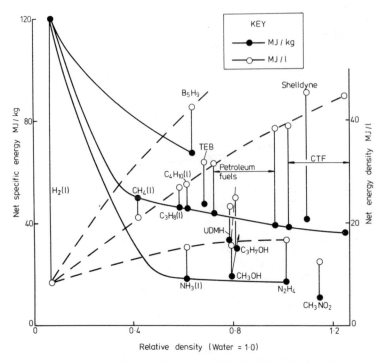

Figure 5.7   Net calorific values of liquid fuels (reference 4)

Figure 5.7 shows comparable plots for the liquid fuels and includes values for liquid hydrogen, liquid ammonia and the liquefied hydrocarbon gases. These conclusions reflect broadly those drawn from figure 5.6 with the hydrocarbon curve continuing smoothly through the ranges of conventional petroleum fuel blends and the coal tar fuels (CTF). The additional points to note are as follows.

9. Pentaborane lies significantly higher than the hydrocarbons.

10. Hydrogen and the nitrogen hydrides form curves comparable with those of the hydrocarbons, but at lower levels.

11. Alcohols show low levels, rising steeply with molecular size.

12. Nitromethane shows very low values.

It is interesting to note that the specific energy of hydrazine (16.68 MJ/kg net) is greater than that of the equivalent mixture of 12.5 per cent hydrogen and 87.5 per cent nitrogen by mass (15 MJ/kg), the additional energy being locked in the molecular structure in the form of bond energy. Thus nitrogen does not act entirely as a diluent in the case of hydrazine, although it does so with ammonia.

72

In the case of the solid fuels in figure 5.8, the values of relative density shown are the 'lump' values, as explained in section 3.4, and the following conclusions drawn.

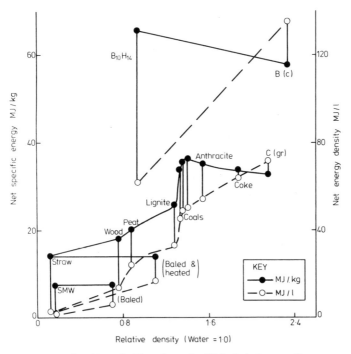

Figure 5.8   Net calorific values of solid fuels (reference 4)

13. Over the wood—anthracite range, both specific energy and energy density rise with relative density (and thus maturity), with a particularly rapid rise in the change from lignite to soft coals.

14. The specific energy level falls slightly through the manufactured fuel coke to graphite.

15. The energy densities of straw and SMW are improved substantially by baling under compression.

On a basis of unit mass of stoichiometric *air/fuel mixture*, specific energy is given by

$$Q/\text{kg stoichiometric mixture} = \frac{Q/\text{kg fuel}}{1 + (a/f)_s}$$

73

This expression differs only marginally from that for the specific energy per unit mass of stoichiometric *air*, given by

$$Q/\text{kg stoichiometric air} = (Q/\text{kg fuel})\,(f/a)_s$$

$$= \frac{Q/\text{kg fuel}}{(a/f)_s}$$

For hydrogen, carbon and the hydrocarbons, values of $(Q/\text{kg fuel})$ and $(a/f)_s$ are found to be related directly in a near linear manner, as shown in figure 5.9, consequently their quotients (giving the gradient of the line) are approximately equal. This relationship is seen to apply also to the non-hydrocarbon alternatives hence, with the exception of the boranes, the resulting stoichiometric mixture specific energies lie within a narrow band, mostly from 2.5 to 3.5 MJ/kg stoichiometric mixture, as shown in figure 5.10 for all the fuels considered, ranging from gases to solids, conventional and alternative. In consequence

16. the specific energy of a fuel/air mixture fed at approximately stoichiometric proportions to a combustor is largely independent of fuel type

17. the boranes and nitromethane show particularly high values.

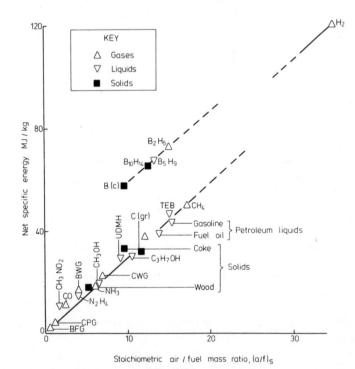

Figure 5.9   Relationship of net specific energy with stoichiometric air/fuel mass ratio (reference 4)

74

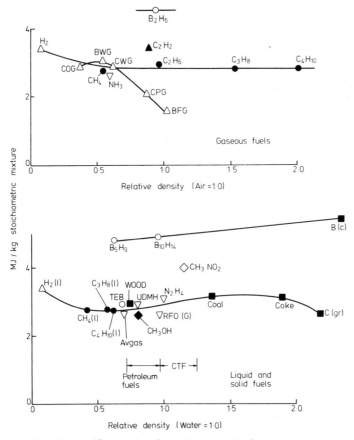

Figure 5.10   Net specific energies of stoichiometric fuel/air mixtures (reference 4)

In some heating applications where changes in fuel type are available, a constant rate of heating is required irrespective of the fuel in use. This is particularly important in gas-fired furnaces where differences in fuel type can be marked, consequently the prime requirement for fuel interchangeability is a common thermal throughput. Since the law of fluid flow through a fixed orifice is such that volumetric flow rate is approximately proportional directly to (pressure drop)$^{1/2}$, and indirectly to (fluid density)$^{1/2}$, interchangeability is given by constancy of the following parameters

$$\text{Wobbe number} = Wo = \frac{\text{energy density}}{(\text{relative density})^{1/2}} \quad \text{MJ/m}^3$$

where the supply pressure remains common (see section 4.3), and

$$\text{extended Wobbe number} = Wo(\Delta P)^{1/2} \quad \text{MJ N}^{1/2}/\text{m}^4$$

where ΔP = change in supply pressure when using different fuels. The gross value of energy density is frequently used in practice, but the net value is likely to be more appropriate. In France, a modified form of Wo is used, incorporating constants to allow for the concentration of oxygen and/or carbon dioxide.[5]

5.5 Combustion Temperature

In many instances, the level of temperature achieved during combustion is a measure of the efficiency of the overall conversion of stored chemical energy to heat and/or work. Experimental methods of determination of combustion temperature are available, in many cases based on optical methods, but calculation is also possible from knowledge of the proportions of product together with the resulting quantity of energy absorbed by the products in comparison with that released by the reactants. The maximum temperature is reached, of course, when all the reaction energy is released and then absorbed by the products, with no transfer of work or heat to the environment. This situation is seen to arise in isochoric (constant volume) adiabatic reactions in non-flow, and in isobaric (constant pressure) adiabatic reactions in steady-flow. The following treatment, as before, is based on the latter case, in terms of enthalpy, and the resulting isobaric adiabatic maximum temperature of combustion (the flame temperature) is here given the symbol $T_{p\,\mathrm{ad}}$. However, comparable arguments apply to the former case, in terms of internal energy, and flame temperature $T_{v\,\mathrm{ad}}$.

The re-presentation of the combustion enthalpy changes in figure 5.11 illustrates that the enthalpy of reaction released during combustion must be exactly equal to the enthalpy absorbed by the products in the $T_{p\,\mathrm{ad}}$ case, since no enthalpy leaves the system as W or Q. Consequently, allowing for the sign convention

> enthalpy absorbed by products = enthalpy released by reactants

$$(\Delta H_{T_{p\,\mathrm{ad}}})_\mathrm{P} = -\Delta H_\mathrm{r}^0$$

where ΔH_T = rise in sensible enthalpy from 298.15 to T K. But

$$\Delta H_\mathrm{r}^0 = (\Delta H_\mathrm{f}^0)_\mathrm{P} - (\Delta H_\mathrm{f}^0)_\mathrm{R}$$

Thus

$$(\Delta H_{T_{p\,\mathrm{ad}}} + \Delta H_\mathrm{f}^0)_\mathrm{P} - (\Delta H_\mathrm{f}^0)_\mathrm{R} = 0$$

Rather than deal with individual values of ΔH_T at different values of T, and then in each case add the constant value of ΔH_f^0, the author has found it convenient to define the sum of these two terms in parentheses as the 'algebraic total enthalpy change', give it the symbol ΔH^*, determine its values for all the products and temperature levels of interest and, at the same time, convert

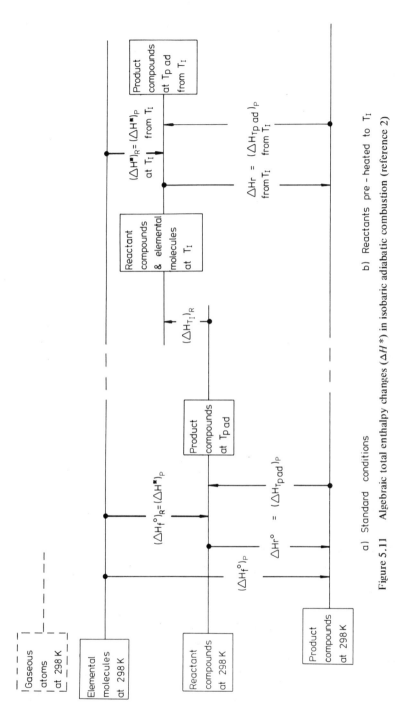

Figure 5.11   Algebraic total enthalpy changes (ΔH^*) in isobaric adiabatic combustion (reference 2)

a) Standard   conditions

b) Reactants   pre - heated   to T_I

77

these from the former standard units of kcal/mol to kJ/mol, as given in table 5.2. Thus with

$$(\Delta H^*)_P = (\Delta H_{T_{p\,ad}} + \Delta H_f^0)_P$$

the above expression may be written as

$$(\Delta H^*)_P - (\Delta H_f^0)_R = 0$$

and also as

$$\Sigma n_j(\Delta H^*)_j - \Sigma m_i(\Delta H_f^0)_i = 0$$

Since, for fuel–air mixtures

$$\Delta H_f^0 O_2 = \Delta H_f^0 N_2 = 0$$

the above expression simplifies further to

$$\Sigma n_j(\Delta H^*)_j - (\Delta H_f^0)_{fuel} = 0$$

The method of solution is by iteration, using selected temperatures, and calculating the related n_j values as in section 5.2.[2]

The significance of the ΔH^* simplification is emphasised in the case where the flowing reactants are pre-heated to some initial temperature T_I, absorbing the sensible enthalpy ΔH_{T_I} in the process. This term, shown in the centre of figure 5.11, consists of the total enthalpy absorbed by the reactant compounds of fuel and elemental molecules of air components. Since the reactants then release this sensible enthalpy to the reaction, the equation becomes

$$(\Delta H_{T_{p\,ad}} + \Delta H_f^0)_P - (\Delta H_{T_I} + \Delta H_f^0)_R = 0$$

which simplifies to

$$(\Delta H^*)_P - (\Delta H^*)_R = 0$$

and

$$\Sigma n_j(\Delta H^*)_j - \Sigma m_i(\Delta H^*)_i = 0$$

The sensible enthalpies of the atmospheric oxygen and nitrogen now *must* appear in the right-hand term, and it must also be remembered that $(\Delta H^*)_j$ is read at the $T_{p\,ad}$ level of temperature, and $(\Delta H^*)_i$ at T_I.

Values of $T_{p\,ad}$ have been calculated manually for stoichiometric mixtures with air of most of the fuels of interest here, with all reactants and products in the gaseous phase (approximately equivalent to the net calorific value condition) for the simple cases of dissociation to carbon monoxide, and molecular hydrogen and oxygen only. The results presented in figure 5.12 show that, although hydrogen has a particularly high specific energy, the very high specific heat capacity of its product water has an inhibiting effect on the resulting combustion temperature. Consequently, values of $T_{p\,ad}$ for the acetylenes are higher than those for the paraffins (for example, C_2H_2

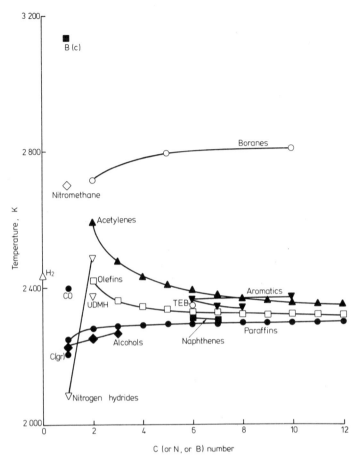

Figure 5.12   Dissociated stoichiometric flame temperatures ($T_{p\,\mathrm{ad}}$) in isobaric adiabatic combustion (reference 2)

compared with C_2H_6). A similar effect is seen with hydrazine, N_2H_4, and ammonia, NH_3 ($\equiv N_2H_6$).

With blends of hydrocarbon fuel components, the flame temperatures of the lighter hydrocarbons are particularly significant since they represent the temperatures reached by those portions of the blends that are first to vaporise and burn, and also by the materials resulting from thermal cracking of the heavier fuel molecules under the action of combustion heat. Consequently, many commercial blends of liquid, solid or gaseous fuels exhibit adiabatic flame temperatures in the region of 2300 K. Flame temperatures are slightly higher for fuels rich in carbon monoxide and/or hydrogen, and lower for fuels containing such inerts as carbon dioxide, nitrogen and ash. In heat-transfer

79

applications, flame temperatures may be significantly lower owing to the intentional loss of energy by radiation.

5.6 Electrochemical Oxidation

The basic reaction in this case is stoichiometric oxidation, as before, but directly to electricity, and in the absence of heat and light, with the reactants meeting only indirectly through the intermediary of some form of ionised species. The reactants are fed separately to the electrodes separated by an electrolyte. The latter must be a good conductor for ions but an insulator for electrons which are required to be stripped from the reactants and to flow through an external circuit to do work. The fuel cell represents the ultimate in conversion efficiency since it not only minimises the number of conversion stages, each with its associated inefficiency, but it is not dependent on high-temperature heat release, and is therefore freed from the restraint of the Carnot efficiency of $(1 - T_{min}/T_{max})$.

The output work flow from a fuel cell may be expressed in terms of either thermodynamic or electrical quantities. Equating these expressions gives the following equation for E, the electrical potential developed, in volts

$$E = \frac{-\Delta G_r^0}{386.088 m_s} \quad V$$

where ΔG_r^0 = standard Gibbs free-energy function of reaction, kJ/mol,
m_s = stoichiometric moles of oxygen/mole fuel, as before.

Chemical–electrical conversion efficiency may be expressed in various ways, but the absolute value is given by

$$\text{Absolute efficiency} = \eta_{abs}$$

$$= \frac{-\Delta G_r^0}{-\Delta H_r^0}$$

where ΔH_r^0 = standard enthalpy of reaction, as before. The gross values are appropriate, with liquid water resulting from low temperature reactions.

Since each atom of oxygen tends to approach the stability of neon by absorbing two electrons to produce the ion $O^=$, one molecule of diatomic oxygen, O_2, is associated with four electrons, consequently the number (n_e) of electrons flowing in the external circuit per molecule of fuel oxidised is given by

$$n_e = 4 \text{ (stoichiometric molecules } O_2/\text{molecule fuel)}$$

$$= 4 \text{ (stoichiometric moles } O_2/\text{mole fuel)}$$

$$= 4 m_s$$

The type of ion actually involved in the electrochemical reaction depends

Table 5.4 Representative electrochemical data

Fuel	Gross ΔG_r^0 (kJ/mol)	Gross ΔH_r^0 (kJ/mol)	m_s (mol/mol)	E (V)	η (%)	n_e
H_2	-237.2	-285.8	0.5	1.23	83	2
C	-394.4	-393.8	1	1.02	100	4
CH_3OH	-706.3	-726.5	1.5	1.22	100	6
CH_4	-818.5	-891.0	2	1.06	92	8

largely on the selection of the electrolyte, but all the above expressions hold whether the ion is $O^=$, H^+, OH^-, H_3O^+, $CO_3^=$ or anything else.

Values of ΔG_r^0, ΔH_r^0, m_s, E, η_{abs}, and n_e are shown for a number of fuels in table 5.4, and the values of n_e permit the derivation of reactions occurring at the electrodes. These are shown in the following examples for hydrogen, and the general hydrocarbon C_xH_y, using the H^+ ion in each case. The reactants and products are identified as $[X]_R$ and $[Y]_P$ respectively and, for convenience, the cathode reaction is written from right to left.

1. Hydrogen $H_2 + 0.5O_2 = H_2O$

Thus $n_e = 4m_s = 4\,(0.5) = 2$

ANODE $[H_2]_R \longrightarrow$ $2H^+$ $+$ $2e^-$
                                    electrolyte   circuit

CATHODE $[H_2O]_P \longleftarrow$ $2H^+$ $+$ $2e^-$ $+$ $[0.5O_2]_R$

2. C_xH_y $C_xH_y + (x + 0.25y)\,O_2 = xCO_2 + 0.5yH_2O$

Thus, $n_e = 4m_s = 4x + y$

ANODE

$[C_xH_y]_R$ $+$ $2xH_2O \longrightarrow (4x + y)H^+ + (4x + y)\,e^- + [xCO_2]_P$

CATHODE   electrolyte   electrolyte   circuit

$[0.5yH_2O]_P$ $+$ $2xH_2O \longleftarrow (4x + y)H^+ + (4x + y)\,e^- + [(x + 0.25yO_2]_R$

Table 5.1 Stoichiometric data of individual fuel compounds with air (approximate basis)

Name	Formula	MM (g/mol)	Non-dissociated stoic. mol/mol fuel					$(A/F)_s$ molar	$(a/f)_s$ mass	$(P/R)_s$ molar
			$O_2(=m_s)$	CO_2	H_2O	N_2	B_2O_3			
Hydrogen	H_2	2	0.5	—	1	1.88	—	2.38	34.48	0.852
HYDROCARBONS	C_xH_y	$12x+y$	$x+0.25y$	x	$0.5y$	$3.76x + 0.94y$	—	$4.76(x+0.25y)$	$\dfrac{137.9(x+0.25y)}{12x+y}$	$\dfrac{4.76x+1.44y}{4.76(x+0.25y)+1}$
Methane	CH_4	16	2	1	2	7.52	—	9.52	17.24	1.000
Propane	C_3H_8	44	5	3	4	18.8	—	23.80	15.67	1.040
Butane	C_4H_{10}	58	6.5	4	5	24.44	—	30.94	15.46	1.047
Octane	C_8H_{18}	114	12.5	8	9	47.0	—	59.50	15.12	1.058
Acetylene	C_2H_2	26	2.5	2	1	9.4	—	11.90	13.26	0.961
Benzene	C_6H_6	78	7.5	6	3	28.2	—	35.70	13.26	1.014
Carbon (graphite)	$C(gr)$	12	1	1	—	3.76	—	4.76	11.49	0.826
Carbon monoxide	CO	28	0.5	1	—	1.88	—	2.38	2.46	0.852
ALKYL ALCOHOLS }	$C_xH_{2x+1}OH$	$14x+18$	$1.5x$	x	$x+1$	$5.64x$	—	$7.14x$	$\dfrac{206.85x}{14x+18}$	$\dfrac{7.64x+1}{7.14x+1}$
Methanol	CH_3OH	32	1.5	1	2	5.64	—	7.14	6.46	1.061
Ethanol	C_2H_5OH	46	3	2	3	11.28	—	14.28	8.99	1.065
Propanol	C_3H_7OH	60	4.5	3	4	16.92	—	21.42	10.34	1.067
Butanol	C_4H_9OH	74	6	4	5	22.56	—	28.56	11.18	1.068

NITRO-PARAFFINS	$C_xH_{2x+1}NO_2$	$14x+47$	$1.5x-0.75$	x	$x+0.5$	$5.64x-2.32$	—	$7.14(x-0.5)$	$\dfrac{206.85x-103.43}{14x+47}$	$\dfrac{7.64x-1.82}{7.14x-2.57}$
Nitromethane	CH_3NO_2	61	0.75	1	1.5	3.32	—	3.57	1.70	1.276
Nitroethane	$C_2H_5NO_2$	75	2.25	2	2.5	8.96	—	10.71	4.14	1.149
NITRO-HYDRIDES	N_aH_{a+2}	$15a+2$	$0.25a+0.5$	—	$0.5a+1$	$1.44a+1.88$	—	$1.19a+2.38$	$\dfrac{34.48a+68.95}{15a+2}$	$\dfrac{1.94a+2.88}{1.19a+3.38}$
Ammonia	NH_3	17	0.75	—	1.5	3.32	—	3.57	6.08	1.055
Hydrazine	N_2H_4	32	1	—	2	4.76	—	4.76	4.31	1.174
UDMH	$(CH_3)_2N_2H_2$	60	4	2	4	16.04	—	19.04	9.19	1.100
BORANES	B_bH_{b+4}	$11.8b+4$	$b+1$	—	$0.5b+2$	$\dfrac{3.76\times}{(b+1)}$	$0.5b$	$4.76(b+1)$	$\dfrac{137.9(b+1)}{11.8b+4}$	1.000
Diborane	B_2H_6	27.6	3	—	3	11.28	1	14.28	14.99	1.000
Pentaborane	B_5H_9	63	6	—	4.5	22.56	2.5	28.56	13.13	1.000
Decaborane	$B_{10}H_{14}$	122	11	—	7	41.36	5	52.36	12.43	1.000
Boron (cryst.)	$B(c)$	10.8	0.75	—	—	2.82	0.5	3.57	9.58	0.726
Triethylborane	$(C_2H_5)_3B$	97.8	10.5	6	7.5	39.48	0.5	49.98	14.81	1.049

References

1. D. R. Stull and H. Prophet, *JANAF Thermochemical Tables*, National Bureau of Standards, Washington, D.C. (1971).
2. E. M. Goodger, *Combustion Calculations*, Macmillan, London and Basingstoke (1977).
3. BS 526:1961 Definitions of the calorific value of fuels.
4. E. M. Goodger, Comparative energies of alternative fuels, *Appl. Energy*, 4 (1978) 39–50.
5. W. L. Lom and A. F. Williams, *Substitute Natural Gas*, Applied Science, London (1976).
6. R. C. Weast (ed), *Handbook of Chemistry and Physics*, 55th edn, The Chemical Rubber Co., Cleveland, Ohio (1974/5).
7. B. Kit and D. S. Evered, *Rocket Propellant Handbook*, Macmillan, New York (1960).
8. S. Sarner, Unsummetrical dimethyl hydrazine, Propellants data sheets, *Astronautics*, 4 (1959) 76.

6. Alternative-fuel Combustion Processes

In general, fuels burn only in the gaseous or vapour phase, and in contact with a gaseous oxidant, usually atmospheric oxygen. Gaseous fuels in air therefore require mixing only prior to ignition and combustion, whereas liquid fuels also require vaporisation, and solid fuels need energy from an external source or from the flame itself in order to pyrolyse and provide combustible gases.

With liquid fuels of volatility comparable to that of a petroleum gasoline, vaporisation is so rapid that rudimentary droplet formation only, as in a carburettor, is adequate to provide extensive vaporisation in the air stream leading to the combustor. With liquid fuels of volatility comparable to kerosine, slow vaporisation is possible from the surface of a cotton or asbestos wick into a draught of air. For a more rapid throughput of fuel, vaporisation can take place by fuel flowing over a hot surface, the temperature of which is maintained by added heat or by transfer from the flame itself. Kerosine or gas oil is usable in this way, whereas heavier petroleum fuels would produce deposits from contaminants or from molecular cracking.

Where the actual level of fuel volatility is particularly low, the effective level can be raised significantly by shattering the fuel bulk into droplets by spraying (the so-called 'atomisation' process). By subdividing the bulk of liquid fuel finely and fairly uniformly, and distributing it rapidly in space, the area—volume ratio is raised so substantially that the fuel vaporisation rate becomes comparable to that of a relatively volatile gasoline.

Gas/vapour—air mixing is followed within the combustor by ignition, combustion and the formation of combustion products. The main fuel parameters controlling these various stages of the overall combustion process are listed in table 6.1,[1] together with the dependent parameters of spray, flame and product characteristics. Clearly, such parameters tend to exert influence in more than one stage, but an attempt has been made here to relate each parameter broadly to the stage in which it has most significance.

Table 6.1   *Relevant fuel parameters in combustion applications*

Stage	Controlling parameter	Dependent parameter
Spray formation	Relative density Viscosity Surface tension	} Droplet size distribution Spray penetration
Vapour formation	Boiling point Vapour pressure Liquid heat capacity Vaporisation enthalpy Vapour heat capacity	} Relationship of vaporisation rate with temperature Extent of carburation Mixture distribution to piston engine cylinders
Ignition	Spontaneous ignition temp. Minimum ignition energy	} Ignitability, relight, spark knock, diesel knock
Combustion	Flammability range Flame speed	} Flame stability
	Calorific value (or Wobbe No.) Content of C, H, etc.	Energy release Combustion temperature Radiation Smoke
Post combustion		Combustion deposits Products/reactants ratio Fuel emissions and NO_x
	Contaminants Ash	Contaminant emissions Corrosion Erosion

No universal requirements can be laid down for the controlling fuel parameters since the spray droplet size, penetration, rate of vaporisation, and so on, need to be matched with the geometry and air pattern of the particular combustor. However, requirements generally tend towards low viscosity for small droplet size, high volatility for ready vaporisation and ignition, high or low spontaneous ignitability (compression- or spark-ignition piston engines respectively), high flame speed and wide flammability range for flame stability and economy, and high specific energy for high energy release. Of the dependent parameters, a high combustion temperature generally assists thermal efficiency, but promotes NO_x pollution, whereas increased (products/reactants) molar ratios raise the resulting volume, pressure and/or kinetic energy of the products depending on the conditions of combustion. The carbon content of the fuel is directly related to flame radiation, which is necessary for heat transfer in furnaces but undesirable for work transfer in engines, and also tends to promote combustion deposits and smoke.

The following sections compare the parameters and behaviour of the alternative fuels and commercial petroleum fuel blends within the various stages of the overall combustion process.

6.1 Spray Formation Stage

Atomisation is achieved by forcing the liquid under high pressure through a small orifice (pressure-jet atomiser) and/or by subjecting the liquid to the shearing action of air at a high relative velocity (rotary cup, air or steam assisted, or air-blast atomisers). Both the fall in pressure and the shearing action allow the liquid to break up into sheets or ligaments, while viscosity and surface tension constrain the disrupted liquid into droplets which are basically spherical but modified in shape due to the relative velocity with air. Selection of orifice diameter, fuel pressure and/or velocity and direction of air flow provide control over the mean droplet diameter, penetration and, to some extent, the size distribution of droplets. Comprehensive information on droplet diameters can be gained experimentally by spraying on to coated slides or by freezing and sieving or examining the sprayed droplets, whereas a measure of the mean droplet diameter is obtainable optically by the forward scatter imposed on a parallel beam of monochromatic light directed through the spray.

Of the relevant fuel properties, density alone is not found to have a marked influence on spray formation, apart from a slight direct effect on spray compactness and penetration. The temperature relationships of relative density in figure 6.1 (at end of chapter) show nitromethane and hydrazine to be heavier than the range of conventional petroleum fuels, whereas ammonia, pentaborane and triethylborane are lighter, the alcohols being roughly equivalent to the kerosines.

The viscosity of the fuel, on the other hand, is of great importance in controlling turbulence in the fuel flow, both in the formation of the continuous film immediately after exit from the nozzle, and of the subsequent ligament disruption into individual droplets. Experiment shows that both droplet diameter and penetration are directly related to fuel viscosity. The temperature relationships of kinematic viscosity in figure 6.2 (at end of chapter) show all the alternative fuels discussed here to have viscosities lower than that of conventional gas oil, thus tending to finer atomisation. Surface tension has a direct effect on droplet size, but the temperature relationships in figure 6.3 show little variation between the alcohols and the petroleum fuels. Hydrazine and nitromethane, on the other hand, are relatively high, and the boranes low.

6.2 Vapour Formation Stage

The boiling temperatures (individual fuels) or ranges (fuel blends) are shown in figure 6.4, and the distillation curves of the hydrocarbon blends in figure 6.5. Included also is a broken line showing the effect of blending 10 per cent of methanol with a motor gasoline. The curves in figure 6.6 show the relationships between the temperatures and pressures of the fully saturated vapours of the fuels of interest, the standard boiling points shown representing the equality of the vapour pressures with sea-level atmospheric pressure. From Avogadro's law, it follows that the vapour pressures bear a direct relationship with the fuel concentrations in the mixture with air. Consequently, under conditions of equilibrium, high vapour pressures represent richer mixtures. The curves show all the liquid alternative fuels studied to lie within the vapour-pressure boundaries of gasoline and kerosine, and therefore to be comparatively volatile. Hydrogen, diborane and ammonia, which exist normally as gases, exert correspondingly very high values of pressure, whereas decaborane, normally a solid, is roughly equivalent in vapour pressure to gas oil. This property is important in controlling low-temperature vaporisation, as in a relatively cool inlet air manifold remote from the combustion chamber.

The level of specific heat capacity for a liquid fuel determines the quantity of energy required to bring the fuel up to its boiling point, and the curves in figure 6.7 show that, in comparison with the petroleum fuels, most of the alternative fuels require more energy for a given rise in temperature. Similarly, all the alternative fuels require comparatively more energy for vaporisation, as shown in figure 6.8. In the vapour phase, however, alternative fuels generally show specific heat capacities either equal to or only slightly less than those for the petroleum fuels, as in figure 6.9. Diborane gas has a relatively high level of specific heat capacity, and hydrogen (not shown) a very high level (approximately 9 kJ/kg K at $-254\,^{\circ}C$). The combined effect determines the enthalpy of the vapour at any temperature above the boiling point, and it is this parameter which is significant in controlling the lifetimes of fuel droplets projected into the hot environment of a combustion chamber. Consequently, the liquid alternative fuels would be expected to tend to longer residence times within the chamber, and to greater flame lengths.

6.3 Ignition Stage

The spontaneous ignition of a fuel—oxidant mixture results from the disruption of a few of the more energetic molecules within the mixture, exposing free bonds available for joining with oxygen. Broadly, therefore, a reduction in the minimum spontaneous ignition temperature (SIT) is expected with increasing molecular size and complexity, due to the inability of the less compact molecules to withstand thermal agitation. The plot of SIT values in figure 6.10 is composite in the sense that the gases are plotted against density relative to air on the upper abscissa, and the liquids against density relative to water on the lower. The inverse SIT—density relationship is generally evident for members of a given fuel type. However, the SIT test indicates the temperature level at which ignition occurs, and not the energy supplied to achieve it. Data on minimum ignition energies are sparse, and not always

88

comparable, but these values will be influenced by the specific heat capacities of the vapours or gases as well as the temperature levels at which ignition occurs. This is shown clearly in figure 6.11 by comparing the ignition data of the alcohols, where their noticeable reduction in SIT is over-ridden by the rise in specific heat capacity to give a general increase in minimum ignition energy. However, no marked reduction in minimum ignition energy occurs with the paraffinic gases, despite reductions both in SIT and specific heat capacity measured at 25 °C. The minimum ignition energy of the common petroleum fuel blends is considered to be about 0.3 mJ, whereas values of acetylene and hydrogen are seen to be particularly low, at about 0.02 mJ.

6.4 Combustion Stage

Compared with the petroleum fuels, the data in figure 6.12 show that most of the alternative fuels have wider ranges of flammability which, with the exception of ammonia, are associated with a slightly higher flame speed. Hydrogen, hydrazine and diborane are outstanding in the former case, and hydrogen and the boranes in the latter. This infers that, in general, the alternative fuels are likely to give greater freedom of adjustment of operating conditions without danger of flame-out, coupled with greater flame stability in continuous combustion, and the ability to cope with higher air speeds at the chamber entry.

Relative levels of calorific value, indicated in section 5.4, are seen to favour the compounds of boron and hydrogen, as distinct from those of carbon and hydrogen, and those containing nitrogen and/or oxygen. In the case of the gaseous fuels, the Wobbe number is the preferred parameter. However, as discussed in chapter 7, the proportion of the calorific value convertible to useful work can, under certain circumstances, be determined by such other characteristics as spontaneous ignitability and dissociation. The temperature resulting from combustion is, of course, a joint function of the enthalpy absorption characteristics of the combustion products, as well as the enthalpy released by combustion. In general, as was seen in figure 5.12, the flame temperatures of the alternative fuels are higher than those of the hydro-carbons, particularly those of a paraffinic base, with the exceptions of the alcohols and ammonia. Flame temperature bears a direct relationship to thermodynamic efficiency in engine cycles.

As discussed in chapter 7, the radiation from particulate solids within a flame greatly exceeds that of the hot gases themselves, and radiation is a requirement for heat transfer in a high-temperature furnace, but is undesirable for work transfer in an engine. The extent of particulates within a flame can be controlled to some extent by chamber design, with the elimination of hot over-rich pockets leading to fuel cracking and resultant free carbon. However, the extent of flame radiation is broadly related to the carbon content of the fuel, which is plotted on a percentage mass basis in figure 6.13. This shows the expected decrease from the coals and CTFs through the liquid petroleum fuels to the alcohols, peat and wood, with most of the alternative fuels studied lying at the lower levels. When re-plotted on a unit energy basis, however, some changes in relative levels occur, particularly with the rise of peat and wood.

Some preliminary tests made at Cranfield in a gas turbine chamber comparing the combustion performance of gas oil with a 25 per cent volumetric blend of Class 'G' residual fuel oil in gas oil, showed increases of 36 per cent and 45 per cent respectively in radiation and emissivity as a result of the increase in carbon content of 6 per cent. The increase in combustion liner temperature, however, was 11 K only, as discussed further in chapter 9.

6.5 Post-combustion Stage

The other major effect of fuel carbon content, again influenced by the chamber geometry and combustion conditions, is the incidence of smoke and of carbon deposits. The Cranfield tests reported above gave an increase in smoke number of 29 per cent when changing to the RFO/gas oil blend. Other solid (or molten) combustion products are generally the result of inorganic metallic contaminants in the fuel, as in the case of the residual fuel oils, and not direct features of the fuel itself. One exception to this is the borane group since its main combustion product, B_2O_3, with a melting point of about 580 °C, promotes copious glass-like deposits on surfaces downstream of the combustor.

The gaseous emissions from combustion are very largely controlled by the effectiveness or otherwise of the complete combustion system, although fuel carbon content can again influence broadly the concentrations of carbon monoxide. Flame temperature largely controls the concentration of NO_x, consequently higher concentrations could be expected with nitromethane, the boranes and hydrazine (see figure 5.12). Finally, as outlined in section 5.1, a high products/reactants molar ratio is helpful in generating product pressure and/or velocity and, as was seen in figure 5.2, the highest values are found for nitroparaffins, nitrogen hydrides and, to a lesser extent, the alcohols.

For convenience of location, the diagrams showing the comparative properties of the conventional and alternative fuels have been presented in the following pages at the end, rather than within the text, of this chapter. The data have been collated mainly from references 2 to 10, of which reference 7 has been particularly fruitful.

Where space permits, the names of the various fuels are given in full out, in other cases, the curves are identified by fuel formulae only. Curves for alternative fuels are shown in full line, whereas background data for conventional fuels are given in broken line, and for water in chain line.

90

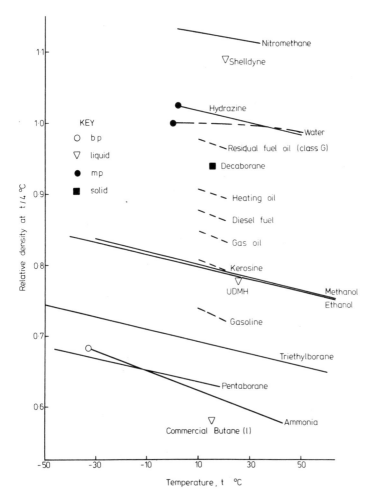

Figure 6.1   Variation of relative density with temperature for petroleum and alternative liquid fuels

91

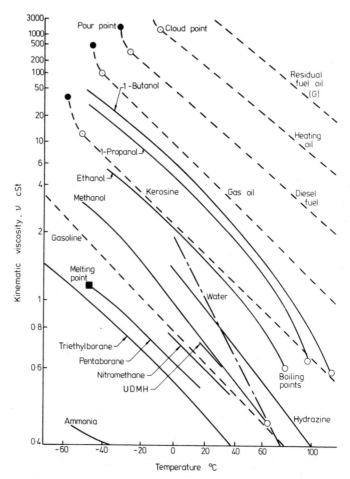

Figure 6.2   Variation of kinematic viscosity with temperature for petroleum and alternative liquid fuels

92

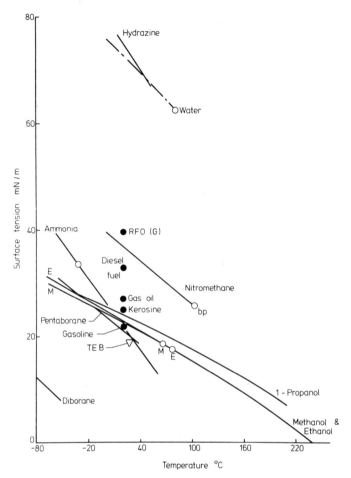

Figure 6.3   Variation of surface tension with temperature for petroleum and alternative liquid fuels

93

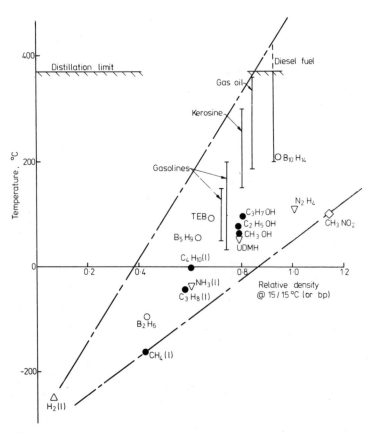

Figure 6.4   Boiling levels of petroleum and alternative liquid fuels

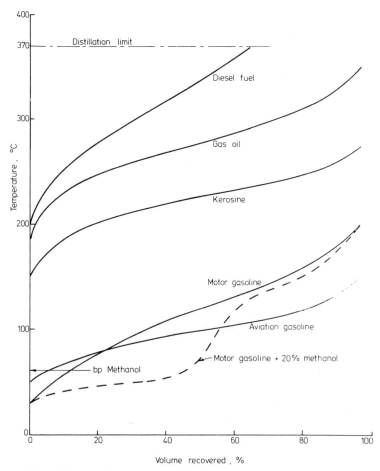

Figure 6.5   Distillation curves for representative petroleum fuel blends

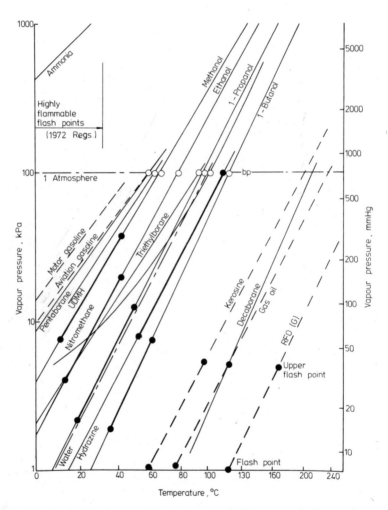

Figure 6.6   Variation of saturated vapour pressure with temperature for petroleum and alternative liquid fuels

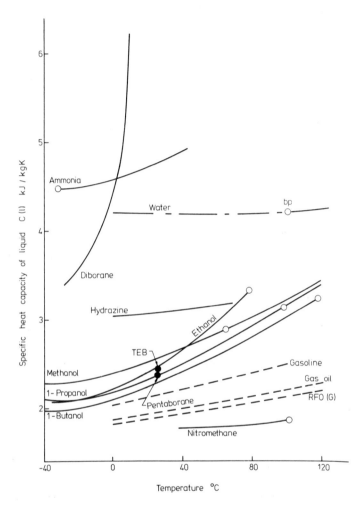

Figure 6.7   Variation of specific heat capacity with temperature for petroleum and alternative fuels (liquid phase)

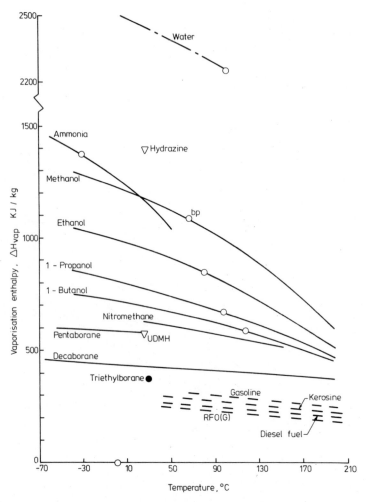

Figure 6.8   Variation of vaporisation enthalpy with temperature for petroleum and alternative liquid fuels

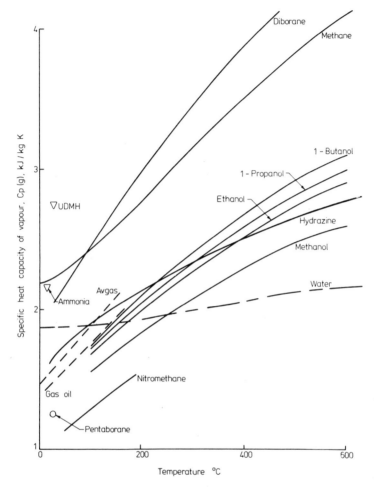

Figure 6.9   Variation of specific heat capacity with temperature for petroleum and
alternative fuels (vapour phase)

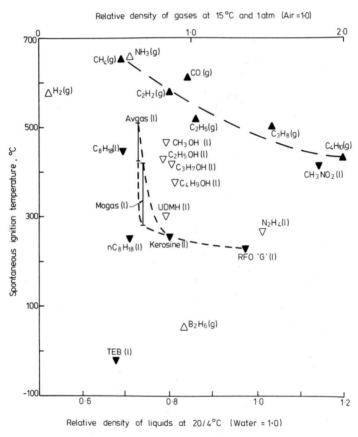

Figure 6.10   Spontaneous ignition temperatures of petroleum and alternative fuels

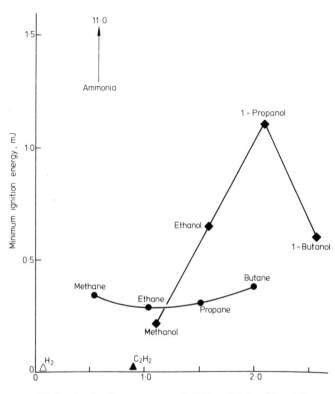

Figure 6.11   Minimum ignition energies of gaseous and vaporised fuels

101

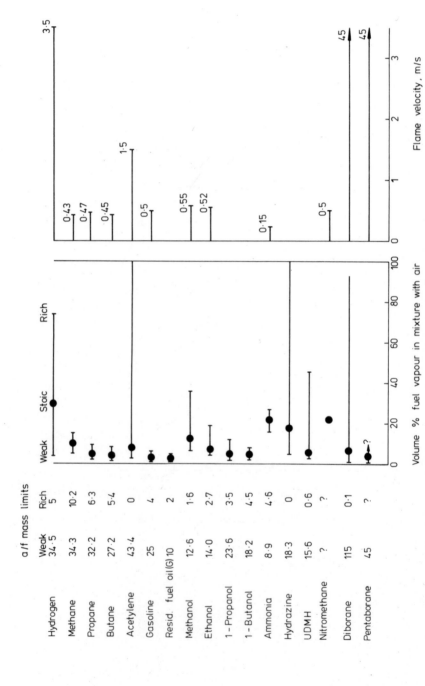

Figure 6.12   Flammability ranges and flame velocities of conventional and alternative fuels

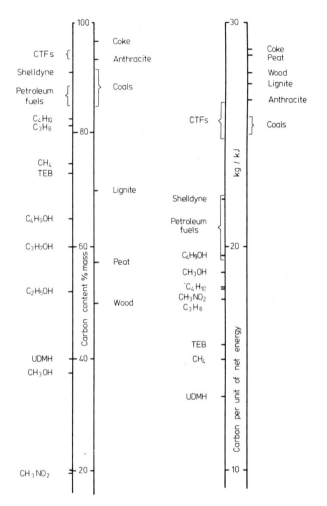

Figure 6.13   Carbon mass per unit mass, and per unit energy, of conventional and alternative fuels

References

1. E. M. Goodger, Alcohol fuel prospects, *J. Inst. Fuel*, **L** (1977) 132–8.
2. *Data Sheet FD/9 – Specific Heat of Fuel Vapour.* Royal Aeronautical Society and Institute of Petroleum (1956).
3. J. W. Rose and J. R. Cooper, *Technical Data on Fuel*, British National Committee, World Energy Conference, London (1977).
4. I. G. C. Dryden (ed), *The Efficient Use of Energy*, IPC Science and Technology Press, Guildford (1975).
5. C. L. Yaws and J. R. Hopper, Methanol, ethanol, propanol and butanol, *Chem. Engng,* **83** (1976) 119–127.
6. *Methanol; Ethanol; Isopropanol; n-Butanol;* Data booklets from BP Chemicals International Ltd, Devonshire House, Piccadilly, London W1X 6AY (1975/6).
7. B. Kit and D. S. Evered, *Rocket Propellant Handbook*, Macmillan, New York (1960).
8. L. F. Andrich and B. A. Ogg, *The Chemistry of Hydrazine*, Wiley, New York (1951).
9. *Diborane; Decaborane; Trialkylboranes;* Technical data sheets, Callery Chemical Co., 9600 Perry Highway, Pittsburgh 37, Pa. (1957/8).
10. *A Guide to the Viscosity of Liquid Petroleum Products, Item No. 67015,* Engineering Sciences Data Unit, London (1967).

7. Alternative-fuel Combustion Performance

In all combustion applications, the fuel—oxidant mixture must be maintained in the correct proportions, and in the correct region within the chamber, for combustion to be as complete as is practicable. With these provisos, most combustor types may be classified into those in which the fuel is

1. vaporised by means of a wick drawing its vaporisation heat from the flame,
2. pre-vaporised and pre-mixed upstream of the chamber, or
3. injected as droplets or solid particles directly into the flame zone.

These combustors may also be classified in terms of intermittent-flow devices depending on flame propagation, or of continuous-flow devices based on flame stabilisation.

The laminar flame velocities of all the fuels considered here, with the exception of the boranes and hydrogen, are relatively low. However, the influences of temperature, pressure and, particularly, turbulence which breaks the flame up and increases the surface area substantially, raise the flame velocity by one or more orders of magnitude. Consequently, in practical combustors, flames can be made to propagate rapidly across the chamber or, alternatively, can be stabilised against a fast approaching mixture or spray. The former process is fundamental to the spark-ignition reciprocating-piston engine, in which the fuel charge is momentarily encapsulated in the combustion chamber, and ignited from one or more discrete points. The latter process is used in the various types of flow device involving furnaces, gas turbines, ramjets and rockets. Ideally this group should also include the compression-ignition reciprocating-piston engine, but ignition must occur a finite period of time after injection and, if this delay is extended, flame propagation occurs first before stabilisation by the remainder of the spray.

Following the discussion of the individual characteristics of combustion for the various conventional and alternative fuels, this present chapter outlines the overall combustion performance within practical combustors, as reported in the literature.

7.1 Timed Combustion Applications

The types of engine considered here are characterised by intermittent internal combustion, the fuel—air charge being confined within a moving solid boundary during combustion, then expelled and replaced. For many years, the two main categories of engine in this group have been based on spark-ignition with gas or gasoline as fuel, and on compression-ignition using either gas oil or diesel fuel depending on the application. Recently, this group has been joined by the Wankel engine which, although rotary in operation, also uses intermittent internal combustion together with a moving solid boundary for for the charge space. The Stirling engine, although based mechanically on reciprocating pistons, is not included here since the combustion, being external, is continuous.

In the spark-ignition engine, fuel metering to provide the required *quality* of mixture is normally achieved by measuring the air flow in some way (by venturi, or by sensing engine speed, air temperature and pressure), and matching the fuel flow accordingly. The *quantity* of mixture entering the cylinders is controlled independently by means of a variable throttle plate. In the compression-ignition engine, the fuel must be injected directly into the cylinder in order to achieve ignition at compression temperatures and pressures, consequently it is customary to dispense with the throttle plate and control both mixture quality and quantity by means of the amount of fuel injected.

Mixture preparation is achieved easily by upstream mixing in the case of gaseous fuels, and by carburation with the volatile gasolines, although some multi-cylinder spark-ignition engines achieve improved mixture distribution by means of continuous injection into the manifold, or by timed injection either into the inlet ports or direct in the cylinders themselves. In compression-ignition engines, timed cylinder injection is essential.

7.1.1 Spark-ignition Engine Characteristics

In charging the engine cylinder with fuel—air mixture immediately prior to compression and spark-ignition, the influence of the fuel is felt in terms of its vaporisation behaviour, and the thermal quantities involved. If these are high, the temperature of the charge is reduced, and the volumetric efficiency of the engine improved. With conventional gasoline, a working figure of 25 °C is generally used as the temperature drop of the charge resulting from complete evaporation. Valuable as this is in improving volumetric efficiency, it could give rise to icing problems in low-temperature humid atmospheres, and most normally aspirated engine intake systems handle both vapour and liquid 'heavy ends' of the gasoline. Vaporisation is completed during compression and mixing with the hot exhaust residuals, and the sparking plug is fired electrically some few crankshaft degrees before top dead centre. A nucleus of flame forms rapidly at the plug electrodes, and the flame moves radially outwards through the combustion chamber by a transfer of both heat and free radicals to each successive layer of unburnt gas. The release of combustion heat promotes a corresponding rise in pressure, which continues until all the mixture is consumed. The pressure rise is augmented if the number of gaseous moles increases (that is, the products/reactants ratio exceeds unity). The pressure—volume diagram therefore shows a rapid rise in pressure during a short combustion period and, for this reason, the performance of the spark-ignition engine is assessed against that of the theoretical Otto cycle in which heat is added at constant volume. The thermal efficiency of this cycle is given by

$$\eta_{Otto} = 1 - (1/r_v)^{\gamma - 1}$$

where r_v = compression ratio = ratio of volume at bottom dead centre to volume at top dead centre.

Weak-mixture operation results in a lower velocity of flame propagation, consequently less heat is converted to mechanical energy, and part of the additional waste heat from the exhaust products is retained in the cylinder walls causing the engine to run hotter and to be more prone to spark knock (see below). With extensive fuel weakening, the flame speed becomes so low that flame is still present when the inlet valve opens for the next admission, leading to back-firing into the inlet manifold.

When cylinder pressures and/or temperatures are particularly high, the unconsumed end gases may be stressed sufficiently to ignite spontaneously before the arrival of the main flame. This explosive form of combustion is termed spark knock, and promotes a sharp rise in pressure followed by violent vibrations of the gases, with sympathetic vibration of the engine components causing a sharp metallic noise. A further abnormal form of combustion arises with the high-compression engine when combustion deposits build up in the chamber. Under high-temperature operation, the deposits tend to glow, and to act as secondary sources of ignition. The fresh charge then ignites early, independent of the spark timing, leading to an uncontrolled over-advance with consequent roughness and hot running. This low-pressure phenomenon is termed surface ignition, and is a function not only of the ignitability of the fuel, but also of the flame temperature of the fuel which had previously determined the temperature reached by the deposits. All these combustion phenomena are illustrated in the pressure—volume diagram in figure 7.1, whereas critical (minimum levels for incipient knock) compression ratios are shown in figure 7.2.

One other engine based on intermittent combustion is the pulse jet unit using a tuned duct with spring-loaded valves at entry, combustion being initiated by hot residual gases from previous cycles. In continuous-flow combustion (section 7.2), the attraction of the ramjet over the gas turbine is the opportunity to dispense with the complex and expensive rotating components, and to gain the required pressure rise merely by the ram effect

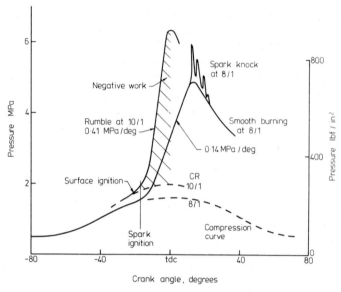

Figure 7.1   Pressure diagrams for normal and abnormal combustion in the spark-ignition piston engine (reference 1)

of the entering air. However, very high air speeds are necessary for any appreciable pressure rise, consequently the early airborne missile, the German V1 operating at 400 mile/h, was powered with a pulse jet tuned to a frequency of 60 to 100 Hz, the reflected pulses providing the required pressure rise at each instant of combustion. Subsequently, a small version was developed by Westland for helicopter tip or target drone propulsion. Suitable fuels include low-quality gasoline, kerosine or gas oil.

7.1.2 Spark-ignition Engine Performance of Alcohols

Comparative gasoline and alcohol bench tests have been conducted on single- and multi-cylinder piston engines, and road tests on the latter, using the alcohols in a variety of ways, as follows

1. as the sole fuel component, with or without water,
2. as a blending agent with gasoline, and
3. as a dual fuel with gasoline.

They have also been used as blending agents with non-petroleum fuel components, and as base stocks for conversion to other fuels. The alcohols discussed here range in type from methanol and methanol—gasoline blends through ethanol and ethanol—gasoline blends to mixed alcohols and their derivatives. The experimental results reported depend largely on test

108

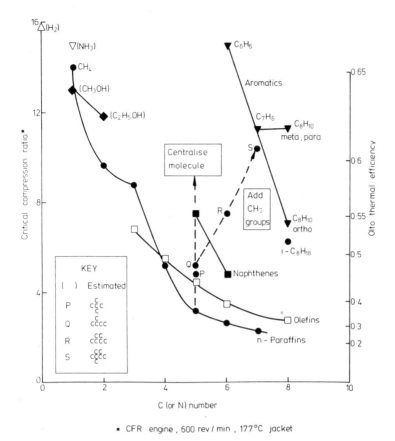

Figure 7.2   Critical compression ratios and Otto thermal efficiencies for conventional and alternative fuels (derived from reference 10 and other sources)

conditions, particularly on any increase of carburettor jet sizes, warming or weakening of the mixture, optimisation of ignition timing, and raising of compression ratio. Nevertheless, in changing from gasoline to methanol fuel, the following broad conclusions can be drawn from a study of the literature (for example[2,3]) including the recent papers at Wolfsburg[4] and at Sydney.[5]

1. With unmodified carburettor jets, a mixture-weakening effect results from the higher stoichiometric fuel/air ratio of methanol, whereas adjustment to the same equivalence ratio promotes a rise in specific fuel consumption of up to 215 per cent in single-cylinder engines, and 100 per cent in multi-cylinder engines. Blending a gasoline with x per cent methanol increases specific fuel consumption by about $0.3x$ per cent. The lean misfire limit extends by about 0.13 units of equivalence ratio, and by 0.2 units in comparison with isooctane.

2. The high vaporisation enthalpy of methanol tends to lower the charge temperature by a further 30 °C, consequently the results depend on whether the manifold temperature, or the heat addition, is maintained constant. In general, the volumetric efficiency rises, together with the thermal efficiency (by about 8 per cent) due to the higher flame speed giving earlier energy release in the power stroke, resulting in a power improvement of up to 12 per cent at the same conditions, and up to about 20 per cent at the higher permitted levels of compression ratio. Cyclic pressure variations are also less with methanol. Blending a gasoline with x per cent methanol raises power by about $0.1x$ per cent.

3. The improved octane rating of about 8 RON permits increases in compression ratio from about 10/1 to 14/1, and the high blending octane number gives a variable octane improvement up to 3.5 numbers for a 15 per cent methanol blend with a 4-star (97 RON) base fuel.

4. Carbon monoxide emissions, on an equal power basis, are slightly reduced with methanol fuel, particularly at the lower engine speeds, but are considerably reduced and comparable with those of gasoline when fuel preparation is improved in the manifold. This applies especially to emissions of unburnt fuel (largely methanol itself, which does not contribute to smog formation), which are otherwise improved by as much as 90 per cent in single-cylinder engines with methanol, but deteriorate by 20 per cent in multi-cylinder engines with a 25 per cent methanol blend with gasoline. Aldehydes also increase by 2 to 4 times with methanol in both types of engine. Emissions of NO_x are generally improved by between 20 to 60 per cent, particularly on the fuel-weak side, and at the higher permissible compression ratios, but this benefit tends to be lost with manifold heating, and also by the higher flame temperature with improved fuel preparation. Concentrations of PANs (peroxyacylnitrates), suspected as carcinogens, are also reduced with methanol. With no carbon—carbon bonds, methanol does not produce soot, and therefore burns with low luminosity and little radiation. In conjunction with the lower flame temperature, about 10 per cent less heat is lost to the engine coolant.

5. The overall influence of lower mixture temperature due to the higher vaporisation enthalpy and the weakening effect is to reduce driveability, appearing as hesitation, surge, stumble and stall, particularly at low temperature, and with low volatility gasoline blending components. The extent of driveability loss appears to be proportional to the percentage fuel unevaporated, and the percentage of methanol—gasoline blend evaporated at 100 °C may be a controlling parameter. However, these detrimental effects were virtually eliminated by proper adjustment of the fuel metering system, by the use of fuel injection, or by stratified charging.

6. The high vaporisation enthalpy and constant boiling point make cold-starting difficult with neat methanol fuel below about 12 °C without auxiliary heating or other starting aid in the form of a volatile auxiliary fuel or additive. Even with such aids, starting below −12 °C is extremely difficult, although

tests with an EAD apparatus (see section A3.3) show that winter starting should be possible down to −30 °C with a blend of 70 per cent methanol and either 30 per cent volatile gasoline, or gasoline with 10 per cent pentanes. With gasoline—methanol blends, the percentage of the base gasoline evaporated at 70 °C may be the best predictor of startability.

7. The addition of water to methanol fuel shows that contamination up to 5 per cent can be tolerated. A 10 per cent addition (M10W) lowers the efficiency and power by about 3 per cent, and doubles the unburnt fuel emissions, although it reduces the NO_x by about 25 per cent, whereas a M20W blend reduces peak NO_x by a factor of about 3. Water also reduces drastically the aldehyde concentrations.

8. The selection of lubricating oil for a methanol-fuelled engine may be critical. Although improved oil economy and deposits have been reported, the oil viscosity may increase significantly, and greater corrosive wear has been found, together with precipitation of some lubricant additives and an alarming build-up of a methanol—water foam in the oil.

Ethanol also has been investigated over the years as a spark-ignition engine fuel, and the literature survey including recent tests with 'Gasohol', a 10 per cent blend of anhydrous ethanol in unleaded gasoline, when compared with conventional gasolines, permits the following broad conclusions.

1. Ethanol produces a power improvement of about 5 per cent, but the 10 per cent blend with gasoline shows no significant variation.

2. The specific fuel consumption can be up to 45 per cent higher under the same conditions of operation, but suitable engine adjustment can reduce this appreciably and, in fact, the 10 per cent blend on road testing showed improvements in fuel economy of about 2 per cent in terms of distance travelled per unit volume of fuel, and 5 per cent in distance per unit of energy.

3. There is an increase in octane rating of about 13 RONs, and the high blending octane number promotes an improvement of about 5 RONs for the 10 per cent blend, permitting a less costly base stock for the preparation of ethanol—gasoline blends.

4. The 10 per cent blend gives 30 per cent less emissions of carbon monoxide, but the variations in unburnt fuel and NO_x were indeterminate.

It is interesting to note that the Maquis, when lacking gasoline during the later stages of the Second World War, used a 90 per cent blend of 100 proof ethanol in gasoline, and started their truck engines by towing.[6]

The alcohols have also been of interest as blending agents with non-petroleum fuel components, as in the Ricardo Discol fuel comprising methanol, ethanol, benzole, acetone and water, blended in 1921 for long-distance racing cars. More recently, both methanol and ethanol have been considered as feedstocks, with isobutane, for the production of methyl tert-butyl ether, $CH_3OC_4H_9$, or MTBE, and also ethyl tert-butyl ether,

$C_2H_5OC_4H_9$, or ETBE. In comparison with the base alcohols, these blending agents have higher specific energies and energy densities, and lower enthalpies of vaporisation. Their anti-knock quality is superior to that of the alcohols, particularly with the front-end fractions which influence knock during acceleration, and emission reduction is also claimed due to more complete combustion. The effects on vapour pressure of the blends with gasoline are very much less than those of the alcohols. They also lack problems of azeotrope formation in production, and of water separation in blends with hydrocarbons due to their high miscibility with all hydrocarbons, and low solubility with water.[4]

7.1.3 Spark-ignition Engine Performance of Hydrogen and Other Fuels

Hydrogen has been of some interest as a fuel for spark-ignition engines since the turn of the century, one of the early attractions being the possible use in airship engines of the hydrogen vented to adjust the buoyancy following consumption of the conventional propulsive fuel. Also attractive is its ability to burn efficiently at relatively weak mixtures, giving good fuel economy. However, all early attempts to burn either hydrogen-enriched fuels or hydrogen itself were plagued with abnormal combustion in the form of pre-ignition, back-firing and spark knock, particularly when the mixture strength approached the region of stoichiometric and maximum power. Ricardo investigated this problem in the early 1920s, using the single-cylinder variable-compression E35 engine, and attributed pre-ignition as the main cause of the abnormal combustion. Erren, in the late 1920s, and Oermichen in the 1940s, eliminated the back-firing problem by means of direct hydrogen injection during the compression stroke after closure of the inlet valve. This also provided some degree of supercharging, and improved the thermal efficiency, but did not influence the heavy knocking.

This readiness for abnormal combustion in its various forms is no doubt due to the very low requirement of ignition energy, the high flame speed, and the very small quenching distance which allows flame to pass through the narrow openings of inlet valves causing back-fire. In connection with the first-named property, the work of King[7] showed carbon deposits in the combustion chamber to be a major cause of pre-ignition, which in turn promotes knock. By adopting a 'clean engine' technique, and lowering the jacket coolant temperature from 100 to 60 °C, knock-free operation at 900 rev/min was possible up to a compression ratio of 10/1. A maximum limiting compression ratio of only 8/1 was found by Downs,[8] and by Anzilotti,[9] because of knock arising from spontaneous ignition reactions within the end gases. In one sense, a high flame speed is helpful in reducing knock since the end gases are consumed by the advancing flame before they can complete their spontaneous ignition pre-reactions and delay period. Nevertheless, the compression heating effect on the end gases during combustion of hydrogen, coupled with the very low minimum ignition energy serves to augment the tendency to knock. Flame speeds of about 48.3 m/s were reported for the hydrogen engine at a compression ratio of 12/1 and engine speed of 1500 rev/min, whereas the corresponding value for gasoline engines would be about 16.5 m/s only. Because of this threefold rise in flame speed, ignition timing in the hydrogen engine is usually found to optimise at about top dead centre, but may be advanced to about $10°$ before tdc at weak mixtures when the flame speeds are lower.[10] Attempts to reduce the flame speed have been made using exhaust gas recirculation.

By further adapting a CFR engine with a sodium-cooled exhaust valve, a cool variety of sparking plug, and eliminating the introduction into the combustion chamber of lubricating oil from the top ring groove, King[7] found normal combustion possible up to 14/1 compression ratio, and also at 16/1 compression ratio with engine speeds restricted to 1100 rev/min. The maximum imep reached was 986 kPa (143 lbf/in.^{2}), and maximum indicated thermal efficiency was over 51 per cent.

In more recent work using the Oklahoma State University (OSU) engine reported by Murray,[11] close attention was paid to emissions. One significant advantage of the hydrogen engine is that it does not generate carbon dioxide, carbon monoxide, unburnt hydrocarbons, lead or sulphur pollutants. When operating with atmospheric air, however, the combustion temperatures are such that NO_x is formed. In fact, comparison of the theoretical flame temperatures of stoichiometric mixtures of hydrogen–air and gasoline–air show the former to be in excess by about 100 K, predicting a corresponding increase in NO_x by a factor of about 2. However, Murray's results show a marked *reduction* in NO_x with hydrogen fuel in comparison with gasoline. This was no doubt due to the fact that the hydrogen was injected directly into the cylinder, coupled with a wide-open air throttle, the power output being controlled by the fuel injection period alone, as in diesel and stratified charge practice. However, as shown by Varde,[12] when compared with the conventional gasoline engine, the stratified charge gasoline engine shows an even greater reduction in NO_x than does the hydrogen engine.

The power output with hydrogen appears to be comparable to that of gasoline. On the other hand, the specific fuel consumption of the OSU engine was slightly higher, but this was considered to be due mainly to frictional losses in the injection system, and partly to poor utilisation of air in the chamber design. Later work by Billings[13] has confirmed the very low concentrations of NO_x at weak mixtures, and the sharp increases with equivalence ratio to peak at about $\phi = 0.8$. Water injection reduces the concentration of NO_x, but also the power output and efficiency. All NO_x emissions would be eliminated by the adoption of oxygen alone as the oxidant, but this brings added complications of storage of oxygen in the liquid, pressurised gas, or metallic oxide form (see section 8.1). In contrast to King's action in reducing the jacket temperature to help control knock, Murray found it preferable to adopt a boiling water cooling system in order to provide uniform jacket temperature and so eliminate cylinder distortion, compression leaks and high oil consumption.

The high proportion of unburnt mixture normally found in the blow-by gases traversing the piston-cylinder gap and entering the crankcase draws attention to the need either for re-design of piston rings, or inert-gas purging of the crankcase, when using hydrogen as fuel, otherwise violent explosions might result from an overheated bearing or other hot-spot. In the Hillman Imp car modified at Cranfield to operate on hydrogen gas, nitrogen at 3.3 times the estimated rate of blow-by was used to purge the crankcase, and then vented back to the carburettor intake.[14] Successful operation of a Wankel engine on hydrogen has been achieved at the Brookhaven National Laboratory, U.S.A., but no emission data were published.

In summary, the hydrogen spark-ignition piston engine, when compared with its conventional gasoline counterpart, appears to offer the following.

1. Wider range of operating mixture strength.

2. High thermal efficiency but low power at weak mixtures.

3. Comparable power but high fuel consumption at stoichiometric and rich mixtures.

4. Theoretically more NO_x emissions, but in practice much less if timed fuel injection and unthrottled air flow are adopted, as in some stratified charge engines.

5. Strong tendencies to pre-ignition and back-firing unless timed fuel injection after inlet valve closure is adopted, together with elimination of hot spots and carbon particles in the cylinder, and ignition timing retarded to near tdc.

6. Fairly strong tendencies to knock unless weak mixtures and cool operation adopted, with pre-ignition eliminated, in which case high compression ratios are possible.

With regard to LPG and compressed natural gas (CNG) as alternatives to gasoline, dynamometer and road tests tend to confirm the reduction in emissions, particularly of the smog-forming hydrocarbon type (olefins), and the possibilities of lean operation, but also show losses of about 10 to 15 per cent in power and economy, with reduced driveability. Marked improvements generally follow by exploiting the superior anti-knock quality of the gases using higher compression ratios, and also by allowing for the lower flame speed through advancing the ignition timing. Interestingly, the customary reduction in knock-limited ignition advance at lower engine speed, due to the greater time available for spontaneous-ignition reactions, is not evident with the light hydrocarbon gases which shown an inverse relationship over the low-speed range.

As fuels for S—I piston engines, the nitroparaffins have received minor attention only. Starkman[15] reports improvements in peak power of over

40 per cent when comparing nitroethane with methanol in a CFR engine at 1800 rev/min, due largely to the high levels of specific energy of the stoichiometric mixture (3.3 compared to 2.67 MJ/kg), and of products/reactants ratio (1.15 compared to 1.06). The peak power with nitroethane occurred at a slightly higher equivalence ratio. A blend of 80 per cent nitromethane in methanol gave a power improvement of over 50 per cent. Tendencies to pre-ignition were controlled by lowering the air and jacket temperatures.

Some research has been conducted with anhydrous ammonia as an alternative fuel in S–I engines.[16,17] Although ammonia exists as a gas at ambient conditions (boiling point $-33\,°C$), it would be stored more compactly as a liquid. Its high enthalpy of vaporisation would then make necessary pre-vaporisation and possibly controlled partial decomposition in a heated catalyst chamber following carburation. A relatively high jacket temperature ($180\,°C$) has been found helpful to assist decomposition during the compression stroke. In comparison with isooctane in a CFR engine at 1800 rev/min, the power output reached about 70 per cent when pre-vaporised and partly decomposed (theoretical value = 77 per cent), and the sfc was greater by a factor of about 2.4. However, the high anti-knock quality of ammonia (130 + RON) would permit increased compression ratio and thermal efficiency. Furthermore, analysis shows that the use of *liquid* ammonia should result in a power gain of approximately 14 per cent due to the increased products/reactants molar ratio. The low flame speed of ammonia requires advanced spark timing (or multiple plugs, particularly as ammonia has been reported as difficult to ignite), but excess decomposition of ammonia to give more than about 5 per cent of hydrogen in the charge resulted in over-rapid combustion roughness.

Exhaust emissions are eased by the complete lack of any carbon-based products with ammonia fuel. It is true that the moles of nitrogen per mole of stoichiometric mixture are less for ammonia (0.726) than for a gasoline represented by octane (0.777), but on the basis of equal energy supplied by these stoichiometric mixtures, the ammonia mixture contains about 15 times as much nitrogen as the octane mixture. However, the lower flame temperature of ammonia imposes the most significant control on the formation of oxides of nitrogen, and calculations by Starkman[16] show concentrations of nitric oxide (NO) to be only 43 per cent of those of stoichiometric octane–air, that is, about 46 per cent on an equal energy basis. Engine tests at the University of Tennessee also show reductions, of about 80 per cent, in NO from ammonia in comparison with octane.[17] However, the related CFR engine tests of Starkman showed such benefits to apply only on the fuel-rich side of stoichiometric, and that at fuel-weak, the NO peak from ammonia was some 45 per cent *higher* than that for octane. Any unburnt ammonia can be expected to be largely dissociated at the high temperature of the exhaust system, the remainder being either absorbed by plant life, or dispersed upwards into the atmosphere to be washed out by rainfall.

Some preliminary tests have been reported by Schmidt[18] with hydrazine injected directly into the throat of the carburettor fitted to a CFR engine. Operation was smooth, and the sfc reduced with the addition to the fuel of water, up to about 30 per cent by mass, but was still about three times that obtained with gasoline. One technical advantage of hydrazine over other fuels is that, with certain catalysts, it decomposes as a monopropellant to give hot ammonia, hydrogen and nitrogen which can be used for engine starting, with consequent engine mass savings of about 10 per cent in starter motor, battery and generator.

Proving S–I engine tests with bio-derived fuels have been reported from Finland. A Saab passenger-car engine has been adapted with a lower compression ratio and a pre-heated dual-fuel system in which motor gasoline is used for starting, idling, warm up and heavy load, but turpentine or other liquids from wood for the cruising condition. Extensive road tests during a very hard Lapland winter have confirmed both reliability and emissions control. These fuels are less expensive than either gasoline or diesel fuel, and the vehicles are reported to have better acceleration and less engine noise than a comparable diesel engine.

7.1.4 Compression-ignition Engine Characteristics

Under normal operating conditions in the compression-ignition engine, air only is admitted during the induction stroke and is then compressed to a relatively high pressure and temperature. Near the end of the compression stroke, a heavy distillate fuel of either gas oil or diesel fuel type is injected into the combustion chamber under a high pressure to achieve fine atomisation. The fuel droplets vaporise rapidly and then, due to their relatively low spontaneous-ignition temperature, the first portions of fuel ignite spontaneously early enough after the start of injection to act as igniting agents for the remainder of the fuel charge as it injects in turn. The rate of pressure rise in the cylinder is therefore controlled to a great extent by the rate and period of fuel injection, that is, by the design of the fuel-pump element and cam. Mixture distribution is thus no problem, but the speed of the engine and the general level of cylinder temperature set a time limitation on the amount of fuel that can be injected and burnt efficiently. Hence air utilisation is an important parameter, and the compression-ignition engine, in contrast with the spark-ignition engine, generally runs on the fuel-weak side of stoichiometric.

When the compression-ignition engine is off condition, for example when starting from cold, the end-of-compression temperatures are lower than the design values, and both vaporisation and ignition delay periods become extended. However, the fuel delivery rate is insensitive to cylinder temperature, and fuel continues to inject into the combustion chamber during the extended delay. When the first portions of the fuel spray do eventually ignite, the ensuing combustion of the excess fuel in the chamber is very rapid, being no longer controlled by the injection rate. This explosive form of combustion is known as diesel knock, and leads to rough running, heavy vibration and smoke. It is interesting to note that diesel knock occurs when conditions are too mild and spontaneous ignition is hesitant, in contrast with spark knock in which conditions are too severe and spontaneous ignition too vigorous.

7.1.5 Compression-ignition Engine Performance of Alternative Fuels

In C–I engines, as in other applications, the less-expensive heavy fuels are attractive, consequently the effects of their lower quality have been investigated on many occasions. In terms of SIT levels, the heavy fuel oils are slightly more ignitable than gas oil or diesel fuel, but they require greater energy for pumping, atomisation and vaporisation, and have higher levels of corroding, and possible eroding, contaminants. Nevertheless, particularly in the marine sector (see section 9.4.4), heavy fuel oils are finding increasing use in the larger C–I engines, and developments in engine design and operation are tending to resolve successfully the problems of fouling, wear, corrosion and slow-burning due to the higher concentrations of carbon, asphaltenes, sulphur, vanadium, sodium, sludge and ash.

When used in a C–I engine, methanol poses a major problem owing to its very low cetane number of about 3, making necessary the addition of from 10 to 20 per cent of an ignition accelerator to bring the cetane number up to about 33. However, this is uneconomic, and an alternative system is to operate on diesel fuel at low load, with methanol added at high load to the injection pumps, direct to the injectors, or by aspiration. The last-named method gives higher part-load efficiency and lower smoke. In the high-speed engine, the concentration of methanol in diesel fuel is limited to about 50 per cent. The dual-fuel approach appears more promising, with two separate fuel injection systems, the high ignition-quality fuel being injected first in order to promote ignition, followed by the methanol or methanol blend. Smoother and less noisy running is reported in view of the pilot type of ignition, together with lower emissions of unburnt fuel and smoke. Spark-ignition has also been considered, with some success, for truck engines, but much higher voltages are required at the high compression pressures. However, the complication of transient conditions makes methanol usage more attractive in the larger single-speed industrial type of engine.

The use of ethanol as the principal fuel in a dual-fuel 5 hp 16.5/1 compression ratio diesel engine has also been reported in the Wolfsburg literature,[19] the alcohol supplying over 80 per cent of the total energy requirement, and the remainder by a diesel oil (presumably gas oil) injected under high compression for purposes of pilot injection. The alcohol was carburetted in with the air, and the maximum amount tolerated by the engine fixed by either misfire or diesel knock. The main problems encountered were long delay and slow, inefficient, combustion at low dual-fuel rates, and explosive combustion at high dual-fuel rates. In comparison with the use of diesel fuel alone, emissions of unburnt fuel with dual-fuel operation rose by a factor of 2 to 5 due to lower efficiency, whereas NO_x was reduced by about 30 per cent due to the lower compression temperatures from the high enthalpy of vaporisation of alcohol. The higher proportions of alcohol fuel were usable when the fuel injection timing was advanced from the standard 27° up to 33° before tdc. Part-load operation was less efficient than with diesel fuel alone, but this discrepancy was less with increase of compression ratio to 20/1. Since diesel knock commenced somewhat earlier with dual-fuel operation, ignition accelerating additives were tested. These had negligible effect when used in the pilot diesel fuel; but 0.5 per cent of aniline added to the alcohol reduced the ignition delay period by about 11° of crank angle. Nitromethane was not effective as an additive in the alcohol. These additives also reduced the unburnt fuel emissions significantly, but the higher temperatures resulting from the reduced delay periods virtually doubled the NO_x concentrations.

The airship hydrogen tests conducted by Ricardo in the 1920s also included the diesel engine. A single cylinder sleeve-valve engine with open combustion chamber was used, the hydrogen being fed into the induction air, and ignition being initiated by diesel fuel injection in the conventional manner. The proportions of hydrogen limited by pre-ignition roughness were established, and compared with the valving mass ratio of 1/13 for hydrogen/diesel fuel required for constant buoyancy of the airship. The test engine was found to be capable of consuming all the valved hydrogen up to a bmep of 550 kPa (80 lbf/in.²).

The use of ammonia in the C–I engine appears to date from a patent in 1905, through limited work by Ammonia Casale Ltd in Italy during the mid 1930s, to the operation of a fleet of about 100 motor buses in Belgium using the Gazamo process in 1943. The compression ratio was reduced from 16/1 to 8.5/1, and ignition initiated by coal gas containing about 50 per cent hydrogen by volume. The ammonia was carried in the liquid phase within propane-type steel bottles at about 20 MPa, and vaporised by heat from the engine cooling water. The energy consumption per unit distance travelled showed an increase of 13.5 per cent in the ammonia–coal gas mode compared with the original gas oil under high compression, but the buses were estimated as being overloaded with passengers and fuel equipment by some 25 per cent. No abnormal wear or corrosion was discovered, nor any additional consumption of lubricating oil.[20]

Confirmation of this compatibility of ammonia and its products with engine equipment is given by Gray,[21] although some degradation of the lubricating oil occurred. Ammonia injected into the combustion chamber of a CFR engine would not ignite below a compression ratio of 35/1, but combustion could be initiated at 30/1 using a gas oil of 53 cetane number for pilot injection at 12° before tdc. Again, because of the low flame speed, ammonia needed to be injected no later than 40° before the end of the pilot injection, and a timing of 80° before tdc was adopted. Combustion was also found possible down to a compression ratio of 12/1 using pilot fuel of high cetane number, and a special high-temperature glow coil appeared as a promising alternative source of ignition. No improvements were found with additives in the fuel or intake air. Values of indicated mep of up to 700 kPa were obtained, at a mass flow ratio of ammonia/gas oil of about 2.6.

7.2 Continuous-flow Combustion Applications

This section covers the performance of both conventional and alternative types of fuel in continuous-flow combustors including the furnace intended for heat transfer, and the gas turbine, ramjet and rocket engines which provide work transfer (as shaft torque and/or propulsive thrust). In the type of furnace relying on forced convective heating, and the gas turbine, the combustion gases necessarily make contact with solid surfaces in the form of steam tubes, loaded stock, nozzle guide vanes, turbine blades, etc., the metallurgical limits of which set a maximum on the temperature of operation, and thus on the overall equivalence ratio of the mixture. In these cases, the specific energy of the fuel provides a relatively simple comparative basis of fuel combustion performance, augmented by its flammability characteristics discussed earlier.

In the ramjet and rocket engines, on the other hand, no such solid surfaces protrude into the gas stream, consequently higher combustion temperatures are permitted, using richer mixtures. However, the significance of the resulting chemical dissociation and recombination taking place in the propelling nozzle is such as to over-ride the specific energy as the main parameter of perform-ance. As a result, reactant performance is assessed on the basis of specific impulse, I_{sp}, defined as the thrust produced per unit mass flow rate of reactant. For the ramjet, the most frequently used form of this parameter is the air specific impulse (in units N s/kg *air*) since this relates to the size of engine required for a given thrust level. The fuel specific impulse (in units N s/kg *fuel*) is also useful since it relates to vehicle range, particularly at high altitudes. For low altitude operation where aerodynamic drag is significant, the fuel volume impulse (in units N s/l *fuel*) is more representative. For the rocket, on the other hand, specific impulse I_{sp} is based on the total mass flow rate of reactants (in units N s/kg *mixture*) since the oxidant also has to be carried in the vehicle. Analysis shows the ratio $(T/M)^{1/2}$ to be an important feature in the calculation of I_{sp}, where T is the combustion temperature of the mixture, and M is the mean value of molar mass of the combustion products leaving the propelling nozzle. For rocket flight within the atmos-phere, volume of the liquid reactants is again important, and performance is expressed in terms of volume impulse, I_v (in units N s/l *liquid mixture*).

7.2.1 Stabilised-flame Combustion Characteristics

As outlined on p. 105, the flame within a continuous-flow combustor is required to be stabilised in a defined location against the entering stream of oxidant over a range of conditions, consequently a balance must be maintained at all times between the velocities of the flame and the approaching mixture. For relatively low-output heating devices using kerosine, a wick-feed system is effective in holding the flame stationary in space against an air flow generated by natural convection. For higher rates of energy release, the flame may be spray stabilised in conjunction with an air swirl inducing flow to the core of the flame by providing a zone of low pressure within it. Alternatively, the fuel may be pre-vaporised immediately upstream of the flame zone. At even higher rates of entry air flow, stabilisation is assisted by the presence of a solid baffle which reduces and reverses the axial mixture flow. For bi-reactant combustion, as in rocketry, the fuel and oxidant sprays may be arranged to impinge upon each other to give rapid and intimate admixture in a fixed location.

In view of the velocity balance existing between the flame and the approaching mixture, the region of flammability defined by the flame velocity-mixture curve also represents the operating area of a continuous-flow combustor, and this is usually plotted in the form of a stability loop, as in figure 7.3. Optimum chamber stability is given by the largest obtainable area requiring not only a wide range of steady operating conditions but also reduced possibilities of flame-out during rapid changes from one steady condition to another, when the operating point might otherwise stray over

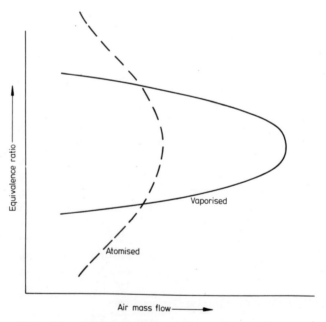

Figure 7.3   Stability loops for continuous-flow combustors

the boundary. Consequently, alternative fuels of high flame speed and wide range of flammability are preferable. Where space is available, flame shape and length are less important, and the chamber can be designed on generous proportions to suit. Under more restricted circumstances, however, the fuel—air distribution patterns must be matched to provide a short flame yet with a suitably uniform temperature distribution at outlet. Droplet lifetimes, as determined by volatility and ignition characteristics of the fuel, together with the quality of atomisation, then become critical, otherwise fuel will either reach the chamber wall and cause carbon deposition, or persist through the combustion zone and give rise to emissions of unburnt fuel and smoke.

7.2.2 Furnace Performance of Alternative Fuels

In this context, 'furnace' represents a continuous-flow air-breathing combustor designed for the transfer of heat, and therefore includes applications of heat to some stock for processing, as in a metallurgical furnace, and also to water for steam raising, as in a boiler. (A fuller description, and differentiation, is given later in section 9.4.1.) The transfer of combustion heat from the flame takes place by a combination of forced convection and radiation, with volumetric heat release rates ranging from about 55 to 670 kW/m^3. The former process is used in the low-temperature furnace, augmented by an air fan, the heat transfer coefficient increasing at each change in gas velocity and boundary shape. At temperatures above about 750 °C, radiation becomes dominant since this varies with the fourth power of absolute temperature, and the heat transfer may take place either directly from the flame or indirectly from heated refractory surfaces. The ability to radiate energy is determined by the emissivity, which reaches about 0.8 for refractory brickwork. The presence of particles of solid carbon or contaminants in the flame thus increases the emissivity, consequently residual fuel oils, for example, with relatively high carbon content, are more suited to heat transfer in furnaces than to work transfer in engines.

Of the individual fuels, the gases are the most convenient for furnace use because of their control flexibility and clean burning. Pre-heating of air and fuel is used with the lean gaseous fuels in order to achieve the required combustion temperature, but cannot be used with carbon-rich gases because of cracking and soot formation in the heat exchanger at high temperatures in the absence of air. Liquid fuels used in furnaces range from gas oil through the heaviest residual fuel oils to the coal tar fuels. The specific energies of the petroleum fuels tend to be higher, and the viscosities lower, but the CTFs exhibit lower concentrations of sulphur.

Industrial furnaces and boilers mainly use natural gas or oil since electrical heating is expensive, and coal is both inconvenient to handle and difficult to burn, except in the case of the large power station boiler furnace. Here, solid fuelling has progressed from hand-firing through the chain-grate and other mechanical types of stoker to pulverised coal firing and, more recently, the fluidised bed combustor. When pulverised to a high fineness fraction of about 90 per cent through a 200 BS mesh (76 μm) sieve, coal can be handled, sprayed and burnt in a manner comparable to liquid fuels, but its main difference lies in the concentration of inorganic ash which can be appreciable and must be removed continuously from the combustion chamber to avoid clogging and surface attack. In a steel-making furnace, for example, ash particles of low fusion temperature may find their way into the charge and become rolled into the steel. In cement manufacture, on the other hand, the ash can become usefully incorporated with the cement. The costs of partial prior ash removal by washing can often be offset by the saving in subsequent ash handling after combustion, otherwise ash separation is achieved during combustion itself by controlling the ash temperature below the level at which it becomes sticky prior to melting, and also the flow patterns within the combustor to avoid surface contact of the hot ash particles.

An effective method of achieving high reaction rates and combustion efficiency at temperatures low enough to avoid problems of ash melting is by means of combustion in a fluidised bed. Greater economies are possible because of the reduction in heat transfer surface areas due to better heat conduction following removal of the boundary gas layers, and because a coarser coal particle size with high ash content is acceptable. If removal of emissions within the bed, and subsequent particulate carry over, become practicable, the resulting pressurised gas will be sufficiently clean for use in a gas turbine component of a combined-cycle system of improved efficiency. Alternatively, it may become economic to burn the coal in two stages, removing most of the ash in the first stage.

When applied to furnaces, the two major substitute fuels that have emerged from this study, hydrogen and alcohols, both suffer from a fundamentally low level of emissivity which inhibits their transfer of combustion energy as heat. Hydrogen, for example, with its non-luminous flame, is rarely discussed in terms of an industrial furnace fuel, but it might be adaptable to heating refractory brickwork and/or heating by convection, particularly in a total-energy concept where it is already in use in engines. It also improves the thermal efficiency of steel manufacture, where the present two-stage system of producing pig-iron from the coke reduction of iron ore, with subsequent heating for the controlled removal of carbon, can be replaced by direct production of low-carbon steel using a single hydrogen-fuelled heating process. Hydrogen also has some promise as a domestic heating fuel in view of its non-toxic products which require no chimney, making possible a more efficient decentralised heating system, and also for less expensive cookers.

Although more complex from the aspect of reactant supply, the use of oxygen, as distinct from air, with hydrogen fuel permits both a higher flame temperature, and therefore higher efficiency, and a complete lack of NO_x emissions. In the aphodid system,[22] for example, the hydrogen—oxygen reaction is used to provide high-temperature steam for subsequent use in processes or engines.

Alcohol fuels, despite their low flame emissivity, have shown some promise as energy sources for steam-raising boilers. From the comparison of flame velocities, flammability ranges and combustion temperatures in chapter 6, alcohol fuels are expected to show superior flame stability, temperature traverse and NO_x emissions. In fact, methanol tests with a simple water-cooled duct[23] showed a good stable flame with low NO_x emissions in comparison with natural gas. The Vulcan–Cincinnati study both of methanol and of 'Methyl fuel', a blend of methyl and higher alcohols, was based on the concept of conversion from natural gas at remote fields for easier shipment as stable, rather than cryogenic, liquids in conventional tankers. Initial small-scale boiler tests showed marked reductions in emission of carbon monoxide. Subsequent full-scale tests were conducted in the 49 MW boiler unit at the A. B. Paterson generating station at New Orleans, using a centrifugal type of fuel pump in parallel with the existing pumps. The optimum type of atomiser for 'Methyl fuel' was found by experiment, the resulting flame being similar in general appearance to that of natural gas. Tests were conducted up to 100 per cent load, and emissions of carbon monoxide and NO_x were found to be lower than those corresponding to both a No. 6 fuel oil (equivalent to Class G fuel oil in the United Kingdom) and natural gas. No sulphur dioxide, and negligible quantities of aldehydes, organic acids or unburnt fuel were found. One useful bonus was the burning off of previous soot deposits by the methanol flame.[24] If the fluidised bed system can be developed to reduce the temperature sufficiently to give combustion without flame, comparable to several petrochemical processes of vapour-phase catalytic oxidation, emissions of NO_x will be reduced further. Methanol would be more applicable than hydrocarbon fuels to such a process.

As with hydrogen, ammonia appears to have been given little attention as a fuel for furnaces, but inferior performance is expected in view of the endo-thermic nature of the dissociation of ammonia in the flame, coupled with the low specific energy and flame speed in air. In the case of liquid ammonia, the high enthalpy of vaporisation will also have an inhibiting effect. Some work has been reported on the effect of the ammonia content of natural gas fuel on the generation of NO_x.[25] Pre-mixed laboratory flames showed that NO_x concentrations could exceed the equilibrium values, since NO_x formation is controlled kinetically, but that ammonia promotes a self-inhibiting effect to its own oxidation which reduces the relative proportion of ammonia conversion to NO_x, with increase in ammonia content, even though the absolute emission rate of NO_x increases. Full-scale tests in two multi-burner furnaces at excess air conditions showed much lower conversion of ammonia to NO_x in the turbulent diffusion flames, with an increase of NO_x by a factor of about 7 for a 0.35/1 ratio of ammonia to natural gas fuel. At stoichiometric mixtures, all the ammonia appears to pyrolyse to molecular nitrogen and hydrogen, with

123

little formation of NO_x. Strong heating of the ammonia prior to contact with oxygen has a similar effect.

7.2.3 Continuous-flow Engine Performance of Alternative Fuels

In continuous-flow engines, the entry air is compressed and the release of heat promotes a transfer of kinetic energy to the gaseous throughput which is then constrained to do mechanical work by change in velocity and/or pressure in a turbine, and/or provide thrust by a change in momentum through a nozzle. The thermodynamic cycle that most closely matches this set of processes is the Joule (or Brayton) cycle in which the heat transfers occur at constant pressure, and the work transfers are isentropic. The resulting ideal thermal efficiency is given by

$$\eta_J = 1 - \left(\frac{1}{r_p}\right)^{(\gamma-1)/\gamma}$$

where r_p = cycle pressure ratio. Thus, thermal efficiency increases with pressure ratio and also, from the relationships between pressures and temperatures, with temperature ratio. Upper pressure levels are set by the mass of the engine, whereas upper temperature levels are limited by the metallurgy of the turbine blades which are already under mechanical stress due to the high rotational speed.

The practical gas turbine engine emerged primarily as a high-performance unit for aircraft, satisfactory combustion depending mainly upon proper mixing of fuel vapour and air. The kerosines proved to be good compromise fuels since their low viscosities and medium level of volatility give effective atomisation and/or vaporisation over wide ranges of inlet air temperature, pressure and velocity. Adaptation to the less expensive and rigorously specified gas oils and diesel fuels has been successful for the industrial version of the gas turbine. In fact, the gas turbine combustor can be designed and developed to operate on virtually any fuel, whether gaseous, liquid or solid, provided it is contaminant free and clean burning. As outlined briefly in section 4.2, operation with alternative types of conventional fuel, in the form of crude and residual fuel oils and pulverised coal, is attractive economically, but incurs problems of turbine blade deposition and corrosion. The major contaminants in these heavy fuels are classified as either sediment or ash. The former consists of finely divided inorganic solids comprising drilling mud, sand, chlorides from evaporated brine, and so on, and can be measured by extraction of the sample with condensed toluene flowing through a refractory thimble filter until the mass of residual sediment remains constant. Ash, on the other hand, is the non-volatile inorganic material which remains as residue on incineration, consisting of natural salts and dissolved metal soaps, tank scale, wind-blown dust and dirt generally. Total ash concentrations are determined by burning the sample and then heating the residue at high temperature until the constancy of mass indicates the absence of combustible matter.

Trace quantities of sodium occur in the ash of crude oils, particularly in the form of sodium chloride, owing to their association with brine from their marine origin. Correspondingly small quantities of vanadium also occur as oil-soluble organo-metallic compounds, such as the multi-ring porphyrin complexes. Sulphur is indigenous to fossil fuels due to its abundance in the soil, and can exist either in corrosive forms as free sulphur, dissolved hydrogen sulphide gas and mercaptans, or as stable non-corrosive sulphides, polysulphides and thiophenes. Operation of gas turbines with the heavy fuels appears to be satisfactory at turbine entry temperatures below about 650 °C but, at higher temperatures, turbine blade problems arise due largely to relatively low ash melting points, since solid ash particles tend to pass through the turbine disc whereas liquid droplets deposit on the blades by impact or eddy motion. The influence of the contaminant oxides is illustrated by the following factors.

1. Sodium chloride decomposes on heating, leading to the formation of hydrogen chloride, with corrosive attack on blades and other hot turbine parts.

2. Vanadium oxidises progressively through V_2O_2 to V_2O_4 (mp 1967 °C) and V_2O_5 (mp 690 °C). In liquid form, these deposits permit the through transport of oxygen to the blades with consequent solution of the metal oxide layer of Cr_2O_3 in the resultant V_2O_5.

3. Sodium and vanadium together form complex compounds of low melting point. Sodium vanadyl vanadates exist in various proportions, including $5Na_2O.V_2O_4.11V_2O_5$ (mp 535 °C) and $Na_2O.V_2O_4.5V_2O_5$ (mp 625 °C), the latter being highly corrosive, particularly in the presence of nitrogen and sulphur trioxide, by oxidising to $Na_2O.6V_2O_5$ and then releasing the oxygen atom to the blade metal.

4. Sodium sulphate (mp 880 °C) deposits on blades as a liquid flux, and strips off the protective oxide layer, exposing the metal to rapid oxidation.

5. Sulphur burns to obnoxious sulphur dioxide, then converts to sulphur trioxide and, in contact with water, sulphuric acid which is corrosive when condensed on cool metal surfaces. Under localised reducing conditions, sulphur forms sulphides with chromium and nickel in the blades, offering no protection to the underlying metal.

Thus sodium and vanadium tend to set an upper limit to the turbine entry temperature, and sulphur a lower limit to the flue gas temperature in relation to the dewpoints of its oxide and acid products. Hence the presence of fuel contaminants inhibits both ends of the range of turbine operating temperature, and the corresponding efficiency; also the problems of blade protection are aggravated by the industrial engine life requirement of some 40 000 h, which provides ample time for serious deposit build up and corrosion damage.

Present practice in the treatment of heavy fuels for gas turbines is to reduce the sodium concentration to about 0.5 ppm by water washing, and to raise the melting point of the vanadium oxides by the use of magnesium additives.

A current application of this treatment relates to the use of a Class G residual fuel oil in a 31.5 MW Westinghouse industrial electrical generating unit at Mol, Belgium.[26] The average concentrations of sodium and vanadium in the fuel were 14 and 78 ppm respectively, the former being reduced to 0.5 ppm by water washing, and the latter controlled by the addition of magnesium at the Mg/V ratio of 3/1. The fuel cost, in comparison with gas oil, represented about 67 per cent, and about 73 per cent including treatment. Turbine entry temperatures of over 800 °C have been achieved, and levels of 1012 °C are envisaged. Blade deposit build up does occur, as indicated by a loss in power of about 8 per cent after 500 hours operation, but this was alleviated to a certain extent by the temperature cycling of daily operation together with the occasional use of a gaseous fuel, and was effectively removed by water washing the blades through the existing atomising air system. Promising results are also reported from the use of a Class E fuel in an aero-derived Pratt & Whitney FT–4 free turbine engine fitted in 'Asialiner', using homogeneous water–fuel mixtures for finer atomisation.[27] Gas turbine operation on crude oil is reported by the Brown Boveri plant at Riyadh power station,[28] the crude having nominal concentrations of 5 ppm sodium + potassium, and 7 ppm vanadium. Similar progressive reductions in power were seen, with improvement by water washing, and silicon additives were found particularly effective in reducing the quantity and adhesion of the blade deposits.

At the other end of the density scale, natural gas is not normally considered as a standard fuel for industrial gas turbines, apart from remote locations where it is the only fuel available, because of its inherent value for a wide variety of applications. It is, however, occasionally adopted in large industrial complexes when it is economically favourable and, being a gas, it does not lead to major problems of flow control, mixing, combustion, temperature distribution or emissions.

As substitute fuels, the alcohols show some promise for the gas turbine application, particularly for land-based generating units. Reference has already been made to the satisfactory flame stability found in a simple water-cooled combustor duct,[23] as expected from the discussion in chapter 6. In comparative tests at the Florida Power Bayboro generating station on a full-scale FT4C–1 industrial gas turbine using gas oil as a standard fuel,[29] methanol was found to give normal acceleration and improved temperature distribution at turbine entry, and consequently higher engine life, together with greater stability and control. This later improvement was due largely to the lower specific energy of methanol, which effectively reduced the control gain by a factor of about two. In tests on a GT-225 experimental passenger-car gas turbine engine, up to 8 per cent additional power was found with methanol in comparison with a representative kerosine at equal turbine entry temperatures.[30] However, with preliminary tests conducted at Cranfield on a single Rolls-Royce Dart chamber restricted to atmospheric pressure and an outlet temperature of 1173 K, the peak combustion efficiencies were roughly common at 97 per cent for both methanol and kerosine.[31] The higher fuel consumption on a volumetric basis with methanol in the GT-225 tests reflected the lower specific energy, but insignificant differences were found when plotted on an energy basis.

With regard to emissions, the lower level of combustion temperature of methanol in comparison with hydrocarbons suggests lower concentrations of NO_x, and the Bayboro FT4C–1 tests showed a reduction of 74 per cent in comparison with gas oil over the operating range from 9 to 19 MW electrical output, whereas the GT–225 tests showed reductions of 65 to 70 per cent in comparison with kerosine. The Dart tests showed a comparable reduction of about 90 per cent in NO_x. However, corresponding *increases* in carbon monoxide concentrations of up to 100 per cent were found with methanol in the FT4C–1 tests, and up to 700 per cent and 400 per cent in the GT–225 and Dart tests respectively, particularly at the high power outputs. In the GT–225 tests, these increases were almost entirely eliminated by enlarging the fuel passages in the air-assist atomising nozzle, and using a higher atomising-air pressure drop.

Higher concentrations of unburnt hydrocarbons are also likely with methanol in comparison with hydrocarbon fuels due to the fact that the combustors tested have invariably been developed for the latter fuels, and to flame quenching by primary and film-cooling air with the doubled rate of fuel flow. Increases in unburnt hydrocarbons of about 20 to 50 per cent were noted during both the GT–225 and Dart tests, and also in aldehydes during the former tests.

Little carbon build up on nozzles was found with methanol as fuel, and there were no problems of smoke. The absence of contaminating sulphur and metals is also an advantage, but the lack of lubricity makes necessary the addition of lubricating oil upstream of the fuel pump. The general conclusions reached from these studies suggest that methanol is an attractive fuel for land-based stationary gas turbines used for power generation, particularly for peak shaving. Little work has been reported with ethanol in gas turbines, but the fuels tested in the Dart combustor at Cranfield included methylated spirits (85 per cent ethanol, 5 per cent methanol and up to 2 per cent pyridine) which showed a significant reduction in peak thermal efficiency from the former 97 per cent to about 89 per cent,[31] together with a further increase in carbon monoxide, but less of an increase in unburnt hydrocarbons. It also showed an *increase* in NO_x in comparison with methanol, but this may be due in part to the presence of pyridine (C_2H_5N) and other denaturing agents.

The potential of hydrogen as a fuel for continuous-flow engines can also be predicted to some extent from the studies of combustion processes in chapter

6. Most of this work has been concerned with aircraft propulsion, and the performance parameter adopted is the specific impulse, as discussed in section 7.2. In comparison with kerosine and most other hydrocarbon fuels, the considerably higher specific energy (by a factor of about 2.8) is reflected in the jet thrust obtainable. For comparable thrusts, corresponding reductions would be expected in specific fuel consumption. As a gaseous fuel, problems of fuel atomisation and vaporisation are eliminated, and mixing with air would be more effective, giving improvements in temperature traverse quality at combustor outlet. This, in conjunction with the low emissivity of the flame, minimises metal temperatures and thermal stress. These factors, together with the absence of eroding or corroding contaminants help to reduce maintenance costs and lengthen engine life. The wide range of flammability and high flame speeds assist combustion stability during changes in operating conditions, and give high rates of heat release leading to smaller combustion chambers. Comparable improvements apply also to ramjet combustors.

The superior heat transfer properties of hydrogen, and its high specific heat as a liquid, permit its use as a heat sink to cool engine parts, in contrast to the loss of performance represented by the standard use of engine bleed air, the absorbed heat being used regeneratively for pre-vaporisation. This heat capacity would also permit higher turbine entry temperatures and pressure ratios, with corresponding improvements in thermal efficiency.

As before, the absence of carbon and fuel contaminants virtually eliminates such emissions as carbon dioxide, carbon monoxide, unburnt hydrocarbons, aldehydes, smoke and particulates, apart from minor concentrations from lubricating oil. Slightly greater concentrations of NO_x are expected since the flame temperature of hydrogen is marginally above those of the hydrocarbon fuels, but the flame temperature of 110 K for hydrogen at its weak limit of flammability is considerably lower than the 1900 K level for kerosine at its corresponding limit. Furthermore, the improved mixture distribution and shorter residence times should both help to reduce NO_x emissions.

Engine experience of hydrogen fuel has been gained by Pratt & Whitney in 1956 with a converted J—57 engine in which the pre-gasified fuel was injected via an axial tube system. No performance or emission data are reported, but the resulting performance is described as excellent, and it was found possible to reduce the fuel flow to such an extent that the combustion temperature rise was only 100 °C, with an engine speed sufficiently low to be able to count the first-stage blades! In the Pratt & Whitney 305 engine for high-altitude work, the hydrogen was vaporised in an exhaust-heated exchanger, the resulting expansion driving the compressor-turbine. The gasified hydrogen was then burnt in the combustor, and the energy utilised for thrust. This engine also realised its performance predictions within a test programme of a few hours. In 1957, NACA further demonstrated the compatibility of hydrogen fuel with standard aero gas turbines by flight tests with a B—57 bomber aircraft modified to burn hydrogen in one of its two J—56 engines.

The liquid hydrogen was supplied from a wing-tip tank using helium pressure, and pre-vaporised in a ram-air heat exchanger immediately prior to injection.[32] Since the energy levels required in ramjet and rocket propulsion are such as to demand fuels of a high energy nature, rather than alternatives in the present sense, these materials are dealt with in section 9.4.5.

It is reported that the prospects of ammonia as a fuel for gas turbines were first explored in an exciting, and unrepeated, experiment by Whittle prior to adopting kerosine, but subsequent studies by Verkamp[33] concern tests conducted on flame stability using a flat-flame burner, and also a single combustor from a T63—A—3 gas turbine operating at engine air-flow conditions conditions. The burner tests showed a marked deterioration in the stability loop with ammonia—air in comparison with methane—air. Partial dissociation of the ammonia was also simulated by the addition of nitrogen and hydrogen, and this resulted in improvements, with a 28 per cent dissociated mixture giving stability comparable to that of methane.

The rated outlet temperature of the above gas turbine chamber at maximum power conditions is 1210 K, but the maximum temperature obtainable with injection of liquid ammonia was only 727 K. A wide range of flame tube designs was tested, with ammonia in the liquid, gaseous and simulated dissociated states. However, as inferred from section 7.2.2, blow-out occurred with liquid ammonia as soon as the torch igniter was switched off, and with gaseous ammonia at an air velocity of only 40 per cent of that when using hydrocarbon fuels. Despite the attainment of a combustion efficiency of 97 per cent, it was concluded that satisfactory combustion with gaseous ammonia, even using continuous ignition, would be possible only by doubling the diameter of the combustor. On the other hand, stable combustion, of 92 per cent efficiency, was obtained with the hydrogen enrichment resulting from dissociation simulated to 28 per cent, indicating that, provided it is partially cracked prior to injection, ammonia could be acceptable as an alternative fuel for gas turbine chambers optimally sized for hydrocarbon fuels. As shown in figure 9.9, the performance of ammonia for rocket propulsion is not outstanding on either basis of comparison.

Further evidence of exotic fuels burned with some success in the gas turbine is provided by reference to the turbine-powered Plymouth automobile which ran on peanut oil.[34]

References

1. E. M. Goodger, *Hydrocarbon Fuels*, Macmillan, London and Basingstoke (1975).
2. *Alcohols: a Technical Assessment of their Application as Fuels*, American Petroleum Institute Publication No. 4261 (July 1976).
3. D. L. Hagen, *Methanol as a Fuel: a Review with Bibliography*, SAE 770792 (1977).

4. International Sumposium on Alcohol Fuel Technology, Volkswagenwerk A. G., Wolfsburg, W. Germany (1977).

5. Conference on Alcohol Fuels, Institution of Chemical Engineers, NSW Group, Sydney (August 1978).

6. G. Lucy, George Starr's secret war. *Reader's Digest*, (June 1978) 179–204.

7. R. O. King, S. V. Hayes, A. B. Allen, R. W. P. Anderson and E. J. Walker, The hydrogen engine: combustion knock and the related flame velocity, *Trans. E.I.C.*, **2** (1958) 143–8.

8. D. Downs, A. D. Walsh and R. W. Wheeler, A study of the reactions that lead to knock in the spark ignition engine, *Trans. R. Soc.*, **A243** (1951) 517.

9. W. F. Anzilotti, J. D. Rogers, G. W. Scott and V. J. Tomsic, Combustion of hydrogen as related to knock, *Ind. Engng. Chem.*, **46** (1954) 1314.

10. J. Levi and D. B. Kittelson, *Further Studies with a Hydrogen Engine*, SAE 780233 (1978).

11. R. G. Murray, R. J. Schoeppel and C. L. Gray, *The Hydrogen Engine in Perspective*, SAE 729216 (1972).

12. K. S. Varde and G. G. Lucas, Hydrogen as a fuel for vehicle propulsion, *Proc. Instn. mech. Engrs*, **188** (1974) 26–74.

13. R. E. Billings, A hydrogen powered mass transit system, *Int. J. Hydrogen Energy*, **3** (1978) 49–104.

14. N. R. Beale, *The Cranfield Hydrogen Car*, Cranfield Institute of Technology Memo 141 (1974).

15. E. S. Starkman, Nitroparaffins as a potential engine fuel, *Ind. Engng. Chem.*, **51** (1959) 1477–80.

16. E. S. Starkman, H. K. Newhall, R. Sutton, T. Maguire and L. Farbar, *Ammonia as a Spark-ignition Engine Fuel: Theory and Applications*, SAE 660155 (1966).

17. J. W. Hodgson, Alternate fuels for transportation. Part 3: Ammonia for the automobile, *Mech. Engng*, **96** (1974) 22–25.

18. E. W. Schmidt, Hydronitrogens as future automotive fuels, in J. M Colucci (ed) *Future Automotive Fuels*, Plenum Press, New York and London (1977) 320–41.

19. N. R. Panchapakesan, K. V. Gopalakrishnan and B. S. Murthy, Factors that improve the performance of an ethanol-diesel oil dual-fuel engine, International Symposium on Alcohol Fuel Technology, Wolfsburg, W. Germany (1977).

20. E. Krock, Ammonia – a fuel for motor buses, *J. Inst. Petrol.*, **31** (1945) 213–23.

21. J. T. Gray, E. Dimitroff, N. T. Mechel and R. D. Quillian, *Ammonia Fuel: Engine Compatibility and Combustion*, SAE 660156 (1966).

22. R. L. Savage (ed), *A Hydrogen Energy Carrier, Vol II, Systems Analysis*, NASA – ASEE (1973).

23. D. Garrett and T. O. Wentworth, Methyl fuel: a new clean source of energy, *Am. Chem. Soc.*, **18** (1973) 111.

24. R. W. Duhl, Methanol: a boiler fuel alternative, *A. I. Ch. E. Symposium Series*, **73** (1977) 338–48.

25. J. O. L. Wendt and C. V. Sternling, Effect of ammonia in gaseous fuels on nitrogen oxide emissions, *J. Air Pollut. Control Ass.*, **24** (1974) 10551–6.

26. E. B. E. S. burning bunker C in 31.5 MW W 251 plant, *Gas Turb. Wld*, **6** (1977) 20–2.

27. Converting aero-derivative gas turbines to burn blended fuel, *Mot. Ship*, **58** (1977) 106–13.

28. P. C. Felix, Problems and operating experiences with gas turbines burning residual and crude oil, Paper 78-GT-103, ASME Conference, Wembley, London (April 1978).

29. R. C. Farmer, Methanol — a new fuel source? *Gas Turb. Int.*, **16** (1975) 38–40.

30. L. W. Huellmanetel, S. G. Liddle and D. C. Hammond, Combustion of methanol in an automotive gas turbine, International Symposium on Alcohol Fuel Technology, Wolfsburg, W. Germany (1977).

31. M. J. Bowyer, Alternative fuels, Cranfield Institute of Technology, unpublished MSc thesis (September 1978).

32. Lewis Laboratory Staff, Hydrogen for turbojet and ramjet powered flight, *NACA RM-E-57D23* (1957).

33. F. J. Verkamp, Ammonia combustion properties and performance in gas-turbine burners, 11th Symposium (International) on Combustion. The Combustion Institute, Pittsburgh, Pa. (1967).

34. A. T. Bruno, Peanuts: people's pâté to gourmet's delight, *Reader's Digest*, (September 1978) 107–110.

8. Alternative-fuel Handling Characteristics

Throughout its lifetime from production to ultimate combustion in the chamber, a fuel is subjected to storage, movement, contamination, and changes in ambient conditions, and may itself promote hazards to safety, structural integrity and health. All these features, and any others not directly concerned with end use by combustion, are jointly grouped within the province of fuel handling, and the major ones are discussed in turn in the following sections. These discussions cover the significance of the results obtained from relevant standard test procedures. The procedures themselves, together with the background philosophy, are covered in appendix 3.

8.1 Storage Dimensional Requirements

In general practice, gaseous and liquid fuels are handled by volume, and solid fuels by mass. For a given energy load, therefore, a preliminary comparison of fuel quantity requirements can be made in terms of the reciprocal values of energy density for the gases and liquids, and of specific energy for the solids. The over-riding factor, however, is whether the application concerned is limited in fuel storage either by volume or by mass. A classic example is found in aviation where subsonic aircraft are mostly mass limited, whereas supersonic aircraft, because of the necessarily thin wing sections, tend to be limited more by volume; consequently the light petroleum fuels are favoured for storage in the former case, and the heavier fuels in the latter. The earlier conclusions from figures. 5.6, 5.7 and 5.8 were that energy density reduces from the dense solids through the liquids, less dense solids and liquefied gases to the gases themselves, whereas specific energy falls from the liquefied gases through the liquids and solids to the gases. On both bases of comparison, the boranes are attractive, but the alcohols and nitroparaffins less so. Reciprocal values of these data have been collated on to the bar chart shown in figure 8.1.

The temperature variation of relative density (Figure 6.1), and thus of energy density, can have a significant effect on the overall storage volume required for a given energy load or, alternatively, on the energy storable

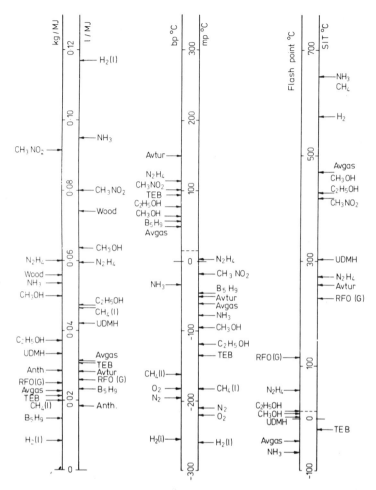

Figure 8.1 Data on unit energy mass and volume levels, and on significant temperatures, in fuel storage

within a given volume. This fact gave rise to a reduction of some 7 per cent in volume found with gasoline in tanks opened in Antarctica at $-50\,^{\circ}$C, having been packed in Melbourne at $15\,^{\circ}$C.[1] Fuel pre-cooling has also been exploited on occasions for the storage of additional fuel for long-distance flights, as in the 4957 mile light-aircraft record reported in *Shell Aviation News* of May 1949. The fuel was pre-cooled from 27 to $-7\,^{\circ}$C using solid carbon dioxide, giving an additional fuel mass load of 4 per cent. Although this technique is not attractive commercially, it is understood that some facilities do exist for such special applications. From figure 6.1, ammonia is seen to have a particularly high variation with temperature, that is, a high coefficient of expansion, consequently overfilling of tanks must be avoided.

133

The above values of storage requirements apply to the fuels alone and, in an engineering sense, are incomplete since they take no account of such factors as the insulation necessary for cryogenic tanks, the reduced volume of gases stored under pressure associated with the mass of rugged containers necessary, and so on. Further factors are the possibilities of storing hydrogen in the form of an alkali metal hydride from which hydrogen is released by the addition of water or, with more promise, stored within the interstitial spaces of the crystalline structure of intermetallic alloys of magnesium—nickel, iron—titanium, or lanthanum—nickel, some of which are capable of hydrogen absorption and desorption fairly rapidly at moderate temperatures and pressures. These hydrides would be stored in fine particulate form with a large surface-area/volume ratio. The exothermic reaction heat on absorption must be removed, but the desorption heat can be supplied readily by the engine cooling water or, for the lighter metallic hydrides, by the exhaust system of the combustor.

These alternative proposals have generated considerable interest for future transport applications. A comparison of various systems of hydrogen storage for an automobile is given in table 8.1. A representative fuel tank size of 50 l (11 UK gal) has been taken for this example, giving a total energy content of 1590 MJ for a standard motor gasoline of 0.74 relative density and 43 MJ/kg (31.8 MJ/l) calorific values. The 'fuel' values for this table are, of course, fundamental, with the exception of that for metallic hydrides which depends on the actual alloys envisaged. The 'fuel + tankage' values are dependent on the design of the tankage and nature of the material used, but have been averaged out as representative from the values given in the references quoted. It is interesting to note that, in this case, the volume of metallic hydrides is somewhat greater than that of liquid hydrogen but that, nevertheless, this trend is reversed in the case of the overall tankage volume. The hydride method of storage thus appears to offer a relatively safe (see section 8.3), reliable and portable method of storing hydrogen, but the cost of suitable high-purity metals puts this system at a disadvantage in comparison with liquefied hydrogen. Since nitrogen is inert, the nitrogen hydrides ammonia,

Table 8.1   Comparison of automobile fuel storage systems for 1590 MJ (derived from references 2, 3, 4)

Fuel type	Fuel		Fuel + tankage	
	kg	l	kg	l
Motor gasoline	37	50	46	57
H_2(l) Cryogenic	13.30	187	105	276
Metallic hydrides	183	208	214	234
H_2(g) at 13.79 MPa (2000 lbf/in.^{2})	13.25	1136	710	1700

NH_3, and hydrazine, N_2H_4, can also be considered as hydrogen carriers, containing 296 and 535 kJ/mol respectively in comparison with 241 kJ/mol for diatomic hydrogen. These values are reflected in the liquid volumes required per unit of energy in figure 8.1, although the corresponding levels of fuel mass are less attractive.

In aircraft applications, hydrogen would best be stored in the liquid phase. The low energy density, coupled with the need for cryogenic insulation, will increase the structural mass fraction, possibly by about 50 per cent for a Mach 3 aircraft, together with the aerodynamic drag. However, for a given fuel load, the improved propulsive performance results in an approximate doubling of the aircraft range in the subsonic regime, and makes hypersonic operation more feasible. Furthermore, the fuel density is particularly low so that, for a given range and payload, liquid hydrogen is claimed to provide reductions in vehicle *gross* mass of about 25 per cent for subsonic aircraft, and 33 per cent for supersonic aricraft.[5] This discussion of energy storage is extended in section 9.4.5 in connection with some special 'high energy' (as distinct from 'alternative' in the present sense) fuels for aerospace.

8.2 Volatility

The volatility of a fuel is represented by the relationship of vapour pressure with temperature, and this in turn is pinpointed, in an inverse manner, by certain specified temperature levels, namely the critical temperature, the boiling point and to a lesser extent the freezing point and, in the case of the liquid fuels, the flash point (see section 8.3). The critical temperature denotes the boundary between the vapour—liquid mixtures and the true gases, being the temperature above which a gas cannot be liquefied by isothermal compression. The boiling point indicates the temperature where the vapour pressure of the fuel reaches atmospheric level, permitting vaporisation to take place vigorously with the rapid evolution of vapour bubbles. The boiling points of the alternative liquid fuels are plotted in figure 6.4, together with the boiling ranges of the conventional petroleum fuels. As expected, a general rise is seen with increase in relative density. The distillation curves for the petroleum fuels, obtained as outlined in appendix 3, are shown in figure 6.5. The curves for the gasolines are the more significant because these fuels are commonly vaporised by carburation without atomisation or substantial added heat. Consequently, particular distillation temperatures can be cross-related to service experience, as shown in figure 8.2.

For purposes of combustion, a high volatility has been seen to be preferable, since this leads to ease of ignition and shorter, more stable, flames. In fuel handling, however, high volatility makes venting of the storage tank necessary in order to limit pressure stresses, and this invariably leads to vapour loss which, in the case of blended fuels, is preferential to the lighter components, and therefore means the loss of *quality* by weathering, as well as in overall *quantity*.

135

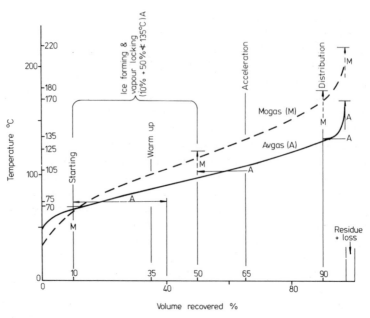

Figure 8.2 Relationship of distillation temperatures to engine behaviour for representative motor and aviation gasolines, showing specification limits

The problems of vapour loss from static fuel tanks are usually tackled by restricting storage temperatures through external tank treatment with reflecting paint, insulating layers and/or sun shielding, or more effectively by submerging the tank to just below ground level. In aviation, the tendency for increased fuel loss at altitude caused by the drop in ambient pressure is partly compensated by the corresponding drop in ambient temperature, but the increase in flight speeds, particularly in the supersonic range, gives rise to substantial levels of stagnation temperature, and a mild degree of tank pressurisation may be used by means of a differential-pressure valve at the tank vent.

Severe problems can also arise from vapour locking within the fuel system. For road vehicles, this tendency is best represented by plotting the V/L ratio against temperature, as discussed in section A3.3, where V is the volume of vapour produced at a given temperature, and L is the original volume of unvaporised liquid. In a vehicle, the most common condition for vapour lock arises from sustained high-speed full-throttle driving followed by a stationary 'soaking period' of about 15 min during which the maximum under-bonnet temperatures are reached. Road tests using a system of rating against reference fuel blends of steep and flat V/L–temperature relationships respectively indicate the limiting V/L ratio for the vehicle, together with the temperature of the critical component of its fuel system. In general, vapour locking with a motor gasoline is found to occur at a temperature of about 55 to 60 °C, giving a V/L ratio of about 36/1.[6]

The level of volatility is very high in the case of the fuel gases which are, of course, well above their boiling points at ambient temperature and pressure, and their liquefaction has been seen to be necessary in order to save storage space. When the boiling point is not too far below ambient, as with the petroleum gases, it is practicable to maintain the liquid phase by storage under moderate pressure at ambient temperature. As shown in figure 8.3 these storage pressures are approximately 7 and 2 atm for the petroleum gases propane and butane respectively. Methane, on the other hand, has to be maintained at −162 °C, its boiling point at ambient pressure, for storage in the liquid phase (for example, LNG). This necessitates substantial tank coatings with effective insulating properties.

As outlined in appendix 3, the rises with temperature of the vapour pressures of liquid fuels are usually plotted on axes of logarithmic pressure and non-uniform temperature in order to give straight-line relationships.

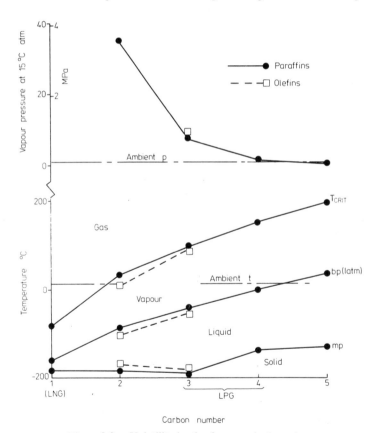

Figure 8.3   Volatility levels of gaseous hydrocarbons

137

These are shown for the alternative fuels in figure 6.6, which also includes the boiling points (at 1 atm pressure) together with both lower (conventional) and upper flash points. The curves show that pentaborane, triethylborane, UDMH, nitromethane and the light alcohols all lie within the volatility range from gasoline to kerosine. An interesting point arises in connection with the alcohol–hydrocarbon blends. In comparison with, say, a motor gasoline, the vapour pressure of the alcohols is lower, no doubt due to the hydrogen bonding of the polar molecules. However, in admixture with gasoline, the alcohol molecules are physically separated from each other, and they tend to form low boiling point azeotropes with the gasoline which raise the vapour pressure of the blend above the levels of either component alone. This effect occurs particularly with the aromatic portions of the gasoline component. In order to limit the vapour pressure of the blend to specified levels, therefore, it may be necessary to remove some of the more volatile fractions of the gasoline for use elsewhere. In this event, the introduction of alcohol into the motor fuel scene adds to the *total* stock of fuel, but has virtually no net effect on the pool of motor gasoline. If, on the other hand, gasoline has to be imported, whereas alcohol is available indigenously, as in such countries as Brazil, alcohol blending with gasoline makes a direct saving. Gaseous ammonia is seen, of course, to be exceptionally volatile, and solid decaborane to be almost equivalent to a gas oil.

8.3 Fire Safety

Like volatility, the readiness of a fuel to burn is an essential feature within the combustor, but is undesirable in handling. For fuel in the liquid phase at normal, near ambient, levels of handling temperature, fire safety is represented by a high flash point since at all temperatures below this level the vapour–air mixture in the ullage space above the liquid surface is too fuel-weak to support combustion. Consequently, no flame or explosion can result from the application of some localised source of ignition. In the United Kingdom, a liquid fuel is classified as highly flammable if its flash point lies below $32\,^{\circ}C$, hence the gasolines, methanol and ethanol all fall within this category. The flammable ranges of pressure and temperature lie between the lower and upper flash points, both of which are shown on the curves in figure 8.4 (and figure 6.6), consequently, both methanol and ethanol are seen to be flammable under ambient conditions. The conventional flash points are the lower values, shown plotted on a linear comparative basis in figure 8.1.

Clearly, with a fuel of particularly low flash point, as with gasoline at about $-50\,^{\circ}C$, the volatility is such that the upper flash point also is low, consequently the ullage vapour–air mixture at ambient temperature exceeds the rich limit of flammability and will not support combustion in the presence of some localised ignition source. Nevertheless, a fuel of such high volatility needs to be vented in storage, the over-rich efflux mixing with atmospheric

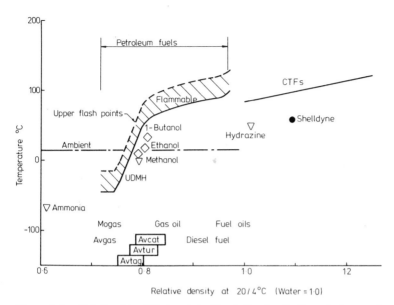

Figure 8.4   Relationship of flash point with relative density for petroleum and alternative fuels

air and passing through the flammable mixture range in the process. This generation of flammable vapour *outside* the tankage is considered particularly hazardous, and protection from local sources of ignition is vital.

With hydrogen fuel stored in the liquid phase, the fact that the boiling point lies appreciably below the melting points of both oxygen and nitrogen makes it necessary to purge the system completely with hydrogen gas in order to eliminate blockages by the formation of slugs of frozen air. As a bonus, this absence of air ensures that flammable mixtures cannot form within the tanks of a liquid hydrogen system. Hydrazine, on the other hand, is stored in an atmosphere of nitrogen, owing to the high rate of oxidation and wide flammability range in the vapour phase. Nitrogen padding raises the lower explosion limit of hydrazine from its value of 4.7 per cent by volume in air to 38 per cent. In aqueous solutions, ignition cannot occur at hydrazine concentrations below 40 per cent. For fuels already in the gaseous phase, fire safety is assisted by a high level of the weak mixture limit of flammability and, from this viewpoint, the gaseous fuels are rated in the following descending order: ammonia, methane, hydrogen, propane and butane. Since natural gas, with methane as the major component, has no distinctive odour, fire safety in the event of a gas leak is improved by the addition of mercaptan or some other stenching agent which becomes detectable at a mixture concentration of about one-fifth of the weak flammable limit.

For fuels subjected to high temperatures in storage, fire safety is represented by a level of spontaneous ignition temperature above that of

139

storage, thus eliminating possibilities of ignition arising from the general heat input alone, irrespective of the presence of localised initiators. With liquid fuels in supersonic flight, for example, kinetic heating raises the temperature level of storage, but this does not exceed about 85 °C at Mach 2.2, whereas aviation kerosine has a spontaneous ignition temperature of about 254 °C. With the exception of the heavy hydrocarbons, most of the fuels of interest are seen in figure 8.1 (and figure 6.10) to have SIT values above about 400 °C at atmospheric pressure, indicating a general resistance to the possibilities of spontaneous ignition under moderately heated storage.

Solid fuels tend to absorb oxygen exothermically during storage, particularly in the presence of moisture, as with freshly won coal, but the reaction ceases if the resulting heat is permitted to escape. The retention of this heat within a stored mass of coal, for example, can lead to a rapid rise in temperature above the safe level of about 40 °C, leading eventually to spontaneous ignition unless the affected coal can be removed and either used immediately or allowed to cool without the addition of water. For this reason, air is excluded as far as possible from a coal heap by packing uniformly, with different sizes in order to fill the interstices, and covering with a layer of wet fine coal wich can easily lose its reaction heat to the atmosphere. Damp hay within a stack can heat to spontaneous ignition by the same chemical process.

A special instance of spontaneous ignition arises over the pyrophoric nature of finely divided metals. The method of storing hydrogen in the form of metallic hydrides depends on a substantial surface area/mass ratio provided by the fine particulate nature of the metallic carrier and, should this be adopted for, say, road transport vehicles, movement of the particles through the tank atmosphere might lead to danger of ignition unless the tank is continuously purged to reduce the oxygen content to a safe level. On the other hand, the endothermic nature of the release of hydrogen gas from the metal ensures that the process will cease due to self-cooling in the event of tank puncture.

Other factors contributing to fire safety are low volatility, which controls the rate of burning at the surface of a pool of fuel, and low flame radiation which does not subject adjacent surfaces and fuel batches to high temperatures. The heavy hydrocarbon fuels fall into the former category, and both hydrogen and the alcohols into the latter. Water is the most commonly recommended fire extinguishing medium, although some authorities prefer carbon dioxide or dry chemicals for the alcohols since water raises their flammable temperature range closer to the temperature of combustion. Protective padding (blanketing) using inert gas (but not carbon dioxide or halogenated hydrocarbons) is also customary for many of the alternative fuels.

8.4 Storage Stability and Compatibility

The chemical stability of a bulk of fuel in storage is a function intrinsically of the structure of its component molecules, together with, in practice, its purity. With the hydrocarbons, for example, stability is provided by saturation of the carbon–carbon bonding in the straight-chain paraffins and close-chain naphthenes (above C_5). The aromatic benzene ring is also inherently stable. Multiple carbon–carbon bonds in olefins, on the other hand, tend to polymerisation to give long-chain gums, whereas the acetylenes are particularly unstable under pressure. The naphthenes below C_5 suffer from ring strain, and tend towards cyclohexane.

As a class, the alcohols are stable compounds but, having polar molecules, are active solvents. Methanol is infinitely soluble in water, and readily soluble in aromatic hydrocarbons. It is, however, less soluble in the non-aromatic (aliphatic) hydrocarbons, and therefore its solubility in commercial petroleum fuels depends largely on the hydrocarbon constituents of the latter. Solubility also increases with temperature level. Ethanol and the higher alcohols dissolve more readily in hydrocarbons, and their presence in an alcohol–hydrocarbon blend increases the solubility of methanol. These features are shown in figure 8.5 for methanol and for ethanol blended separately with kerosine using

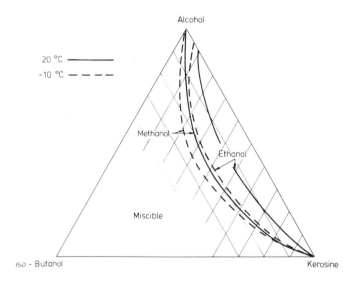

Figure 8.5   Solubility of alcohols in kerosine (derived from reference 21)

iso-butanol as a stabiliser. The presence of even small quantities of water in alcohol–hydrocarbon mixtures, however, leads to direct hydrogen bonding between the alcohol and the water resulting in phase separation, particularly at low temperature, with the paraffinic hydrocarbons in the upper phase, and a combination of alcohol, water and aromatic hydrocarbons in the lower. This effect is shown in figure 8.6 for methanol and for ethanol blended separately with gasoline. Since small quantities of contaminant water are inevitable in any fuel distribution system involving water-borne transport, with vented tanks exposed to rain and diurnal breathing cycles in humid atmospheres, alcohol blending is usually effected at the point of delivery rather than upstream. The BASF approach[8] is to delay mixing even further by using a dual-fuel system incorporating a twin-choke carburettor, feeding one choke with gasoline and the second with the alcohol—water mixture.

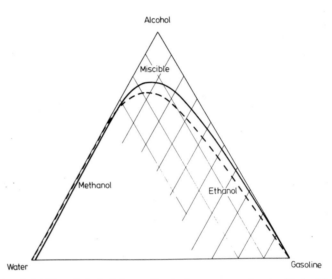

Figure 8.6   Solubility of alcohols in gasoline in the presence of water (derived from references 7, 22 and 23)

The diatomic hydrogen molecule is stable, but the liquid phase exists in either the *ortho* or *para* forms, the natural ortho—para conversion releasing more than sufficient energy to boil the hydrogen completely. For long-term storage, therefore, the para form is essential, and is derived by catalysis. The problems of hydrogen embrittlement of metals are reviewed by Gray.[24]

Of the nitrogen hydrides, only the first two of all the theoretically possible compounds are sufficiently stable for practical storage. Ammonia is an active solvent, being exothermically soluble in water and alcohols, but is stable at moderate temperatures. In either the vapour or liquid phase, ammonia can form explosive compounds with mercury, and must therefore be excluded from mercury manometers. It can also react explosively with chlorine and the hypochlorites. The marked reaction of ammonia gas with the fumes of burning sulphur, generating white clouds of ammonium sulphate, was formerly used in the simple 'sulphur candle' test for detecting the presence of ammonia.

Hydrazine is a stable chemical, insensitive to shock, friction or electrical discharge. No rapid decomposition has been observed in the absence of catalytic agents. Inhibitors are available to reduce the rate of catalytic decomposition promoted by the surfaces of the container. Hydrazine is a highly polar solvent, miscible with other polar solvents, and it reacts exothermically with many oxidising agents including iron oxide, nitric acid, and the chlorates, peroxides and permanganates generally. Spontaneous ignition may result in the vapour phase, but does not propagate through the liquid. Satisfactory long-term storage is possible using a clean system and an inert atmosphere (for example, 'nitrogen padding'). Nitromethane is not stable, and tends to detonate if contaminated and/or subjected to heat or shock.

Fuel stability at moderate temperatures, below the level for spontaneous ignition, is an important feature in cases where fuel systems operate in hot environments, as with the kinetic heating effect of high-speed flight, the proximity of a hot combustor, or the use of fuel as a coolant. Over a period of time, the slow oxidation or recombination reaction can lead to degradation in the form of either gum or sand-like particulates, with subsequent blockage of filters or injectors. One of the standard tests for aviation kerosine is a measure of the high-temperature stability based on the amount and type of deposits on an aluminium heater tube over which the fuel is pumped, together with the rate of blockage of a heated precision filter located immediately downstream, using the Jet Fuel Thermal Oxidation Tester (JFTOT). The thermal instability of hydrocarbon-based jet fuels appears to be related to the concentration of fuel-bound nitrogen, which is high in the case of fuels derived from shale oil and coal.

Ammonia decomposes to nitrogen and hydrogen when heated to about 500 °C, whereas hydrazine has been found stable up to 250 °C provided catalysts are absent. Of the boron hydrides, diborane gas decomposes extensively at room temperature, and is therefore stored under refrigeration and also at high pressure. It must be handled in a clean, dry system completely devoid of oxygen. Decomposition is more rapid at higher temperatures, and leads to complete dissociation above 500 °C. Solid decaborane is stable indefinitely at room temperature, and does not react with air or oxygen up to 60 °C, but explodes with oxygen gas at 100 °C. In the absence of air, it can be maintained stably at 150 °C, but begins to produce hydrogen above 200 °C, and to dissociate slowly at 300 °C. Decaborane is soluble in the light paraffins and other organic solvents. Liquid triethylborane is stable at room temperature, but decomposes slowly above about 100 °C. It is pyrophoric in that it ignites spontaneously with air at room temperature, and with oxygen at 0 °C.

The compatibility of the above fuels with the materials used for the construction of fuel systems is presented briefly in table 8.2.

Table 8.2   Material compatibility in handling (derived from references 9, 10 and 13)

Fuel	Materials	
	Compatible	Incompatible
Hydrogen	Austenitic stainless steels Aluminium and alloys Copper and alloys Monel Pure titanium	High-strength steels Nickel and alloys Titanium alloys Cobalt and alloys Low-strength steels
Methanol	Stainless steels Clean carbon steels Certain plastics	Lead—tin tank coatings Zinc Copper and alloys Aluminium Magnesium Some elastomers, sealants, plastics, rubbers, and fibre gaskets
Ethanol	Iron Mild steel Copper	Aluminium Copper (if pyridine present)
Isopropanol	Mild steel Copper	Aluminium (if fuel hot)
n-Butanol	Mild steel Copper Aluminium	Aluminium (if fuel anhydrous and hot)
Ammonia	Iron Steel Aluminium Lead 300/400 stainless steels Some rubbers and polymers Asbestos	Copper Brass Zinc Tin Aluminium alloys (unless fuel dry)
Hydrazine	Titanium Cadmium Beryllium Molybdenum 300/400 stainless steels Aluminium PTFE High-density polythene Asbestos	Stainless steels of over 0.5% molybdenum Magnesium Zinc Lead Rubbers Cork PVC Halogens
Unsymmetrical dimethylhydrazine (UDMH)	Mild steel Stainless steel Aluminium and alloys Magnesium PTFE Polythene Graphite	Copper and alloys

8.5 Pumping

The energy required to transfer a fuel from storage tanks through a system comprising pumps, pipelines, filters, control valves and, eventually; injectors is largely determined by the resistance arising from the fuel viscosity. Methods of measuring viscosity are discussed in section A3.8, together with the effects of temperature. The extreme effects of low temperature are covered in the following section 8.6, but difficulties can arise well above these levels, and temperature limitations are therefore set for acceptable storage and pumping, and also for satisfactorily small droplet sizes on atomisation. These temperatures, and their corresponding viscosity limits, are shown for the residual petroleum fuel oils in table 8.3.

Pump suitability depends not only on viscosity, but also on lubricity, which is defined as a low tendency to produce friction, wear and/or scuffing. Fuel lubricity can be promoted by the presence of certain impurities, particularly polynuclear aromatic sulphides, which act as boundary lubricants. The standard four-ball test machine has been found unsatisfactory, but tests with a pin-and-disc machine[15] have shown fuel treatment in the refinery to be very significant. For example, chemical treatment to convert objectionable mercaptans RSH to innocuous disulphides RSSR' does not appear to affect lubricity, whereas severe hydrogenation reduces mercaptans to alkanes and hydrogen sulphide, thus removing the polar impurities that act as boundary lubricants, and leading to pump seizure. Fortunately, corrosion-inhibiting additives tend to improve lubricity as a side effect.

Single- or double-acting reciprocating-piston, or rotating gear, types of pump were formerly in wide general use for the transfer of crude oil and its products, and are still used for pumping at very high pressures, or for fuels of high viscosity. Because of their low speed, they are driven by electric motors through reduction gears, or by direct drive from low-speed diesel engines. In some engine fuel systems, multiple reciprocating pumps are arranged with parallel axes, the pistons being operated by a rotating inclined surface acting through slipper pads. Lubricity problems of sulphiding of the silver-plated

Table 8.3   *Minimum handling temperatures and associated maximum viscosities, x °C (y cSt) (derived from reference 14 and other sources)*

Fuel oil class	Storage	Pumping (Dependent on pump type)	Atomisation
E	10 (330)	10 (330)	62 (24)
F	25 (600)	30 (400)	90 (24)
G	35 (1000)	45 (500)	113 (24)

slipper pads were found due to fuel treatment, and inert carbon inserts were adopted subsequently.

Because of their pulsating flow, the positive displacement pumps have largely been replaced by single- or multi-stage centrifugal pumps, connected in series or parallel, since these are mechanically simpler and require less maintenance over long periods of operation. The clearance between impeller and casing is larger than in a gear pump but, with the lower viscosity fuels, the slippage is not excessive. Centrifugal pumps operate most effectively at high speeds, and are driven directly by electric motors. For large capacity pumps used on infrequent occasions, drive is by diesel or gas engines, expansion turbines when high-pressure gas is available, or combustion turbines with any suitable fuel. For highly viscous or slurry fuels, screw type pumps are sometimes necessary. Methanol, for example, with low levels of viscosity and lubricity, is best handled with a centrifugal type pump. Liquid hydrogen and other cryogenic liquids, on the other hand, appear to be better suited to reciprocating piston type pumps. In view of the material compatibility problems with some of the more aggressive alternative fuels, the magnetic drive pump may offer a solution. This pump incorporates a plastics encapsulated magnetic impeller with ceramic self-lubricating bearings, and operates submerged, being suited to most acid, alkali and salt solutions at temperatures up to 100 °C.[16]

To some degree, pumping resistance is also determined by the extent of filtration. This varied widely between fuel types and applications, but, apart from a level of 5 to 10 μm for diesel fuels, the general trend is towards the aviation standard of 1 μm.

8.6 Low-temperature Behaviour

Each individual material has its own freezing, or melting, point consequently each fuel consisting of a single element or compound freezes at a single temperature, whereas those composed of blends of a number of materials freeze progressively over ranges of temperature. This latter behaviour is characteristic of the commercial hydrocarbon fuel blends in which the heavy fractions freeze first and promote a cloud of fine wax crystals (at the cloud point), the light fractions freezing progressively until apparent solidity is reached (the pour point). In fact, as outlined in section A3.9, the lightest fractions are still liquid at this point, and mechanical agitation demonstrates the thixotropic nature of the fuel by the generation of a liquid–particulate slurry as the wax structure is broken apart. The pour points of the representative petroleum fuels residual fuel oil Class G, Avtur and gasoline are shown in figure 8.1.

The melting points for most of the fuels under discussion are seen from the figure to lie below -100 °C, whereas those for the nitrogen hydrides are somewhat higher. In particular, hydrazine freezes at 1.5 °C, but contracts in

146

the process and so does not damage storage tanks. Antifreeze agents are necessary to achieve practical freezing requirements down to about $-50\,^\circ$C. Water and/or ammonia are promising anti-freeze additives, and a ternary mixture TF-1 is described by Schmidt[17] consisting of 64 per cent hydrazine, 10 per cent ammonia and 26 per cent water. The presence of the water depresses the specific energy, but the ammonia improves the anti-knock quality.

8.7 Health Factors

As a guide, a brief summary is given in table 8.4 of the major physiological reactions on exposure to the conventional and alternative fuels considered in this text. These reactions may be localised and/or have systemic (remote) effects, such as from absorption into the bloodstream, and are tabulated under the following headings

Ingestion	— swallowing of liquid into the digestive tract
Inhalation	— in-breathing of vapour to the lungs
Aspiration	— introduction of liquid into the lungs either through inhalation or by vomiting
External contact	— contact with skin and, particularly, with eyes.

The table attempts to relate the main causes and effects but, clearly, a hazard arising from, say, inhalation can also follow aspiration, and possibly even external contact. Furthermore, some materials are either slow to eliminate (for example, methanol) or are cumulative (for example, decaborane).

The evaluation of atmospheric quality with regard to the presence of contaminants is commonly expressed in terms of the threshold limit value (TLV) defined as the acceptable airborne concentration of the given contaminant in occupational exposures for up to eight hours daily without adverse effects. These values have been established by the American Conference of Governmental Industrial Hygienists, and are published in the United Kingdom by the Health and Safety Executive as *Guidance Note EH 15/77*. However, since the volatility of the contaminant determines its vapour concentration at ambient temperature, it is helpful to use the hazard index, defined by (vapour pressure/TLV), and these values are included in table 8.4.

To ensure overall safety in handling, reference to the manufacturers' handbooks is recommended in all cases, taking due note of the TLV or hazard index in relation to the concentration giving detectable odour. The broad conclusions from such an exercise appear as follows.

1. Maintain adequate ventilation, and provide respirators where necessary.
2. Wear protective clothing.
3. Provide plentiful safety shower and eye-irrigation facilities.
4. In event of ingestion, do not induce vomiting (to avoid aspiration).

Table 8.4 Health factors (derived from references 11, 12, 17, 18, 19, 20)

Fuel	Hazard index (mm Hg/ppm)	Liquid ingestion	Vapour inhalation	Liquid aspiration	External contact
LNG			Oxygen deprivation		Cold burns
LPG	1.4		Drowsiness Narcotic at high concentration particularly butane		Cold burns
Gasolines	0.75	Drowsiness Loss of consciousness	Loss of consciousness	Pneumonitis	Irritation by de-fatting Dermatitis
Kerosines		Moderately toxic	Dizziness	Pneumonitis	As gasolines
Gas oils Fuel oils		As kerosines, but to reducing degree			
Aromatics	5.7	Vomiting Loss of consciousness	Drowsiness Loss of consciousness	Respiratory paralysis Cardiac arrest	As gasolines

Substance	Value			
Methanol	0.5	Blindness	Headache Trembling Vomiting	
Ethanol	0.05		Milder than methanol. Oxidises rapidly in body, and eliminates	
Liquid hydrogen				Cold burns
Liquid ammonia	208		Irritation of mucous membrane Bronchitis Immobilisation	Caustic and cold burns Eye damage Blindness
Hydrazine	20	Nausea	Irritation of mucous membrane Nausea Haorseness	Caustic burns Nausea
Nitromethane	0.46			
Diborane			As toxic as phosgene.	Affects kidneys and liver
Pentaborane	28000		As toxic as chlorine.	

5. Summon medical aid for anything other than the obviously minor accident.

With regard to the inhalation safety of combustion products, the non-carbon-based fuels all have the advantage of lack of toxic carbon monoxide.

References

1. *Engineers Australia*, Institution òf Engineers, Australia (14 July 1978), 15.
2. W. F. Stewart and F. J. Edeskety, Alternate fuels for transportation. Part 2: Hydrogen for the automobile, *Mech. Engng*, **96** (1974) 22–8.
3. K. C. Hoffmann, W. E. Winsche, R. H. Wiswall, J. J. Reilly, T. V. Sheehan and C. H. Waide, Metal hydrides as a source of fuel for vehicular propulsion, Paper No. 690232, International Automotive Engineering Congress, Detroit (1969).
4. K. S. Varde and G. G. Lucas, Hydrogen as a fuel for vehicle propulsion, *Proc. Instn mech. Engrs*, **188** (1974) 26–74.
5. G. D. Brewer, *The Case for Hydrogen Fueled Transport Aircraft*, AIAA Paper No. 73–1323 (1974).
6. G. F. Sheppard and J. G. Withers, Assessment of car and fuel factors affecting vapour locking tendency, *Proc. Auto. Div. Instn mech. Engrs*, **7** (1954/5).
7. *Alcohols: a Technical Assessment of their Application as Fuels*, American Petroleum Institute Publication No. 4261 (1976).
8. Technical Editor, To drive or to drink? *Autocar*, **144** (1976) 20–2.
9. *Methanol; Ethanol; Isopropanol; n-Butanol;* Data booklets from BP Chemicals International Ltd, Devonshire House, Piccadilly, London W1X 6AY (1975/6).
10. J. W. Hodgson, Alternate fuels for transportation. Part 3: Ammonia for the automobile, *Mech. Engng*, **96** (1974) 22–5.
11. *Hydrazine Data Sheet*, Olin Chemicals Division, 745 Fifth Avenue, New York 10022 (1959).
12. S. Sarner, Unsymmetrical dimethyl hydrazine, Propellants data sheets, *Astronautics*, **4** (1959) 76.
13. A. W. Thompson, Structural materials use in a hydrogen energy economy, *Int. J. Hydrogen Energy*, **2** (1977) 299–307.
14. BS 2869:1970 Petroleum fuel for oil engines and burners.
15. R. A. Vere, *Lubricity of Aviation Turbine Fuels,* SAE 690667 (1969).
16. Literature on magnetic pumps, Totton Electrical Sales Ltd, Southampton, UK.
17. E. W. Schmidt, Hydronitrogens as future automotive fuels, in J. M. Colucci (ed), *Future Automotive Fuels*, Plenum Press, New York and London (1977) 320–41.

18. *Health Guide to B. P. Petroleum Products*, B.P. Trading Ltd, London.

19. *Shell Petroleum Products Guide to Health and Safety*, Shell International Petroleum Co. Ltd, London.

20. *Boranes data sheets*, Callery Chemical Co., 9600 Perry Highway, Pitsburgh 37, Pa. (1957/8)

21. W. J. Mackenzie, Alternative fuels, Cranfield Institute of Technology, unpublished MSc thesis (September 1975).

22. J. D. Rogers, *Ethanol and Methanol as Automotive Fuels*, E I du Pont de Nemours & Co. Inc., Petroleum Chemicals Division Report No. P 813–3 (November 1973).

23. *Use of Alcohol in Motor Gasoline – A Review,* American Petroleum Institute, Committee for Air and Water Conservation, Report No. 4082 (August 1971).

24. H. R. Gray, H. G. Nelson, R. E. Johnson, W. B. McPherson, F. S. Howard and J. H. Swisher, Potential structure material problems in a hydrogen energy system, *Int. J. Hydrogen Energy,* **3** (1978) 105–18.

9. Conclusions and Prospects

An attempt has been made to survey all the materials of possible interest as alternative fuels for the future, leaving options open to consider any other materials that may emerge. However, experience to date highlights those fuels which appear to hold particular promise. These are the products of fluidised solid fuels, the alkyl aclohols, and hydrogen. The following sections deal with possible future production methods of these fuels, and these in turn are followed by comments on alternative fuel prospects within the main fuel-consuming sectors.

9.1 Solid Fuel Fluidisation

Of the fossil fuels, the coals possess the very significant advantage of substantial reserves, with a resource lifetime of some 200 years or more. On the other hand, the need to handle the fuel in solid lump form, and subsequently the solid particulate ash, complicates industrial combustion plant, is inconvenient domestically, and totally unsuited to the majority of transport applications. Many of these problems are eased if the constituents of coals are first converted chemically to gases and/or liquids, with ash removal in the process. Several techniques are available but, as indicated in chapter 3, all involve the following two basic steps.

1. Rupturing of the polynuclear aromatic rings of the coal platelets into a variety of straight-chain paraffinic structures, together with some naphthenic and single aromatic rings.
2. Increasing the hydrogen/carbon atomic ratio from about 0.75 to some appropriate level up to about 2 by the removal of carbon, addition of hydrogen, or both.

In such fluidisation processes, performance can be assessed in a variety of ways, typical parameters being operating pressure, fluid yield, and thermal efficiency of conversion. Representative values, where available, are discussed in the following two sections, but comparisons must be made with caution since performance definitions are not universal. Furthermore, some of the many new processes have not yet produced sufficient data for representative assessments to be made.

The level of operating pressure determines the wall thickness necessary for the reactor plant, and thus the capital costs. As with conventional techniques of fuel processing, the adoption of catalysts can often bring down the operating pressure to a more economic level.

The yield of a conversion process is usually defined as the mass ratio of finished product to feedstock material, and the most significant basis for the determination of yields from a solid fuel conversion process is that of the self-sufficient plant in which the solid fuel also meets the requirements of process energy, needing an input of water only for the generation of process hydrogen.

The thermal efficiency is usually defined in overall terms as the ratio of the energy content of the output fluids to the total input of energy comprising that of the feed coal, the hydrogen source and any process heat required, as well as any heat losses, although some estimates are made in terms of carbon efficiency, based on the ratio (carbon in product/carbon in coal). Typically, thermal conversion efficiencies of solid fuels vary from about 45 to 75 per cent.

The following sections outline the processes either commercially available, or under active development, for the gasification and/or liquefaction of coals and other solid fuels.

9.1.1 Coal Gasification

The gasification of coal has been practiced since the late 18th century, largely for the manufacture of either a town gas of intermediate energy content, or a synthesis gas for processing to ammonia or methanol. Early methods tended to two distinct stages, that is, carbonisation to drive off the volatile matter, followed by gasification of the residual coke. The production rates of these systems suffered due to the variability of the properties between different batches of coal, and even between different portions within a given feedstock. In the later processes derived for SNG as the major product, therefore, this and other factors have led to the following developments.

1. Coal pre-treatment by blending, pulverisation and/or briquetting in order to improve uniformity of heating and diffusion of gases.

2. Agitation of the coal particles to enhance penetration and reaction rates, using mechanical stirring, fluidisation or entrainment.

3. Control of reaction temperature either below the ash fusion point to ensure ash removal as solid, or sufficiently above this level in order to drain the ash as a liquid slag.

4. Maximising the methane content of the product gases by increasing the

pressure, reducing the temperature or by subsequent methanation reactions. High pressure also limits the physical size of the plant.

A number of processes have been devised, and may be classified in various ways (table 9.1). In the following treatment, the processes are characterised in three classes according to the manner in which the necessary heat for gasification is supplied, that is

1. direct oxidation of some carbon in the feedstock
2. external oxidation, with heat-carrying medium
3. external heat conduction.

Oxidation of some carbon in the feedstock not only provides the gasification heat but also helps to increase the hydrogen/carbon ratio. In the commercially developed Lurgi process, for example, illustrated in figure 9.1A, the two major steps are as follows, with reactions shown in full arrows, and material transfer in broken arrows

1. Gasification

$$
\begin{array}{c}
\text{volatile hydrocarbons} \xrightarrow{\text{cracking}} \left[CH_4 \right] + C_x H_y \\
\uparrow \\
coal \longrightarrow coke + \text{volatile hydrocarbons} \\
\downarrow \\
coke + H_2O + O_2 \xrightarrow{\text{carbonisation}} CO_2 + H_2 \xrightarrow{\text{methanation}} \left[CH_4 \right] + H_2O
\end{array}
$$

2. Shift

$$(\text{part}) \; CO + H_2O \longrightarrow CO_2 + H_2 \tag{6}$$

The added steam acts both as a source of hydrogen and a temperature regulator. The gasifier functions also as the main steam boiler, and fuel agitation is achieved by means of a rotating grate. The diameter of the gasifier is limited to about 3 m in order to ensure efficient stirring without channelling, consequently multiple units are required for higher throughputs. With a feed rate of about 1 tonne of coal per hour for each m^2 of grate area, the gaseous output rate is about 300 000 m^3/day.

The Winkler process is also commercially available. In the original version, coal pulverised to 8 mm diameter is gasified with steam and oxygen in a fluidised bed at atmospheric pressure and 800 °C (below the ash fusion point), the fuel ash carrying over with the gas stream. The output in this case is limited by the low level of operating pressure, and by carry-over of raw fuel with the ash.

In the Koppers—Totzek process, the pulverised coal is entrained in oxygen and steam, and injected at high speed through diametrically opposing jets. The high temperatures of oxidation ensure very rapid gasification of the coal particles, together with liquid slagging of the ash. Although the high operating temperature ensures that tars and phenols are cracked, the product gases require extreme methanation. In the Rummel—Otto process, a rotating bath

Table 9.1 Representative coal gasification data (derived from references 1 and 2)

Process	Pressure (atm)	Temperature (°C)	Ash removal	Bed type	Main features	Acceptable feedstock
Lurgi	20–40	1100–1650	Solid from rotating grate in base	Slow moving mechanically stirred	Sized lump coal batches introduced through pressurised lock hopper	Non-coking
Winkler	1	800	Solid from base or carry-over with gas stream	Stationary fluid	Small fuel particles	Lignite
Koppers–Totzek Rummel–Otto	1	1600	Liquid slag drainage	Entrained	High temperature generated to melt slag and crack liquid products	Wide range
Synthane	40–75	1000	Solid from base	Stationary fluid	Char heat used to raise steam	Wide range
Bi-gas	70	930–1670	Liquid slag drainage	Entrained stationary fluid	Fine coal–water slurry	Wide range
Hygas	75–90	1050	Solid from base	Stationary fluid	Coal–oil slurry to three superposed beds. Gasification heat augmented by methanation of char with hot H_2	Non-coking
Agglomerated ash	7	980	Solid excess withdrawn from heat transfer circuit	Stationary fluid	Gasification heat supplied by combustion of char, and transferred via agglomerated ash to gasifier in advance of O_2	Wide range with preliminary reductions of coking tendency
CO_2 acceptor	20	860	Carry-over with gas stream	Stationary fluid	Gasification heat supplied by sensible heat of calcined dolomite, CaO, plus reaction heat with CO_2 to $CaCO_3$	Lignite Sub-bituminous

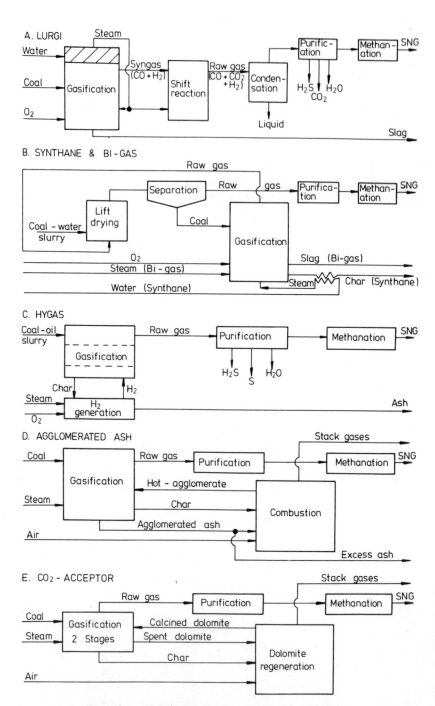

Figure 9.1   Schematic of processes of coal gasification

of liquid slag is maintained, the coal gasifying at and above the slag surface.

With gasifiers operating at high pressure, fuel feed through pressure locks is effected more conveniently in fluid form. Consequently, in the Synthane process (US Bureau of Mines), the coal is introduced as a slurry with water, which is then dried and pre-heated by the main stream of hot product gas. The gasification steam is obtained from water quenching of the resulting char. The BI-GAS process (Bituminous Coal Research Inc.) has a similar system of coal—water slurry feeding, drying and separation for high-pressure operation, the gasification occurring at a temperature sufficient for the ash to melt and be removed periodically as coagulated slag. In the Hygas process (Illinois Institute of Gas Technology), a coal—oil slurry is used. Three superposed fuel beds are fluidised and gasified by hot hydrogen produced by the action of steam and oxygen (or steam and electrical heat) on the hot char at the base of the gasifier, the three-bed arrangement assisting in methane equilibrium. This process therefore represents an intermediate position between direct heating in the gasifier (class 1) and external oxidation with hydrogen as the heat-carrying medium (class 2).

More representative of class 2 is the Agglomerated Ash process (Union Carbide and Batelle Research Institute) which dispenses with oxygen supplies by using compressed air. A mixture of char and ash is burnt with air, the hot agglomerated particles supplying gasification heat by pumped transfer back to the gasifier, with fluidisation by steam, and removal of excess ash. The CO_2 Acceptor process (Consolidated Coal Co.) also dispenses with oxygen, the gasifying heat being provided by reacting calcined dolomite (oxides of calcium and magnesium) with CO_2 in two interconnected fluidised beds, the spent dolomite being regenerated with air. In both processes, the combustion gases are withdrawn separately in order to avoid dilution of the product gases with atmospheric nitrogen from the combustion air.

Lom[1] and Teggers[2] also report on other gasification processes under development in the United States. These include a catalytic process using molten sodium carbonate to break down the higher hydrocarbons, and a process using molten iron as the gasification medium. Injection of steam and oxygen is used in both cases. Also included is the Hydrane process, a further direct method of hydrogenation in which the coal reacts during free fall in hydrogen gas at high pressure and temperature, the hydrogen being produced by gasification of the resultant char with steam and oxygen in the usual way.

The final group of processes, dependent on gasification heat supply via conduction through external walls, includes the tube process in which a coal—water slurry is transported by fluidising carbon dioxide gas through a metal tube heated either electrically or by external combustion. Eventually, it is anticipated that both gasification heat and steam supplies will be forthcoming from gas-cooled nuclear power plant, and such processes are under development in the Federal Republic of Germany. This method not only eliminates the combustion of part of the coal for heat production purposes, but also lowers the content of inert carbon dioxide in the product gases. A wide range of methods is therefore available, some of which can be expected to reach economic feasibility by the time supplies of other fossil fuels become severely restricted.

9.1.2 Coal Liquefaction

The bulk liquefaction of coal probably stems from the coking process of carbonisation used by Abraham Darby in the late 18th century represented by the by-product tars which subsequently served as feedstock for chemicals and fuels. Complete liquefaction of coal was achieved by Berthelot in 1896, and the direct hydrogen method was developed by Bergius in 1913, and then by the I.G. Farben Industries.

As indicated in section 4.4.2, methods of coal liquefaction may be classified under the following headings[3,4,5]

1. hydrocarbonisation
2. indirect hydrogenation
3. direct hydrogenation (by hydrogen gas or by solvent).

Representative of the hydrocarbonisation route is the coal—oil—gas, or COGAS, process under development by a consortium of American companies, based on carbonisation in a fluidised bed, the coal decomposing through the action of heat, followed by hydrogenation using hydrogen produced by reaction with steam and oxygen with the hot unreacted coke (figure 9.2). The multi-step lower pressure COED process is also based on pyrolysis followed by hydrogenation of part of the char.

The indirect method of hydrogenation is represented by an initial Lurgi or other complete gasification stage in the presence of hydrogen, followed by shift reaction synthesis to liquid products. The Lurgi stage, using coal particles down to about 3 mm diameter and up to 30 per cent ash content, is similar to the coal gasification method but with catalyst type and operating conditions selected to maximise the liquid yield from the Lurgi syncrude. In the process adopted in 1955 by SASOL (South African Coal Oil and Gas Corporation), the major products are waxes, oils, motor fuels and oxygen-containing chemicals. The recently proved Mobil process using a synthetic shape-selective zeolite catalyst converts methanol to high-octane gasoline only, with no other products or major contaminants. This represents the final link in the lique-faction of coal to gasoline, the first two stages being the production of synthetic gas, and combination to methanol. Ethanol is also under considera-tion as a feedstock for gasoline conversion.[6]

In methods of direct hydrogenation, the coal is processed in either the solid or dissolved state. The former methods differ from the earlier hydro-gasification processes in that highly active catalysts (for example, cobalt—molybdenum) are used, permitting lower temperatures and pressures. The

158

A. HYDROCARBONISATION

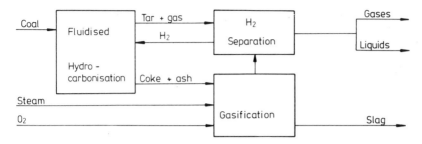

B. INDIRECT HYDROGENATION

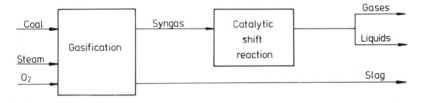

C. DIRECT HYDROGENATION WITH H₂ GAS

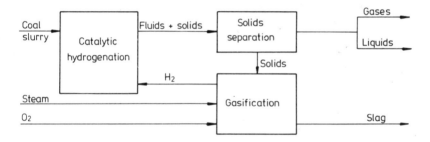

D. DIRECT HYDROGENATION WITH DONOR – SOLVENT EXTRACTION

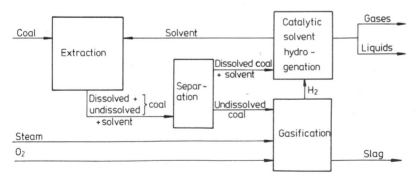

Figure 9.2   Schematic of processes of coal liquefaction

hydrogen is added either as gas or by means of transfer from the hydrogenated solvent, as shown in table 9.2. In the United Kingdom NCB system, the coal is slurried with recycled solvent oil, and then heated to assist the solvent extraction and subsequent filtration of ash. The hydrogen gas is then added for purposes of hydrocracking. Experiments are also under way with a supercritical system in which the extract and solvent are taken jointly from the extractor and then condensed and separated at low pressure. In the Exxon process, the recycled aromatic solvent oil is first hydrogenated in order to act as a vehicle for the required hydrogen.[7]

Data on these liquefaction processes are shown in table 9.3. These processes have reached varying stages of development, sometimes with more than one process in integrated form, as a step towards the creation of an overall 'coal refinery', or 'coalplex'.

In the ideal process of liquefaction in which all the energy from the solid feedstock is transformed without loss to the liquid products, the maximum possible yield of liquids is given by the ratio of the specific energies of the reactants and the products. Thus, a coal with a gross specific energy of 29.8 MJ/kg, liquefied to a naphtha–fuel oil mixture of average gross specific energy of 41.9 MJ/kg, gives a maximum theoretical mass yield of 100 $(29.8/41.9) = 71$ per cent.[7] The overall process is represented schematically in figure 9.3, showing the individual quantities of coal used for conversion, hydrogen generation, and hydrogenation heat provision, with a total mass throughput (excluding combustion air) of 1.357 kg. The theoretical maximum mass yield of 71 per cent is confirmed by the ratio of liquid fuel mass (containing residual traces of nitrogen, sulphur, oxygen and chlorine contaminants) to the total input of coal, that is, $(0.804/1.128) = 0.71$. Inspection of the analysis for the coal shows the reduced formula to be $CH_{0.87}$, and of the resultant liquid mixture to be $CH_{1.40}$. Being entirely self-sufficient, this plant achieves an overall thermal efficiency of 100 per cent. In practice, the process heat may be supplied independently, and allowance made for energy losses, in which case the mass yield will go up, but the overall thermal efficiency will drop to about 65 per cent.

9.2 Alcohol Production

Currently, methanol is a major organic chemical in tonnage production, and is manufactured mainly from synthesis gas derived from light hydrocarbon feedstocks, in some cases with added carbon dioxide. Methanol has a very wide range of uses, including polymers, solvents, resins, adhesives, paints, coatings, plasticisers, dyes, anti-freezes and pharmaceuticals, with a growing list of potential outlets in blast furnaces, food production and sewage treatment. If adopted as a fuel in addition, it is estimated that world production will have to increase fourfold by the mid 1980s.

Chemical routes for the production of methanol through the steam

Table 9.2 Solid fuel liquefaction processes

Coal state	Hydrogen supply	Representative processes	Catalyst
Slurried	Gas in reactor	Synthoil (US Bureau of Mines)	Fixed bed
Slurried	Gas in reactor	H-Coal (Hydrocarbon Research Inc.)	Fluidised bed
Dissolved	High-pressure gas in reactor	Solvent Refined Coal (Pittsburgh Midway Coal Co.)	Nil
Dissolved	Gas in subsequent cracking unit	NCB	Nil
Dissolved	Donor solvent	Exxon	Nil (fixed bed for solvent only)
Dissolved	Donor solvent + subsequent gas in hydrogenation	Consol Synthetic Fuel (Liquefied Fuel Development Corporation)	Nil (fluidised bed in second stage)

Table 9.3   *Representative coal liquefaction data* (derived from references 3, 4 and 5)

Process type	Pressure (atm)	Temperature ($^{\circ}$C)	Gas yield (m^3/tonne)	Liquid yield (l/tonne)
Hydrocarbonisation	1–70	540	110–140	155–230
Indirect hydrogenation	30	1930	225–280	230–310
Direct hydrogenation (H_2 gas)	200	450	55–85	390–545
Direct hydrogenation (donor solvent)	20–200	260	100–125	310–470

reforming of light hydrocarbons are shown schematically below. In each case, $[X]_R$ represents reactants, and $[Y]_P$ products

1. Steam reforming of methane to methanol

$2[CH_4 + H_2O]_R$

$\xrightarrow{reforming}$

$2(3H_2 + CO) \xrightarrow{\text{synthesis}} 2H_2 \quad + \quad \begin{bmatrix} 2CH_3OH \\ \\ CH_3OH \\ \\ CH_3OH \end{bmatrix} \begin{matrix} \\ \\ + H_2O \\ \\ {}_P + H_2O \end{matrix}$

$[CO_2]_R + 3H_2 \xrightarrow{\text{synthesis}}$

$4H_2 + CO_2 \xrightarrow{\text{synthesis}} H_2 \quad +$

$\xrightarrow{reforming}$

$[CH_4 + 2H_2O]_R$

2. Steam reforming of naphtha to methanol

$[CH_2 + H_2O]_R \xrightarrow{\text{reforming}} 2H_2 + CO \xrightarrow{\text{synthesis}} \begin{bmatrix} CH_3OH \\ \\ CH_3OH \end{bmatrix}_P + H_2O$

$[CH_2 + 2H_2O]_R \xrightarrow{\text{reforming}} 3H_2 + CO_2 \xrightarrow{\text{synthesis}}$

The reforming reaction is favoured by low pressure and high temperature, whereas the methanol synthesis reaction requires the opposite. However, the conventional zinc–chromium methanol catalyst requires the fairly high temperature of 350 $^{\circ}$C, with an associated high pressure of about 350 bar.

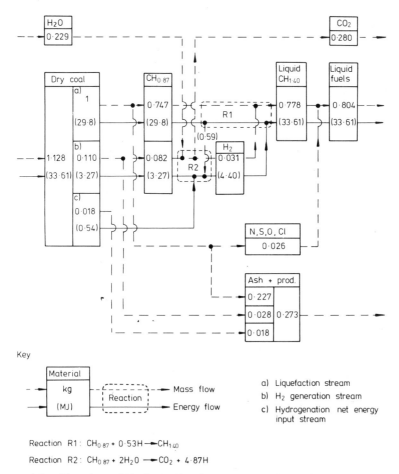

Reaction R1: $CH_{0.87} + 0.53H \longrightarrow CH_{1.40}$

Reaction R2: $CH_{0.87} + 2H_2O \longrightarrow CO_2 + 4.87H$

Figure 9.3   Flow chart of idealised self-sufficient coal liquefaction plant (derived from reference 7 and personal communication, Dr A. Stratton, ICI)

The ICI low-pressure process resulted from the following two developments

1. a copper–zinc–alumina catalyst capable of operating at 220 °C and 50 bar, with a working life of about 4 years.

2. the steam reforming reaction which produces a particularly pure syngas, virtually free of such copper poisoners as sulphur and chlorides.

The first low-pressure plant, which went on stream in 1966, showed substantial improvements in plant costs, design simplicity and operational control. Continuing development by ICI and Davy Powergas has raised the thermal efficiency of the overall process from the initial 58 per cent to about 70 per cent. Methanol plant has also been designed for use in a sea-going vessel as a means of developing gas resources offshore.

The diminishing availability of these premium feedstocks is leading to increasing adoption of the heavier feedstocks including coal, particularly with the emergence of improved methods of coal gasification. The Lurgi pressure (30 bar) gasification process of producing the intermediate syngas, together with some methane, followed by a mild shift conversion to give the required H_2/CO molar ratio of 2, has some attraction here since it is applicable to a wide variety of solid fuels including run-of-mine coal and coals of high caking capacity and high content of ash and moisture. The Winkler process appears to be suited to brown coals. The earlier high-pressure (300 to 500 bar) processes may still be competitive for the larger plants.

When methanol alone, rather than the co-production of methane and methanol, is required from coal, a high gasification temperature of about $1300\,^{\circ}C$ is used, with a moderately high pressure. Following the commercial demonstration of methanol synthesis, it would appear that the future of coal—methanol conversion depends largely on the emergence of the most successful of the proposed schemes for coal gasification, and that the resulting product of a coal-bearing region could be competitive with imported methanol derived from foreign natural gas. In fact, the costs of natural gas conversion and transportation as methanol, in general, are still higher than the shipping of LNG in cryogenic tankers.

From about the middle of last century, industrial ethanol was produced by fermentation of sugar, starch and cellulosic materials, but synthesis from ethylene, via either the ethyl sulphate route or by direct catalytic hydrolysis, was introduced in the 1930s and emerged after the Second World War as more economic. The ethylene itself was derived from natural gas or petroleum cracker gas. The increasing price and eventual loss of these primary feedstocks will no doubt see a full-circle return to the fermentation routes based on vegetable and cellulosic waste, or specially grown, feedstocks. Cellulose and starch are both polysaccharides, that is, naturally occurring polymers made up of very many monosaccharide units held together by glycoside linkages. Both materials have the general formula $(C_6H_{10}O_5)_n$, where n exceeds 1500, giving molar masses of over 250 000 g/mol, but differ in the configuration of the unit linkages. In plants, cellulose serves as the main structural material, and starch as the reserve food. Complete hydrolysis with acid or by means of enzymes gives glucose, which can then be fermented with yeast to ethanol, as shown in the simplified reactions below

$$(C_6H_{10}O_5)_n + nH_2O \xrightarrow[\text{enzymes}]{\text{acid or}}$$

cellulose
or starch

$$nC_6H_{12}O_6 \xrightarrow[\text{fermentation}]{\text{yeast}} 2nC_2H_5OH + 2nCO_2$$

glucose ethanol

The carbon dioxide is removed by high-pressure water absorption.

A typical ethanol mass yield from corn is about 30 per cent. Production is normally on a multiple batch basis, but continuous fermentation appears feasible without the problem of infection by selecting conditions favouring the yeast itself rather than the bacteria present, and by adopting a one-stage process.[8]

Deriving fuels from biomatter is a process of photobiological energy conversion with carbohydrates as the vehicles. Although the celluloses offer a high yield at lowest cost, they are expensive in both money and energy to convert to liquid fuels. The saccharification process to glucose is one of hydrolysis using either a sulphuric acid solution at about 180 °C or, more recently, a micro-organism producing enzymes or 'cellulases'. The more expensive starches and sugars are more easily converted, and produce a less expensive ethanol. Cassava (manioc or tapioca) is the highest known yielder of starch, with a cyanide content providing some degree of pest repulsion, and capability of flourishing on poor soils without irrigation. Sugar beet is tolerant to extremes of weather, and gives a sucrose content of 14 to 21 per cent. Sugar cane is a high-yielding crop, but more dependent on weather and soil conditions. Ethanol productivity from these sources is estimated to reach up to about 8000 l/ha annually. A net gain of some nine times the energy consumed in sugar conversion arises in the resulting anhydrous alcohol, but the economics do not yet compare favourably with conventional gasolines.

9.3 Hydrogen Production

The major proportion of manufactured hydrogen gas is produced currently from sulphur-cleansed natural gas by catalytic steam reforming. As shown in section 4.6.1, the basic reaction is that of methane reforming in the presence of nickel oxide catalyst pellets. The product gases, cooled to about 375 °C, then undergo the water-gas shift reaction with iron-oxide—chromium catalyst, as shown

$$CH_4 + \left[H_2O \right] \longrightarrow CO \; + \; \left[3H_2 \right] \tag{15}$$

$$\left[H_2O \right] \; + \; CO \longrightarrow \left[H_2 \right]_p + CO_2 \tag{6}$$

This is followed by a second shift reaction at 200 °C with a copper—chromium—zinc oxide catalyst. Carbon dioxide is removed mainly by absorption, and the final traces by methanation using some of the product hydrogen. The hydrogen/natural gas volume ratio is about 2.13, and the thermal efficiency of the process approaches 70 per cent. Some commercial plants operate on the partial oxidation of hydrocarbons to synthesis gas, followed by augmentation of the hydrogen yield by shift conversion, as before. Other source materials include the liquid hydrocarbons generally, and the water gas derived from steam reaction with coal, coke or oil shale.

165

However, the hydrocarbons from these solid sources, being compatible with existing handling and combustion equipment, will probably be preferred in the mid term. Hydrogen is also present as a by-product from coke ovens, and refinery and chemical plant.

Methanol and ammonia are suitable for the commercial production of hydrogen by thermal-catalytic dissociation, and small methanol–water plants are available for use either on-site or as mobile field units. For the future, water represents the logical, inexhaustible source and in fact, even in the steam reforming of methane, outlined above, half the hydrogen was derived from the added steam. The dissociation of water can be achieved by electrolytic, thermochemical and, possibly, thermal means.

The application of electrical energy, rectified to give direct current, ionises water to hydrogen and hydroxl ions, and produces particularly pure hydrogen gas at the cathode, and oxygen gas at the anode. The electrical conductivity of water is insufficient for heavy current-carrying capacity, hence a soluble caustic material is added. In electrolysis, the free energy, rather than the enthalpy, of reaction interchanges with electrical energy, and the difference beween these two quantities appears as heat transfer. Theoretically, electrolysis of water at 25 $^{\circ}$C would occur isothermally, with no waste heat, at an applied potential of 1.47 V, producing nearly 7 ml of hydrogen gas per ampere, and requiring 2.8 kW h/m^3 of hydrogen produced.

Electrolysis would still occur at 1.23 V (and even lower at higher temperatures), but with absorption of heat from the environment. On this basis, the electrical energy input is only about 84 per cent of the total, consequently the *electrical* efficiency of the system is equivalent to 120 per cent. However, the corresponding theoretical value for subsequent use in the fuel cell is only 84 per cent, so no overall gain results. In practice, higher voltages are necessary in order to achieve finite and reasonable reaction rates, and a balance is struck between current density, applied voltage, electrolyser size and efficiency. In practice also, of course, some inefficiency is inevitable both in hydrogen production and consumption, giving an energy deficit overall.

Modern electrolyser designs incorporate porous electrodes of high surface area with catalytic components, and an aqueous alkali electrolyte, the input potential ranging up to about 2.3 V, and current densities to about 4000 A/m^2, requiring about 4.6 kW h/m^3 of hydrogen produced. A recent development in solid polymer electrolytes appears to have promising applications to both electrolysers and fuel cells. Despite the high electrical efficiency of the electrolytic process, one inhibiting factor is the low overall efficiency of the initial generation of electricity by nuclear fission (33 to 40 per cent). The economics of this system are therefore determined largely by the cost of electrical energy, and water electrolysis is being undertaken on a small scale in such areas as Vemock, Norway, and Bhakra Dam, India, where relatively inexpensive hydroelectric power is available. Large-scale production may be possible eventually from solar power stations.

Thermal processes of hydrogen production from water have been proposed, but the major drawback is the very high temperature required to prevent re-combination of the hydrogen and oxygen. In the thermochemical route, water reacts with intermediates in two or more reactions to give products which decompose thermally to give hydrogen, and also to regenerate the intermediate compounds. A practical overall efficiency higher than that with electrolysis appears possible, but no process has progressed beyond the laboratory stage to date. One process proposed by de Beni and Marchetti at Euratom[9] is shown schematically below, with reactions represented by full arrows, and material transfers by broken arrows.

$$[2H_2O]_R + CaBr_2 \xrightarrow[50\ atm]{730\ ^\circ C} Ca(OH)_2 + 2HBr \qquad\qquad [0.5O_2]_P$$

$$+ \qquad\qquad\qquad +$$

$$Hg \longleftarrow\cdots\cdots\cdots\cdots\cdots\cdots Hg$$

$$250\ ^\circ C \Big| 25\ atm \qquad 600\ ^\circ C \Big| 10\ atm$$

$$Ca(OH)_2 + HgBr_2 \xrightarrow[10\ atm]{200\ ^\circ C} CaBr_2 + HgO + [H_2O]_P$$

$$+$$

$$[H_2]_P$$

Overall

$$(2-1)H_2O \longrightarrow H_2 + 0.5O_2$$

The maximum temperature of 730 $^\circ$C is available with present nuclear reactors, and a conversion efficiency of 55 per cent is predicted. A number of other processes have been proposed, based on thermochemical, hybrid thermal-electrolytic, chemonuclear, discharge radiation and other advanced techniques.[10]

9.4 Future Fuel Prospects by Sector

The discussion so far has provided a comparative over-view of types, resources, production, combustion and handling of conventional, and candidate alternative, chemical fuels. The selection of any fuel—combustor combination depends, as always, on the particular application in mind, and although based primarily on technical considerations, is controlled eventually to a large extent by economics. As fossil fuels decline, such factors as conversion efficiency in fuel production, and the ability of a given combustor to accept a variety of fuels, will exert a growing influence. The overall pattern of fuel consumption, therefore, is likely to change with the years and, although generally resolved naturally by market forces, an overall integration would seem to be essential, and some degree of control inevitable.

The demands of the energy industry must also be weighed against those for material feedstock in the chemical engineering and manufacturing industries. The latter are outside the scope of this book, but are just as significant if civilisation is to endure and progress. Demands within the energy industry itself can also be preferential. In the transport sector, for example, energy can be either transferred from a remote source, or carried within the vehicle itself. The former category is represented by the electrified rail network, the energy source for which may be a chemically fuelled generating station. However, most independently powered free-ranging vehicles carry their energy store in a chemical form, whereas some use an electro-chemical charge, others a nuclear source, and a very few others store mechanical energy directly in the form of a rotating flywheel.

In comparison with static installations, the restraints on chemical fuel storage within vehicles tend to be more severe owing to space and mass limitations on fuel and combustion system hardware, effects of motion and vibration, and the more extreme and rapid changes in operating conditions. It follows therefore that the transport sector relies heavily on the handling convenience and combustion readiness of fuels storable in the liquid phase. The conclusion that such premium fuels should be reserved almost exclusively for premium purposes would, of course, have repercussions on fuel–combustor selection throughout *all* sectors of the energy industry, and no doubt on other industries also.

This book concludes with brief comments on those patterns of fuel usage within some of the major fuel-consuming sectors which appear probable in the light of all the previous discussion.

9.4.1 Fuel Prospects for Heating Purposes

This section explores the future selection of fuels for heat generation within high- and low-temperature furnaces and boilers in the industrial, commercial and domestic sectors. In the high-temperature industrial furnace used for metal processing, pottery and brick firing, cement manufacture, and so on, radiation requirements will continue to point to the heavier of the liquid fuels and/or those rich in carbon or other radiating solid particulates. As an established fossil fuel, therefore, coal is likely to find increasing use as a furnace fuel, no doubt with wider adoption of the alternative means of feeding and combustion, stimulated by such factors as improved combustion efficiency, ash handling and emissions control.

The successful use of pulverised coal slurries is likely to be extended by such projects as the Shell developments of 'Colloil', a mixture of oil and very fine particles of coal, and also the regular sized pelletising of coal dust in oil.

The water—emulsion practice of providing secondary atomisation by the micro-explosion of the water droplets may also find additional use. However, the importance of flame luminosity can be reduced by the re-radiation effects from heated refractory surfaces, coupled with furnace designs to encourage heating by convection. As a result, the handling convenience, flexibility and good performance of the liquid fuels and natural gas (conventional, simulated and supplemental) can still be exploited. Even the low-energy gases may find increased usage, with air pre-heat by exhaust heat recovery adopted to attain sufficient flame temperatures. In some furnace applications, as in steel manufacture, the use of electrical heating is likely to increase, despite the expense, in view of its high efficiency and cleanliness. The heating may be effected by direct resistance, indirect resistance or by induction.

In the large low-temperature industrial furnace used for drying plant, vat and tank heating, and so on, hot combustion products from the fluidised combustion of coal appear particularly attractive, generated from large lump coal floated in a sand bed held at a temperature below the fusion point of the ash. Heat transfer rates will be high, and pollution problems no doubt reduced further by the addition of lime to give a chemically active bed capable of removing sulphur from highly contaminated fuels. This trend will be strengthened by the long-term availability of coal, and its unsuitability for such applications as transport. Again, the fuel gases, including SNG and the low-energy gases, will no doubt find increasing use, in some cases replacing steam for drying and heating purposes.   .

In the steam-raising boiler, flame luminosity is particularly important, hence gaseous fuels will be less attractive than carbon-rich coal. A significant development here for the smaller package boiler is the 'Vekos' system in which the coal is fed pneumatically, the conveying air comprising part of the secondary combustion air, with arrested grits returned automatically to the static grate which requires unskilled manual de-ashing after each 8 hour period of operation. Fuel flexibility will become increasingly important, so that the fuels available at the time and place can be utilised with consequent savings in fuel transport costs and in wastage through unsuitability. In the boiler world, it is already established practice for burners and combustion equipment to be designed to accept a variety of fuels, either singly or in combination. A marked example of this is the ICI power station at Wilton, Teesside, UK, which can operate on 19 different fuel blends ranging from natural gas through impure LNG, excess refinery gases, used lubricating oils, tars and emulsion residuals to complex petrochemical wastes.[11] On the smaller scale, multi-fuel boilers are already available commercially, with all provision for consuming gas, oil, coal and a wide range of wastes. A wider adoption of furnace designs suited to such varied and heterogeneous inputs is therefore expected, and boiler selection will become an increasingly important exercise in view of possible changes in fuel availability during the ensuing 25 years of boiler life expectancy.

169

With the concept of total energy (or combined heat and power, CHP), supplies of both heat and work are generated by a local energy centre in the most efficient way possible within an overall complex of plant utilising energy which may otherwise flow to waste. In these applications, the fuel available for furnace combustion may well be very much a compromise in that its selection will depend on criteria imposed by other types of combustor. The alcohols provide examples of this since, although they would not rate as obvious primary choices for furnace or boiler work in view of their low specific energy and radiation levels, they might need to be used in this manner in view of overall plant requirements. As seen in section 7.2.2, however, their performance for heat transfer in such combustion chambers is by no means unsatisfactory, and they could well provide a useful service in future furnaces operated in areas of plentiful alcohol supply. Their advantages of low NO_x and zero SO_x emissions are significant, with possibilities of low carbon monoxide also, and alcohols may be used either as the base fuel or as an additional fuel in conjuction with a dual-fuel system. Initially, the most likely appearance of alcohol fuel in the furnaces of industrial countries is in the form of a blend, as in 'Methyl fuel', in which rigorous separation into individual alcohol types is not required, since this can be derived from remote fields of hydrocarbon gases, and transported more easily than the gases themselves. Subsequently, the source of alcohols for furnaces is likely to centre on such 'renewables' as SMW and biomatter. In a corresponding manner, hydrogen does not emerge as an ideal fuel for heat-transfer combustion, but may need to be adapted to total energy furnaces in a hydrogen economy.

Waste materials, whether solid, liquid or gaseous, municipal or industrial, appear to be a logical choice as sources of heat energy largely because they become continuously available, can serve almost no other purpose, and require disposal anyway. As seen in section 4.6.5, there appears to be no easy, inexpensive way of burning such heterogeneous material, but some success has been achieved, and the sheer good sense of using these materials in this way, coupled with social pressures for an environment clear of inelegant dumps of unwholesome rubbish, suggest further development. Biomatter is somewhat more acceptable but, again, may just as well be disposed if not suitable for animal feedstuff, fertilisation, or for manufacture of constructional materials. Waste straw could therefore serve as a heating fuel during the months of its availability and this, in some measure, might reduce the present method of 'burning off' excess vegetation on farmlands. Wood still represents an effective fuel for heat generation, but its resurgence as a widely used heating fuel is conditional on the balance between afforestation and consumption, including its use as a structural material and for paper making. In brief, fuels of a wide variety, including wastes and relatively primitive materials with minimal preparation, can often find their way usefully into an industrial furnace for the generation of heat whereas, in general, chambers for internal-combustion engines are much more demanding with regard to fuel preparation, comtaminant content, and quality generally.

Both the commercial (business premises, public services, agriculture, and so on) and domestic sectors are likely to meet their heating requirements mainly by piped gas (conventional NG and SNG), assisted by off-peak electricity, oil and, occasionally, bottled gas, not only for economic reasons but also in view of the overall convenience. In the domestic sector, solid fuels will no doubt endure, but used in smoke-consuming stoves rather than the inefficient open fire. Currently, wood burnt in a stove represents the least expensive form of space heating, but only well-forested countries such as Sweden are likely to be able to make a significant development in this direction.[12] More applications of district heating are to be expected as part of overall CHP schemes, particularly if power stations are sited close to high-density residential areas. Here again, hydrogen gas could become dominant in these sectors if the hydrogen economy eventuates. Electricity is likely to make an increasing contribution to space heating with the adoption of the heat pump, particularly with the development of a unit for domestic purposes, small enough not to require a three-phase electrical supply.

In essence, the successful development of furnaces suited to a wide variety of fuels will lessen the importance of fuel selection, and availability, in this sector of fuel usage.

9.4.2 Fuel Prospects for Industrial Power Generation

The energy used in industry in the form of work, as distinct from heat, appears most commonly as electricity because of its flexibility, ease of control, and capability of transmission to remote points through complex routes. The electrical energy is derived by conversion from mechanical energy which, apart from comparatively minor contributions from nuclear and hydro sources, is itself derived by conversion from the stored chemical energy of fuels by combustion, in conjunction with a heat engine. On the relatively small scale, the engine may be of the compression-ignition piston type, whereas the large scale involved in peak topping is more suited to an industrial or aero-derived gas turbine. Much of the base load for electrical supply systems, of course, is carried by generating units driven by steam turbines but, since the steam itself is produced in a boiler, the initial task of the fuel in this application is the production of heat, and this is the subject of the previous section.

By definition, compression-ignition engines rely on fuels of relatively high ignitability, such as the medium heavy types of petroleum distillate generally classed as diesel fuels. The less-expensive heavy blends of distillate and residual fuel oil are sufficiently ignitable for diesel application, but bring problems of atomisation, corrosion and erosion. They have, however, seen substantial development for marine propulsion, discussed later in section 9.4.4. Both methanol and ethanol offer some promise for the larger-sized diesel engines, following the dual-fuel pilot injection approach, as discussed in section 7.1.5. Problems still arise with combustion efficiency, smoothness and emissions of unburnt fuel, but if further development brings some easement, this type of engine may well find a growing role in an alcohol economy.

The industrial, or industrialised-aero, gas turbine, on the other hand, is customarily fuelled with gas oil or diesel fuel. As indicated in section 7.2.3, attempts to adapt to crude or residual fuels tend to give rise to corrosion problems of turbine blades due to the combustion products of such contaminants as vanadium, sodium and sulphur. Carbon formation and shedding can also tend to blockage of cooling ports and erosion damage to turbine blades. Currently, the standard techniques of contaminant control are seen to be the removal of sodium by water washing, and inhibition of vanadium by means of additives, coupled with regular washing of the blades themselves after a specified (for example, 8 per cent) drop in power, and the Mol experience in Belgium confirmed the economic advantages of operating a current technology gas turbine with residual fuel oil on normal utility conditions. Removal of some sulphur compounds is technically feasible during refining, but is generally uneconomic. An alternative approach, therefore, is through pre-gasification and sulphur-stripping with lime in a chemically active fluidised bed, as in the Esso system.[13] If present research on the pressurised fluidised bed is successful, this unit could well serve as a generator of clean combustible gases at pressures suited to future designs of power-generating gas turbines. However, the conventional basic designs of gas turbine combustor may still play a significant role with heavy fuels in the future if atomisation can be improved, since the smaller particles of contaminant oxide are more likely to follow the gas streamlines rather than impinge on the turbine blades. Smaller droplet sizes of the heavier fuels may result from the further development of water—emulsion techniques, or of designs of atomiser using air flow, rather than fuel pressure, as the main atomising influence, as used in air-blast and air-assist devices. The successful development of any of the above techniques is likely to result in a growing use of the less refined heavy fuels, including coal—oil slurries in the industrial gas turbine, the deciding factor being initially the relative costs of gas oil and heavy fuels plus treatment, and ultimately the relative availabilities.

Comparatively few problems arise with the use of gaseous fuels in gas turbines since combustion tends to be rapid and complete, and contaminants are minor, hence the use of gas turbines at wellheads and gas-pipeline pumping stations is likely to continue. Industrial power may well be generated locally from the use of manufactured gases in gas turbine units. Recent work has shown satisfactory operation with a low-quality coal gas of 5.7 MJ/m^3 (cf. 17 to 35 MJ/m^3 for conventional town gases), and introduces a novel form of engine design incorporating an array of replaceable sectoral-shaped chambers,

172

each with five fuel nozzles designed for injection of either gas or, below 20 per cent full load, gas oil.[14]

Of the engine applications of alcohol fuels, the land-based turbine generating unit appears most promising, and the full-scale results discussed in section 7.2.3 show satisfactory power and improved emissions of NO_x, SO_x and smoke, but a higher fuel consumption and emissions of carbon monoxide and unburnt hydrocarbons. The miscibility of alcohol with water may lead to problems of turbine blade corrosion from sodium contamination of the water. No such problem occur with hydrogen, and the gas turbine generator unit may well show promise in the event of a hydrogen economy.

Developments in energy policy, as well as in technology, are necessary for a logical solution to the problem of power generation, particularly with those generating authorities whose terms of reference were laid down in a previous era of cheap energy. A broader viewpoint is now required, so that any excess self-generated electricity can be transferred economically by the large industrial consumers back to the central authority, permitting all sources of electrical energy within the community to be integrated to give a technical optimum unhindered by policy restrictions.

9.4.3. Fuel Prospects for Land Transport

Developments in engines and fuels invariably proceed in parallel, as some advance in one of these areas permits, or demands, a corresponding improvement in the other; the changes in automotive fuel quality and engine performance throughout this century provide a classic example. On the assumption that expansion in public transport is unlikely to restrict greatly the pressure for personal mobility, the overall demand for motor gasolines and gas oils will continue to grow, calling for improvements in their availability and/or the economy of automotive engines. A higher yield of these distillate fuels could be achieved by greater use of cracking of the heavier components of crude oils, and the resulting reduction in the heavier fuel oils could well match the increased use of coal and nuclear resources proposed for electricity generation.

On the engine side, the compression-ignition unit is more fuel-economic in operation than its spark-ignition counterpart, although it tends to be heavier, with greater frictional losses and a higher initial cost. Furthermore, the production of its fuel, gas oil, in comparison with a high-octane gasoline, is less expensive in refinery energy. For taxis, public conveyances and heavy commercial vehicles, the compression-ignition engine has already proved its superior economy, but the picture is far less clear in the case of the privately owned vehicle in which overall weight and varying driving conditions render such an advantage almost negligible in the absence of high annual mileage or substantially less expensive gas oil. In comparison with spark-ignition engines, development of lighter compression-ignition engines of

173

improved structural and combustion chamber design would provide advantages of energy thrift in both fuel production and use, whereas turbo-charging would improve the conversion efficiency to mechanical power in both types of engine.

In the spark-ignition engine, current developments lie in the direction of lean burn and stratified charge designs. As an example of the latter, the Ford PROCO engine operates satisfactorily at 11/1 compression ratio with lead-free gasoline of 91 octane number, at a fuel consumption approaching that of a diesel engine. Closed-loop systems of fuel metering, and ignition timing sensitive to exhaust emissions, are also under development. These features not only improve fuel economy but reduce the octane requirement. The fact that production of a lower octane quality also reduces energy consumption in the refinery makes the point that, from now onwards, an advance on the fuel technology side can be represented by a permissible reduction in fuel quality, where quality is assessed on the traditional basis of resistance to spark knock. Such factors as fuel availability and energy thrift in production now become over-riding.

Combination of the above two types of engine into the spark-assisted diesel would not only permit operation with petroleum fuels ranging from gasoline through kerosines to gas oils but, far more valuably, would give rise to the concept of a single wide-ranging distillate requiring separation only from the residuals in the crude, with no further fractionation or major upgrading. This would give rise to further appreciable savings in energy and costs at the refinery (personal communication, J. Boddy, Mobil Oil Co.).

Shortly before the recent energy challenge, the tightening of restrictions on exhaust emissions led to much speculation on alternatives to the conventional internal-combustion engine of the piston-in-cylinder type. These include rotary-element engines of the Wankel type, small-scale gas turbines, piston or turbine type steam engines and, one of the more promising, the Stirling engine with its theoretical attraction of approaching the Carnot level of efficiency, and the practical merits of steady-flow continuous combustion with increased residence time for soot burnout, and ability to burn a variety of fuel. It also has low levels of noise and emissions.

The emergence and subsequent adoption of one of such novel designs of engine as a successful replacement for the conventional type would represent a financial and manufacturing involvement of collossal proportions, and it appears likely that the conventional type of engine will not disappear without a struggle. Equally, the capital investment in fuel production and distribution systems makes it more attractive, as long as it remains possible, for new fuel sources, and their products, to be converted to conventional types of fuel. Consequently, supplemental motor gasolines can be expected from shale oil, tar sands and coal sources. In the United Kingdom, a road demonstration has already been given by the Automobile Association of a motor gasoline derived from coal by the Coal Research Establishment, Stoke Orchard, with the assistance of British Petroleum, Sunbury. In the United States, the Mobil catalytic methanol–gasoline process is expected to develop eventually into a direct conversion of syngas to gasoline.

Ultimately, of course, these various fossil-based routes will all approach their end points, and attention is therefore directed towards such substitute fuels as alcohols and hydrogen. Methanol, derived from coal or biomatter, holds many attractions for engine performance, although would present some difficulties of compatibility in the distribution system. Full-scale tests conducted by Volkswagen confirm the improved volumetric and thermal efficiencies, and reduction in NO_x. The use of methanol in blends with gasoline overcomes the need for major re-design of engine fuel systems, but suffers from the problems of water separation, and the increase in volatility. Similar remarks apply to ethanol, but it seems likely that the alcohols will find some growing use in automotive propulsion as these problems are alleviated, particularly with continuing rise in the price of gasolines. Hydrogen is probably less likely to find favour in anything other than centrally fuelled fleets of vehicles, in view of distribution and tankage difficulties, and the hazards of crankcase explosions, although promising results have been gained during road tests by the Brokhaven National Laboratories and Daimler–Benz, and the heat released during hydride re-charging could be employed usefully for space heating. Vehicle ranges of approximately 400 km (250 miles) are envisaged from a tank containing 200 kg of hydrides, and the tank re-charging time can be reduced to about 10 minutes by permitting the tank to cool beforehand. Ammonia, on the other hand, may not be adopted at all for road vehicles due to its high toxicity, problems of compatibility, and need for some ignition assistance.

In many respects, the electrically driven vehicle appears to offer attractive solutions to the problems of fuel economy and air pollution by combustion emissions and noise.[15] High-capacity re-chargeable batteries are envisaged, and the main obstacle is the lack of a battery unit of power/weight ratio superior to the present 50 W h/kg. Improved units under development include lead–acid, iron–nickel, zinc–nickel, zinc–air, zinc–chlorine, sodium–sulphur and lithium–sulphur types. Low-speed battery-driven vehicles are already a feature in the United Kingdom and elsewhere for roundsman-type duties, together with medium-speed vans and mail deliveries. Taxis, light vans and buses operated on a fleet basis, appear to be best suited to electrical propulsion. Working ranges of about 180 km (112 miles) and speeds of 50 km/h (30 miles/h) have been achieved with a prototype 34 passenger bus designed by Lucas Batteries for service in Manchester, and much development work is under way in the United States, Japan, France, the Federal Republic of Germany, the Netherlands and elsewhere. The present targets are for city and urban commuter vehicles capable of a working range of about 70 km (45 miles) at a maximum speed of 90 km/h (55 miles/h), with (battery/vehicle) mass ratios less than the 0.25 to 0.3 for commercial vehicles.

In the light car sector, valuable experience of electrical fleet operation has been gained by the UK Electricity Council based on the purchase of 66 Enfield 6 kW electric cars in 1966. Each vehicle is fitted with eight 12 V batteries in series/parallel configuration permitting speeds up to 64 km/h (40 mile/h) over a range of 39 to 90 km (24 to 56 mile). An average of over 6000 km (3800 mile) per car has been logged to date, with an average energy consumption of 310 to 370 W h/km (500 to 600 W h/mile). Following improvements in the charger and controller units, the main requirements now appear to be the development of lightweight traction batteries, and a suitable instrument to indicate the energy available in the batteries.

Battery charging would take place overnight using off-peak electricity at central depots in the case of fleet operators, and at service stations, home garages or at specially adapted parking meters for the private motorist. Full re-charge time would probably be about 8 hours, but rapidly exchangeable palletised battery packs may become feasible. Improved range is claimed by Chloride Technical Ltd through better control of the drive system to deliver a constant torque at low speed, and eliminate the high current surges. A very effective method of improving ranges of electrically propelled vehicles and reducing their battery mass is the conjoint use of a transmitted power supply by means of automatic pick-up from either a rail or overhead conductor over less than 20 per cent of the route length, coupled with regenerative braking, as in the French 90 passenger 'Biomode' system, and the German 'Duo Bus'. Hybrid drives, involving both diesel and electric propulsion, probably including hydraulic accumulators for storing braking energy, may also prove useful for some bus routes. A diesel—electric passenger car under test at Queen Mary College, London, incorporates clutches so that the electric motor is engaged for acceleration, and the system charged during stationary idling, giving an overall fuel consumption of 100 mile/UK gal. One of the major factors must be the overall efficiency of energy conversion from central power station to vehicle road wheels, and the future of electric road transporation will no doubt rest not only on a breakthrough in battery technology, but also on the wider adoption of electrical power generation from non-fossil sources. Opinions are divided on the relative running costs of conventional and electric vehicles, but some studies suggest that coal-derived gasoline would be less expensive for the mid term.

Propulsion for rail transport is depending increasingly on schemes of electrification for main-line inter-city and highly populated commuter services, retaining diesel locomotives for rural services, with solid-fuelled steam engines still used in less developed areas. Rail traction will therefore come to depend progressively less on gas oil as electrification is extended, and fuel is con-served by such practices as the collection of injector leak-off. However, the rate of reduction in the latter case tends to be offset somewhat by the trends to higher speeds, and by such cost-saving but energy-expensive practices as leaving engines running rather than shutting down after use. As with the smaller units for the generation of power (section 9.4.2), the trend for diesel locomotive fuels will no doubt be towards the heavier fuel oils, and the extent to which this occurs will be influenced by the success with which these fuels can be burnt without problems of combustion and corrosion. Similar remarks apply to those cases where the small gas turbine is adapted for railway use. Such substitute fuels as the alcohols do not appear to offer any real advantages in this sector in view of their low energy densities and correspondingly high requirements for storage, and hydrogen probably has no role to play at all.

9.4.4 Fuel Prospects for Marine Transport

In the marine sector, diesel engines power the motor ships comprising over 90 per cent (over 60 per cent in gross tonnage) of the merchant fleets, together with the minesweepers and conventional submarines in the world's navies. The diesel engine provides high efficiency with relative insensitivity to fuel type, and flexibility with regard to reduced power for fuel conservation. The slow-speed (110 to 130 rev/min) marine diesel engine is usually of the direct-drive two-stroke design, whereas the medium-speed (500 to 1200 rev/min) engine is a geared four-stroke unit. The remaining vessels are mostly steamships equipped with boilers and either reciprocating engines or, in the case of the larger vessels, steam turbines in order to provide the very high power levels and the smoothness of propulsion required in passenger ships, the steam itself also representing a convenient source of auxiliary energy. Naval fleets, on the other hand, have generally adopted the marinised aero-derived gas turbine in view of its higher specific and volumetric power, instant power availability, wide turn-down ratio and minimal on-board maintenance requirements.

Until recently, the heavier gas oils and diesel fuels, including naval Dieso, were used almost exclusively for diesel engines in motor ships. The continuing and increasing need for such middle distillates will necessitate a wider adoption of cracking and visbreaking in the refinery, resulting in distillate fuels of high density, viscosity and sulphur and wax content, and lower cetane number. The higher viscosities will demand greater pre-heat, following centrifuging, together with increased injection advance and rate in order to ensure effective atomisation, mixing and combustion of the less volatile slower-burning components, and so avoid fouling, wear and performance loss. Automatic control of fuel injection systems based on engine monitoring is likely to be adopted in many cases. Effects of increased concentrations of sulphur on wear rates of cylinder liners, piston rings and exhaust valves will no doubt continue to be offset by such mechanical improvements as valve rotation, cylinder lubricant injection and by controlled levels of alkalinity of the lubricants.

Over the last 20 years, however, fuel oils have steadily been replacing the marine distillates in diesel engines, first in the low-speed range, then the medium-speed, and now with a tendency towards the high-speed range (over 1500 rev/min) used for generating sets, bow thrusters and other purposes.

Heavy fuel quality tends to vary substantially world-wide, depending on the crude oil source and the refinery processes used, and a general degradation is expected as more refinery demands are made for distillates. Consequently, the marine fuel oils of the future will be heavier and more viscous, with higher levels of contamination. Density will no doubt be limited as long as possible to 0.99 kg/l to permit water removal by centrifuging (if necessary, at temperatures near 100 °C to augment the relative density), but a rise to above unity may be unavoidable eventually, with alternative means of treatment by water flashing or fine depth type filtration.

Viscosity can be expected to reach and exceed the BSS Class G level, but a system of automatic viscosity control is already widely adopted. The more significant effects of deterioration will be due to the increased concentrations of carbon and asphaltenes, leading to deposit fouling and abrasive wear in the former case, and slow burning in the latter. Higher proportions of sulphur (up to 5 per cent), sludge and ash are also to be expected. Further adoption of exhaust gas supercharging and/or air pre-heating is likely in order to assist the combustion of the lower-grade fuels. The effects of low-temperature sulphur corrosion, particularly in two-stroke engines, on injector nozzles and exhaust gas turbines would be controlled, as now, by maintenance of metal temperatures above the sulphuric acid dew point. Nozzle-tip temperatures will no doubt be maintained above about 140 °C for this reason, but below the carbon-trumpet forming temperature of about 180 °C. High-temperature vanadium corrosion of piston crowns and exhaust valves will probably continue to be solved by restriction of metal temperatures below about 530 °C, together with sodium washing and lubricant additives. The high concentrations of water and sediment in heavy fuel oils should be amenable to future designs of centrifuge and other purifiers. In particular, the starting, manoeuvring and stopping involved in pier-to-pier operation can lead to deposit build up, but costs can be saved for the short distance ferry vessel if a change-over to distillate fuel for this purpose can be avoided.

For steam generation, heavy fuel oil is widely used, the high sulphur content promoting less environmental impact at sea, until such time as sulphur removal or control becomes both practical and economic. Homogenisation and the use of emulsification with water (and coal) will probably find additional use, together with the fluid-bed boiler, possibly using coal or coal–oil slurries. Liquefaction of coal using expensive hydrogen is unlikely to be an economically attractive method of producing relatively low-grade marine fuels on the large scale. The older steam-powered naval vessels will no doubt continue to use Dieso for logistic reasons dictated by a single-fuel policy, and because the higher fuel costs are more than offset by lower maintenance costs, the fuel costs representing a comparatively small proportion of the life-cycle costs of the vessel.

The most commonly used fuel for naval gas turbines is Dieso, as referred to above. This has proved to be the most acceptable compromise fuel for the heavy-duty gas turbine, as in land-based power units. The 'Asialiner' experience with water-emulsified light fuel oils is helping to show that the gas turbine may also serve the merchant marine. With the emergence of the more efficient second-generation aero gas turbines, incorporating higher by-pass ratios and replacement gas-generator capability, these power units may become even more attractive. In the LNG carrier, for example, the cargo boil-off represents approximately half the propulsion fuel requirement for a loaded voyage, consequently a dual-fuel system is proposed capable of handling both gas and liquid fuels simultaneously over a range of gas/liquid volume ratios from about 0.1 to 9. Furthermore, electrical transmission will permit the deck installation of the turbine, greatly reducing the extent of ductwork required. Again, future trends are likely to be towards heavier fuels, and the successful development of heavy and residual-type fuels for land-based power turbines will no doubt be reflected in the marine world.

Overall fuel economy can be exploited from dual plant designed for conditions of both optimum cruise and full power. A wider adoption can therefore be expected of the combined propulsive power unit represented by such symbols as CODOG, COSAG and COGOG indicating combined diesel or gas turbines, steam and gas turbines, and two alternative types of gas turbine (for example, Olympus and Tyne).

As a future marine fuel, coal again offers the great advantage of enduring availability, and is feasible for the larger merchant ship provided the coal is pulverised, slurried with oil, or otherwise rendered pumpable, and its storage stability can be ensured. In this connection, the petroleum coke derived from very severe cracking may be useful as a marine fuel in a fluidised bed, or as a slurry with oil in a valveless diesel engine. However, the application of solid fuels is less attractive to naval craft which depend on ambient-liquid fuels for replenishment at sea, and in which fuel bunkering space and ash disposal would create problems, even with advanced fluidised-bed combustors. Oil shale and tar sands will no doubt be exploited for hydrocarbon liquid fuels for marine purposes, as in other applications.

The low calorific values of the alcohols, together with their low cetane ratings, render them unattractive for marine propulsion, and their water solubility eliminates the possibilities of using water displacement in the fuel tanks of small ships to improve vessel stability. The nitrogen hydrides, and hydrogen itself, also appear unsuitable for marine use, although the electrolysis of sea water gives rise to the concept of a large nuclear mother ship supporting a small fleet of short-range craft powered by hydrogen-fuelled engines or fuel cells. Nuclear propulsion is only likely to be economic for the larger size of merchant ship, and is unlikely to feature in naval fleets, apart from the nuclear submarine which has little access to air for conventional combustion. The contribution of nuclear power in the marine sector will more likely be determined by environmental acceptance, international agreement, insurance arrangements and initial costs, rather than technical feasibility.

9.4.5 Fuel Prospects for Aerospace

As discussed earlier, fuel and engine developments tend to proceed in parallel, and the urgent need to improve fuel economy in the aviation sector has been reflected clearly in the progressive reduction of specific fuel consumption in both piston engine and gas-turbine powered aircraft. In general, engine efficiency rises with increase in operating temperature and/or pressure, and propulsive efficiency is influenced by the manner in which the propelling jet is created, that is, by propeller, pure jet, or by-pass fan. For commercial aero engines, cruise sfc values range from about 25 mg/N s for turbojets to about 17 mg/N s for high by-pass turbofans, and appear to be approaching an asymptotic value of about 15 mg/N s.

The replacement of the piston engine by the gas turbine as the main unit of aero propulsion has brought a contraction in the number of specifications for aviation gasoline, and a corresponding increase in those for jet propulsion (JP) fuels. The traditional method for producing the JP fuels is to separate from selected crude oils the mid-distillate fractions boiling between about 150 to 280 °C (to meet the requirements for flash point and freezing point respectively), followed by mild hydrogen treatment as necessary to control sulphur content and/or thermal stability. On average, petroleum crudes yield a total of about 18 per cent of kerosine type fractions, including about 12 per cent meeting the aviation specification requirements for smoke point and aromatic content. Although the aviation consumption of the total petroleum production reaches only about 6.5 per cent within North America, and no more than 3 per cent elsewhere, these same middle distillates are also in strong demand for the production of domestic kerosine, industrial gas oils, chemical feedstocks, and as a 'cutter stock' to control the viscosity of the heavier fuel oils; consequently the continuing supply of aviation kerosine to meet current specification does not necessarily follow from these relative percentages.[16]

Some likely trends in jet fuel quality have already been foreshadowed by the temporary shortfalls in suitable crudes arising from the 1973 fuel embargo. Commercial jet fuel supplies were maintained only by the adoption of temporary waivers (in the United States, by Emergency Specification ES-2-74) to relax the maximum permitted volume of aromatics from 20 per cent towards the existing military limit of 25 per cent. Over this relatively small rise in carbon content, laboratory and field tests showed no significant differences in combustion chamber liner temperature or smoke formation,[17] and a relaxed maximum of 22 per cent aromatics, together with a minimum smoke point of 19 instead of 20 mm, were permitted, provided the user was notified, associated with a maximum specified fbp as 300 instead of 280 °C, and a minimum flash point of 38 instead of 40.6 °C.

With the return in 1976 to a more stable pattern of crude oil supplies, the availability of jet fuels improved and, in fact, on a worldwide basis, this could last for several years. However, since the demands for jet fuel, and particularly gas oil, will no doubt continue to grow steadily, further maintenance of an adequate pool of middle distillates will necessitate the re-introduction of such waivers on a more permanent basis, followed by supplementation from alternative sources, and eventually to synthesis and/or outright substitution. In the medium term, therefore, the probable future pattern of jet fuel supply appears as follows.

1. Refining of hitherto unattractive petroleum crudes — for example, crudes high in aromatic content (as Arabian Heavy and North Slope, Alaska) and in sulphur contamination.

2. Hydrogenation of the heavier fractions from current petroleum crude types — as seen earlier, this is expensive in energy consumption and cost.

3. Permanent adoption, and extension, of the 1974 specification waivers — sufficient relaxation in current limits on aromatic content, smoke point and freezing point will permit the specification of a wide-cut heavy kerosine.

4. Supplementation of either conventional or wide-cut heavy kerosine from alternative sources — shale oils and tars are likely first, followed by the less attractive coal syncrudes. (Shale fuels have already been tested.)

All the above cases will promote higher aromatic content and, in fact, the latest British specifications have already raised this limit to 22 per cent, and the American specification for Jet A (internal airline fuel) to 25 per cent, with a minimum smoke point of 18 mm. Figure 9.4 shows that, over the current distillation range for Avtur, a rise in fuel density will follow any appreciable increase in aromatics. Corresponding increases can also be expected in freezing point, flame radiation, liner temperature and smoking tendencies, associated in the supplementation case with increased fuel-bound nitrogen leading to poorer thermal stability, as discussed below.

A relaxation in the current freezing point limit may improve the yield of jet fuel by some 3 per cent per 1 °C rise, and an increase from −50 to −47 °C for Jet A1 (international airline fuel) is under consideration by ASTM, although this may not be suited to polar routes. More generous increases would be necessary for, and would make possible, the adoption of the heavier fuels and sources outlined above. This gives rise to the NASA concept of the heavy fuels Jet C and Jet D, with freezing points of −29 and −18 °C respectively. The inadequacy of the current freezing point test is underlined by the fact that most kerosines remain pumpable at temperatures as much as 10 °C below the measured freezing point, consequently an improved test method is needed. Nevertheless, these proposed broadened specification jet fuels would require substantial heat addition in order to maintain fluidity in

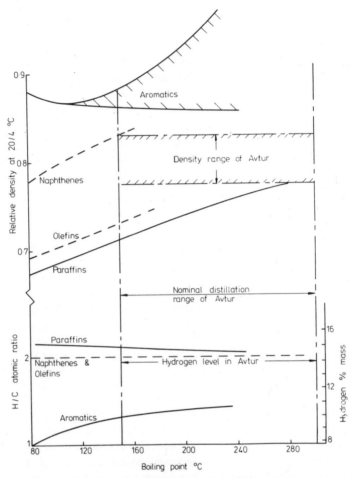

Figure 9.4   Influence of aromatics on density and H/C atomic ratio of Avtur

flight, and an analysis of potential sources of such energy favours the heat rejected from the cabin air-conditioning system, closely followed by the main engine tailpipe, provided safety can be assured. Fuel tank insulation, on the other hand, incurs serious penalties of both cost and weight.[18, 19]

The case for using hydrogen content as a measure of fuel burnability has been stated by Shayeson,[17] and the British specification for Avtur permits the waiving of tests for olefin content, specific energy, aniline gravity product, smoke point and naphthalene content if the hydrogen mass content is 13.8 per cent or above. An instrument for the measurement of hydrogen content of liquid fuels with an accuracy of 0.1 per cent is now available,[21] based on low-resolution nuclear magnetic resonance. As seen in figure 3.1, and again in figure 9.4, an increase in aromatic content corresponds to a decrease in hydrogen content. Although no precise relationship can be derived between these parameters in view of the differing nature both of the aromatic and of the non-aromatic components within different fuels, some broad relationships have been reported in the literature for an appreciable number of jet fuels, fuels,[17,18,20,22] and the resulting mean line from all these sources is found to follow the law

Hydrogen per cent mass = 15 − 0.0625 (aromatics per cent volume)

over the range of 15 to 11 per cent hydrogen, and 0 to 64 per cent aromatics. In examining the effect of these broadened specifications on liner temperature and life, therefore, a composite set of curves has been plotted in figure 9.5, with the following conclusions.

1. Over a given rise in aromatics content from 15 to 24 per cent volume, liner temperature increases by about 20 to 40 °C as the pressure ratio increases from 3.5 to 8, and smoke number increases from 10 to 17 at a pressure ratio of 7.

2. Over this same rise in aromatics content, the liner temperature increase drops to zero at pressure ratios of 10 and above.

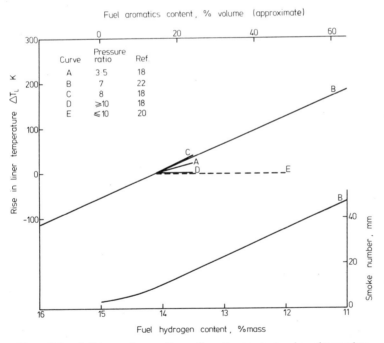

Figure 9.5   Influence of aromatics on liner temperature and smoke number

183

3. Over the larger rise in aromatics content from 15 to 40 per cent volume at a pressure ratio of 7, liner temperature increases of about 100 °C could be expected, with increases in smoke number from about 10 to 30.

The current ultimate limit of 30 per cent aromatics has been set by elastomer compatibility within the fuel system, but this could no doubt be raised by the development of more resistant elastomers, re-establishing liner temperature as the controlling parameter on aromatic content.

All the above comments have been based on the use of these broadened specification fuels in conventional combustion chambers. However, with parallel development in engines, particularly in the direction of staged combustion as in the Vorbix and the double annulus chambers, liner temperatures are seen again to be virtually independent of fuel aromatic content,[18,23,24] even at pressure ratios below 10. An alternative approach is the internal coating of the flame tube with a ceramic thermal barrier, giving reductions in liner temperature of about 100 °C.

The thermal instability of jet fuels appears to be related directly to the concentration of fuel-bound nitrogen; consequently one solution would be a sufficiently severe hydrotreatment to reduce the nitrogen to acceptable limits. However, reduction of the nitrogen content of shale-derived jet fuel to about 0.1 per cent mass resulted in a breakpoint temperature of only 230 °C, and the conventional breakpoint temperature of 260 °C was achieved only with more severe reduction of nitrogen to about 0.01 per cent.[18] Such an extensive hydrotreatment is expensive, consequently a control of maximum temperature in the fuel system, in conjunction with the fuel heating requirements for control of freezing as discussed earlier, would be an attractive alternative. For purposes of research into the long-term effects of all the above relaxations in specification limits, an experimental Jet C type fuel permitting the use of supplemental components has been recommended by NASA,[18] with the following properties

	Experimental Fuel	Jet A
Hydrogen, per cent mass	13	14
Aromatics, per cent volume	35	< 25
Flash point, °C	> 40	> 40
Freezing point, °C	− 29	− 40
Breakpoint temperature, °C	>240	>260

The options available to ensure continued supplies of hydrocarbon type jet fuels of both technical and economic suitably therefore comprise

1. More extensive (and expensive) fuel refining to suit existing specifications, engines and aircraft.
2. Broadening fuel specifications to minimise refining energy and costs.
3. Developing engines and aircraft less sensitive to fuel properties.

The most practical solution for the medium term will probably entail some compromise between all three options. A strong case will no doubt be made by the aviation sector for some priority in the allocation of middle distillates, on the basis that transportation invariably relies on liquid fuels, with aviation of necessity operating under conditions demanding the most rigorous quality standards.

On a long-term basis, hydrocarbon blends closely approaching the conventional kerosines may well be synthesised from copious supplies of inorganic hydrogen and carbon, provided substantial energy resources are available for the purpose, as discussed in section 4.5. Eventually, in the post-petroleum long term, the most promising fuel for aviation appears to be liquid hydrogen. Comparable paper studies have been conducted on liquid methane, since it also offers advantages over JP fuel in terms of specific energy, heat-sink capacity, payload capacity, thermal stability and clean burning, and since its availability, being comparable with crude oil, is greater than that of JP fuels. Nevertheless, once the techniques for high-volume cryogenic storage in aircraft have been developed, they will no doubt be extended sufficiently to accommodate liquid hydrogen, with its further advantages in performance. The alcohols, on the other hand, are particularly unattractive for aviation because of the appreciable oxygen content (50 per cent by mass in the case of methanol) which is an unacceptable burden for a mass-sensitive vehicle operating in an environment of freely available oxygen. (The propect·of an aircraft of Boeing 747 scale having to take on board some 50 tonnes of oxygen as an unavoidable part of its normal fuel load tends to clinch the argument.)

As observed in sections 4.5.1, 5.4, 6.4, 7.2 and 7.3, hydrogen offers the very significant attractions of elemental abundance, maximum specific energy, rapid mixing with high flame speed and wide range of flammability giving good stability and temperature distribution, together with minimal tendencies for pollution. Its attraction for use in aerospace propulsion is shown in figure 9.6, plotted on a basis of specific impulse (see later). On the other hand, its density is particularly low, even in the liquid phase, together with its boiling point. Consequently, it requires large capacity storage with cryogenic insulation and, in comparison with a conventional fuel, its minimum ignition energy is considerably lower, which reflects on fire safety.

As shown in section 7.2.3, the compatibility of hydrogen with standard aero gas turbine engines has already been demonstrated. For hypersonic (Mach 5+) flight, the ramjet or scramjet engine requires internal cooling, but this can be effected by circulating the fuel in cooling ducts which, in turn, provide pre-vaporisation. The heat capacity of a liquid hydrogen fuel load is high, and is calculated to be adequate for hypersonic flight up to about Mach 11, the excess heat capacity below this speed level being available to cool the aircraft structure, possibly through the medium of a secondary coolant (water–glycol mixture). Several experimental hypersonic engines have been

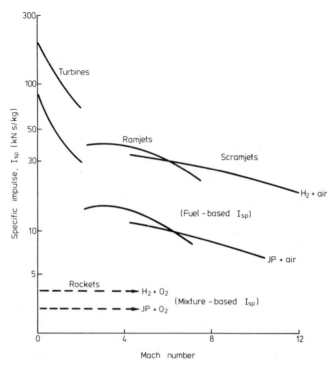

Figure 9.6   Specific impulse of hydrogen and JP fuels (derived from references 25 and 26)

tested, and integrated systems of turbojet and scramjet proposed in order to cover both low- and high-speed regimes. Cruise speeds of approximately 4000 mile/h would then bring most regions of the world within a few hours' flying time.

The changes in the design of the aircraft fuel systems required for the use of liquid hydrogen are largely due to the particularly low energy density, which is only one-quarter that of Avtur, as well as the need for cryogenic insulation, as discussed in section 8.1. Other requirements for a hydrogen fuel system are a method of purging with hydrogen gas prior to fuelling in order to eliminate risk of blockage by frozen air, and a means of variable tank pressure control with hydrogen gas over the regimes of take-off, climb, cruise and descent. With less mass of fuel required for a given mission, wing loadings will be lower consequently hydrogen-fuelled aircraft will fly at higher altitudes. This, combined with the reduced aircraft mass and increased length, will reduce the intensity of sonic boom. Take-off is expected to be quieter, since low wing loading and high power loading will permit throttling.

In the long term, hydrogen as an aviation fuel would appear to be the 'front runner', but parallel developments in surface transport and tele-communications may find aviation reserved mainly for intercontinental overseas routes. In this case, fewer, remote airports, with high-speed links to city centres, may be appropriate, and this would solve the present illogicality of permitting dense housing development in the vicinity of airports where low flying is essential and some noise unavoidable. Although the hazards of handling liquid hydrogen are reported by some to be about equivalent to those of gasoline, which have already been fully accepted by the travelling public, the 'Hindenburg syndrome' still exists, and the introduction of hydrogen is likely to be confined to service use, possibly with jettisonable and/or crash-resistant fuel systems. Furthermore, much experience will probably be required in, say, air freighting before the fire safety characteristics are considered acceptable for passenger transport. In anticipation of this, several preliminary designs of hydrogen-fuelled passenger/freight aircraft have been proposed, with passengers and fuel either sharing the fuselage or separated by means of podding (figure 9.7). A recent proposal by the Lockheed Corporation is that four Tristar airliners be modified as hydrogen-fuelled freighters and operated jointly by the United States, the United Kingdom, the Federal Republic of Germany and Saudi Arabia over a four-point network linking cities close to fossil-based sources, each capable of generating about 20 tonnes of liquid hydrogen per day.

As with the earlier usage of selected fuels for motor racing, one special group of fuels has been classed here with the alternatives in that they (necessarily) replace conventional fuels in view of the severe demands of the application. These are the high-energy fuels intended for high-speed flight with advanced gas turbines and ramjet engines, and for space propulsion with rockets. On a mass basis, fuels rich in hydrogen are seen to offer the greatest specific energy, whereas the compounding with carbon provides the liquid phase at normal conditions with resulting handling convenience. Since carbon has only 27 per cent of the specific energy of hydrogen, it is logical to attempt to replace carbon in the hydrocarbon molecules with some other element to give other liquid hydrides of greater energy content. Boron is a case in point, and the calorific values in table 9.4 show the relative attraction of liquefied diborane and liquid pentaborane. However, despite their considerable improvements over the conventional hydrocarbons, these fuels have become less attractive, even for special high-energy applications, owing to problems of toxicity, abrasive hardness, and preparation costs in terms of both energy and money.

Although heavier-than-air machines are intrinsically mass limited to some degree, the aerodynamic drag arising from high-speed motion through the atmosphere imposes a volume limitation which may be over-riding. This applies particularly in and beyond the supersonic regime where the aerodynamic demands for thin wing sections put a premium on the space hitherto available for storage of fuel. No petroleum fraction is seen to be available between the heaviest fuel oils and solid carbon itself, although some individual high-density hydrocarbons have been proposed for ramjet and other high-speed

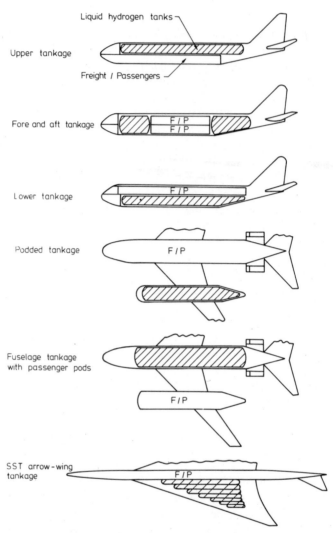

Figure 9.7   Some alternative configurations proposed for hydrogen-fuelled aircraft (references 27 and 28)

aeronautical applications. These fuels are generally derived by close packing of hydrogen and carbon atoms in the molecule into the form of fused, or polynuclear, ring structures, commonly described as bicyclics, or dimers. Several multi-ring high-density fuels have been considered, including those shown in table 9.4. One such polycyclic hydrocarbon (tetrahydronorbornadiene dimer) is available commercially under the name of Shelldyne,[29] and figures in two US military fuel specifications for volume-limited ramjet applications.

Table 9.4   Candidate fuels of high net calorific values (derived from references 2 to 10 of chapter 6)

Fuel	Relative density	MJ/kg	% rel. Avtur (mass)	MJ/l	% rel. Avtur (vol.)
Liquid hydrogen	0.071	120	277	8.5	
Liquid diborane	0.43	73	169	31.4	
Pentaborane	0.63	67.8	157	42.7	123
Liquid methane	0.424	50.1	116	21.2	
Avgas	0.72	44.0	102	31.7	
Avtur	0.8	43.3	100	34.6	100
9-Methylperhyfluorene*	0.934	42.4		39.6	115
Hydromethylcyclopentadiene dimer	0.93	43.0		40.0	116
Dimethanodecalin	1.003	42.2		42.3	123
Solid adamanthene	1.071	41.0		43.9	128
Shelldyne	1.092	41.6		45.4	131
60/40 mass slurry boron/avtur	1.32	52.0	120	68.6	198
Solid carbon (graphite)	2.17	32.8		71.2	206
Solid boron (crystalline)	2.34	57.8	133	135.3	391

* The Latin prefix 'per' (through) signifies a maximum amount of substitution or addition, hence 'perhy' here represents complete saturation by hydrogenation

The main properties are shown below, with comparative values for Avtur in parentheses

H/C atomic ratio	= 1.17 (1.97 approximately)
bp, °C	= 250 to 265 (150 to 300)
fp, °C	= −24 (−50 maximum)
Viscosity @ 37.8 °C, cSt	= 11.29 (1.25)
Flash point, °C	= 59 (38 minimum)
Smoke point, mm	= 6 (20 minimum)

On a basis of viscosity, therefore, Shelldyne is seen to be broadly similar to diesel fuel, and its very high viscosity at low operating temperatures is brought down by blending with methylcyclohexane. The thermal stability is superior to that of Avtur, but the tendency to smoke may be high.

The solid state offers the maximum density for storage of energy, but solid fuels are inconvenient to feed from tank to combustion chamber, and tend to be inflexible in response to flow control. However, compromises may be reached by pulverising the fuel and mixing it with an appropriate liquid carrier to form a slurry, as discussed in chapter 8. Both aluminium and boron have been proposed for use in this way, with kerosine as the carrier fluid.

Since both specific energy and energy density are significant for high-speed applications within the atmosphere, some simple indication of both parameters jointly is made available in the form of a ratio of their arithmetic product to the corresponding product for Avtur, hence

$$\text{performance index of fuel} = \frac{(\text{MJ/kg} \times \text{MJ/l}) \text{ of fuel}}{1500 \ (\text{MJ})^2/\text{kg l for Avtur}}$$

Figure 9.8 shows representative values of performance index plotted against relative density for the hydrogen—carbon, hydrogen—boron and hydrogen—nitrogen compounds, with connecting curves. The performance index of liquid hydrogen is seen to suffer because of the very low density, whereas the value for solid boron is particularly attractive. In practice, of course, the relative importance of the two energy parameters may not necessarily be equal, as is implicit in the performance index, and some different weighting may be needed for the application in hand.

In rocket applications to space flight, both fuel and oxidant must be carried in the vehicle, and fuels are burnt with oxygen-rich oxidants in order both to achieve high thrusts and to avoid carrying the unusable atmospheric nitrogen. In fact, rocket reactants have to fulfill the two roles of combustion and propulsion, by releasing sufficient energy within the combustion chamber and, at the same time, providing oxidation products of appropriate propulsive characteristics. The performance parameter adopted is the specific impulse, in terms of the thrust produced at the exit plane of the propelling nozzle per

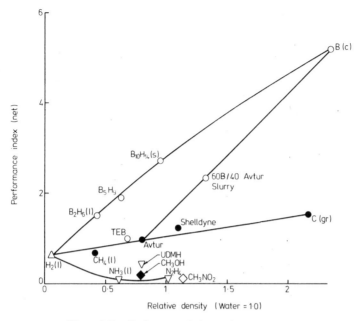

Figure 9.8   Performance index (reference 27)

unit mass flow rate of propelling fluids, and this is equivalent to the effective exit velocity of the propellants. Thus

$$\text{specific impulse} = I_{sp} = \frac{\text{thrust}}{\text{propellant mass flow rate}}$$

$$= F/\dot{m} \quad \text{N s/kg}$$

Analysis shows that reactants giving a high combustion temperature and pressure, and producing propelling products of low molar mass and low γ give high I_{sp}. No combination of fuel and oxidant can meet all these requirements simultaneously, and the result in practice is a compromise. For comparative purposes, the specific impulse parameter may be used also for high-speed air-breathing engines, as shown in figure 9.6. The relatively low level of specific impulse for rocket reactants arises because in rocketry the flow rate is based on the basis of total reactants, comprising both fuel and oxidant, whereas the fuel values only have been used in the air-breathing engines. In rocket applications within an atmosphere, the aerodynamic drag at high speed must be considered, and the parameter used is the volume impulse, I_v, based on the volume in litres of the stored liquid reactants.

Values of I_{sp} and I_v vary markedly with fuel–oxidant ratio but, for comparative purposes, the peak values are adopted at the appropriate ratios.

Values may be calculated on a basis of either 'shifting' or 'frozen' equilibrium: the former allows for the changes in product composition taking place along the propelling duct whereas the latter, for simplicity, assumes that no chemical changes occur, and these results are approximately 5 per cent lower. The 'shifting' values of I_{sp} and I_v plotted in figure 9.9 reflect the superiority of hydrogen on a mass basis, and inferiority on a volume basis, found in the variations of calorific value in section 5.4. It was felt of interest to examine the variation of a combined parameter of impulse, comparable to the performance index as a combined parameter of calorific value. A specially refined kerosine known as RP-1 of relative density 0.801 to 0.815 is specified as a reference hydrocarbon for rocket work, consequently the suggested 'impulse index' is given by

$$\text{impulse index of reactant pair} = \frac{(I_{sp} \times I_v) \text{ for reactant pair}}{8.836 \times 10^6 \text{ (N s)}^2/\text{kg l for Rp}-1}$$

The value of impulse index plotted in figure 9.10 show that, despite the wide difference between the various types of rocket fuel, and of oxidant, the same

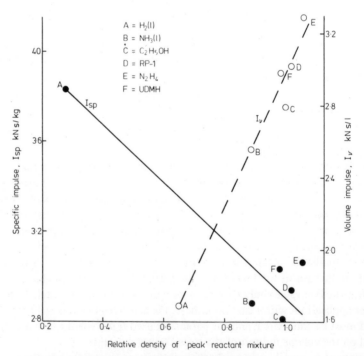

Figure 9.9   Comparative values of peak specific impulse and volume impulse for liquid rocket fuels with liquid oxygen (derived from reference 26)

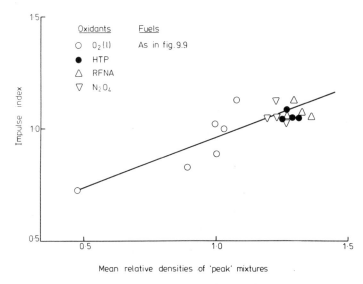

Figure 9.10   Proposed impulse index (reference 27)

general trends appear as with the performance index of the hydride fuels, namely

high gravimetric performance at low relative density
high volumetric performance at high relative density
high combined performance at high relative density

For fuel—oxidant selection, the general conclusions drawn are for heavy reactants during atmospheric operation when drag is significant, as in the early stages of an interplanetary mission, and for light reactants in space where mass performance is paramount. Solid reactants are not capable of the same levels of performance, but they are storable over a longer term, and do not require complex systems of pumping or flow control.

A summary of probable future fuel options by sector is given in table 9.5.

9.5 Fuel Cost Estimates

In this section, an attempt is made to record the recent and present levels of fuel energy costs, and to assess broadly the possible future levels, in terms of the customary unit of US $ per million Btu (1 MBtu = 1.055 GJ), using 1978 values of US $ throughout. The use of fuel costs rather than prices eliminates such complications as taxes, transportation charges and profits. Predictions of this kind are notoriously imprecise, but these estimates are restricted to a single market, namely the United States, and for the conventional fuels use the

Table 9.5 Future fuel options by sector

Classification	Heating	Industrial power	Land transport	Marine transport	Aviation
Conventional	NG Gas oils to RFOs Coal (lump or pulverised)	C–I engines Diesel fuels Steam turbines Gas oils to RFOs coal and crude oils Gas turbines Gas oils/diesel fuels	S–I engines Gasolines C–I engines Gas oils	C–I engines Gas oils/diesel fuels Steam turbines Heavy fuels and Dieso Gas turbines Gas oils/diesel fuels	S–I engines Gasolines Gas turbines Kerosines
Simulated	Simulated NG	—	—	—	—
Supplemental	Supplemental NG Manufactured gases Lower-grade heavy oils (homogenisation, emulsification, fluid beds) Coal (slurried, fluid beds)	C–I engines Diesel fuels from coal Steam and gas turbines As 'heating' + coal-derived fuels	S–I engines Gasolines by additional cat-cracking, and from shale, tar, coal Wide-range distillate C–I engines Wide-range distillate gas oil + alcohol in dual-fuelling	C–I engines Heavy fuels Gas turbines Heavy fuels	Heavy wide-range kerosine of relaxed specn. derived by hydrotreating unattractive crudes, then from shale, tar and coal
Elemental synthesis	—	—	—	—	Kerosine from inorganic H_2 and C
Substitute	Wide range of wastes, residues, etc., Alcohol (total energy H_2(g) schemes)	Steam turbines As 'heating' Gas turbines Alcohols from coal or biomatter	Alcohols from coal and biomatter Possibly H_2 from coal, or from hydrolysed or thermochemically split water	Pumpable coal slurries	Possibly CH_4(l) H_2(l) from coal or from water
(Alternative energy)	(Electric)	(Nuclear, Hydro, Solar)	(Electric)	(Nuclear)	(Nuclear)

194

following forecast ranges of annual percentage cost increases

1980	15
1990	2 to 5
2000	2 to 4

Energy costs of conventional and alternative fuels are shown in broken and full lines respectively in figures 9.11 and 9.12. The break-even years when the cost advantage transfers to the alternative fuels emerge as follows

1993	Methanol in favour of premium gasoline
1993	Liquid hydrogen in favour of JP fuels
1994	Supplemental gasoline in favour of premium gasoline
1996	Supplemental natural gas in favour of natural gas

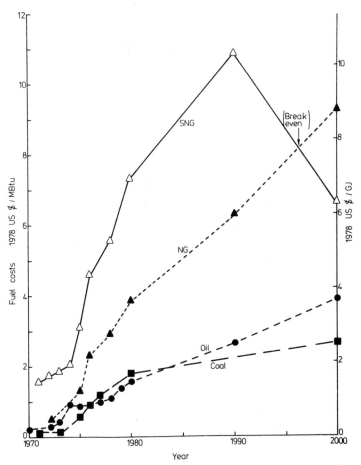

Figure 9.11   Estimated fuel costs to year 2000 (derived from reference 30)

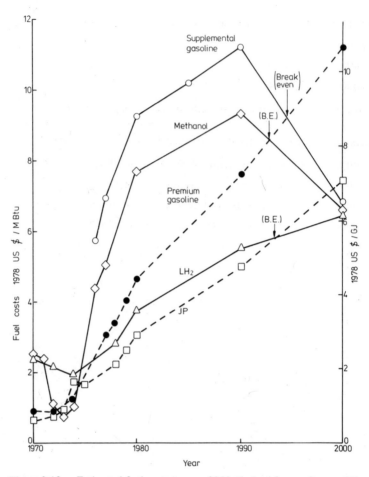

Figure 9.12   Estimated fuel costs to year 2000 (derived from reference 30)

It is entirely possible that prediction errors incurred with the absolute cost values for each pair of fuels may tend to be comparable, with minimal resulting effects on the corresponding break-even years. For the given constraints, therefore, it can be concluded that the major alternative fuels could become economically viable by about 1995.

References

1. W. L. Lom and A. F. Williams, *Substitute Natural Gas*, Applied Science, London (1976).
2. H. Teggers, Gasification of coal and its future aspects regarding the use

of heat from high-temperature nuclear reactors, in J. C. Denton (ed), *Future Energy Production Systems*, vols 1 and 2, Academic Press, London (1976) 489–507.

3. N. P. Cochran, Oil and gas from coal, *Scient. Am.*, **234** (1976) 24–9.
4. K. Goddard, Coal as a source of future transport fuel, *Chart. mech. Engr*, **99** (1977) 50–3.
5. J. Owen, Coal liquefaction, Energy for Industry Symposium Paper, Cranfield Institute of Technology, Pergamon, Oxford (1979).
6. Mobil proves gasoline-from-methanol process, *Chem. Engng News*, **56** (1978) 26–8.
7. L. E. Furlong, E. Effron, L. W. Vernon and E. L. Wilson, The Exxon donor solvent process, *Coal Process Technol.*, **3** (1976) 69–75.
8. W Engelbart and H. Dellweg, Basic data on continuous alcoholic fermentation of sugar solutions and of mashes from starch containing raw materials, Paper 5–3, International Symposium on Alcohol Fuel Technology, Wolfsburg, W. Germany (1977).
9. G. de Beni and C. Marchetti, Mark-1, a chemical process to decompose water using nuclear heat, *163rd Natn. Meeting Am. Chem. Soc.*, **16** (1972) 110–33.
10. D. P. Gregory (ed), *A Hydrogen-energy System*, American Gas Association (1972).
11. M. Kenward, Burn waste and save money, *New Scient*, **62** (1974) 556.
12. I. E. Smith, Energy and our little boxes, Cranfield Institute of Technology Inaugural Lecture (21 March 1979).
13. *Fluidized Combustion*, Symposium Series No. 1, Institute of Fuel, London (1975).
14. N. Dibelius, G. Touchton and R. Vogt, Preliminary design of three combustion turbines to burn low Btu coal in a high-temperature combustion turbine, Paper 78-GT-71, ASME Conference, Wembley, London (April 1978).
15. *Electric Vehicle Development,* Conference Publication 14, Peter Peregrinus Ltd, Hitchin, Herts. (1977).
16. A. G. Robertson and R. E. Williams, Jet fuel specifications: the need for change, *Shell Aviation News*, **435** (1976) 10–13.
17. M. W. Shayeson, Jet fuel quality considerations. *Shell Aviat. News*, **440** (1977) 26–31.
18. J. P. Longwell and J. Grobman, Alternative aircraft fuels, Paper 78-GT-59, ASME Conference, Wembley, London (April 1978).
19. A. J. Pasion and I. Thomas, Preliminary analysis of aircraft fuel systems for use with broadened specification jet fuels, *NASA CR-135198* (1976).
20. H. F. Butze and R. C. Ehlers, Effect of fuel properties on performance of a single aircraft turbojet combustor, *NASA TM-X 71789* (1975).
21. I. J. Richmond, *Measurement of Hydrogen Content of Liquid Fuels by*

Low Resolution Nuclear Magnetic Resonance, Newport Instruments Ltd, Newport Pagnell, Bucks. (1978).

22. R. A. Rudey and J. Grobman, *Characteristics and Combustion of Future Hydrocarbon Fuels*, AGARD Lecture Series 96, London (1978).
23. C. C. Gleason, D. W. Rogers and D. W. Bahr, Experimental clean combustor program, Phase II *NASA CR-134971* (1976).
24. R. Roberts, A. Fiorentino and W. Greene, Experimental clean combustor program, Phase III *NASA CR-135253* (1977).
25. W. J. Small, D. E. Fetterman and T. F. Bonner, Alternate fuels for transportation, part 1: Hydrogen for aircraft, *Mech. Engng,* **96** (1974) 18–24.
26. *Rocket Engine Propellants*, Publication 505-X, Rocketdyne, Canoga Park, Calif. (1959).
27. E. M. Goodger, Alternative fuels for aviation, *Aeronaut. J.,* **79** (1975) 212–4.
28. G. D. Brewer, The case for hydrogen fueled transport aircraft, *AIAA Paper 73-1323* (1974).
29. Shelldyne, Report 59F, Shell International Petroleum Co. Ltd, London (1965).
30. A. P. Haran, Fuel costs, School of Mechanical Engineering, Cranfield Institute of Technology, unpublished report (June 1979).

Bibliography

Alcohols: a Technical Assessment of their Application as Fuels, American Petroleum Institute Publication No. 4261 (July 1976).

Alexander, A. D., Economic study of future aircraft fuels (1970–2000), *NASA TM-X-62*, 180 (1972).

Anketell-Jones, M. W., Marine transport, *The Effective Use of Petroleum*, Institute of Petroleum Annual Conference, London (21/22 November 1978).

Boddy, J. H., and Spencer, E. H., Overall economy of engines and refineries, *The Effective Use of Petroleum*, Institute of Petroleum Annual Conference, London (21/22 November 1978).

Goodger, E. M., Aviation fuel prospects, *The Effective Use of Petroleum*, Institute of Petroleum Annual Conference, London (21/22 November 1978).

Grainger, L., Automotive fuels derived from coal, Paper C9/77, Conference on Land Transport Engines, Institution of Mechanical Engineers, London (18/20 January 1977).

Macnair, E. J., Future fuels for the Royal Navy, *Energy World*, **56** (1979) 4–8.

The Motor Ship, Marine Propulsion and Future Fuels Conference, London (1/2 March 1979).

Mills, G. A. Alternate fuels from coal, *Chemtech* (1977) 418–23.

Pefley, R. K., Browning, L. H., Likos, W. E., McCormack, M. C., and Pullman B., *Characterization and Research Investigation of Methanol and Methyl Fuels*, Environmental Protection Agency, Ann Arbor, Mich. Report 406/3-77-015 (August 1977).

Power from coal, Institution of Mechanical Engineers Conference, London (10 April 1979).

Savage, R. L. (ed), *A Hydrogenergy Carrier, Vol. II, Systems Analysis,* NASA-ASEE (1973).

Sweetman, W., Hydrogen fuel stands by for take-off, *New Scient.,* **82** (1979) 818–20.

The Enfield Electric Car Project, The Electricity Council, London (1979).

Appendix 1 Alkyl Alcohols: Nomenclature and General Properties

As seen in section 4.6.2, an alcohol molecule consists of a hydrocarbon in which one atom of hydrogen has been substituted by the hydroxyl group, and is represented by the formula ROH where R is the remaining hydrocarbon group. If the original hydrocarbon is an alkane (a paraffin) with the general formula C_xH_{2x+2}, the resultant alkyl alcohol appears with formula $C_xH_{2x+1}OH$. More generally, the R group may be any open chain (aliphatic) or cyclic radical, and may contain a double carbon—carbon bond, an aromatic ring, or a halogen atom.

Alcohols are named by three different systems (see table A1.1).

1. Common names. The hydrocarbon group name is followed by the separate word 'alcohol', indicating the presence of the OH group, hence

    propyl alcohol C_3H_7OH

2. Carbinol system. The name 'carbinol' for the methyl alcohol group is prefixed by the name of any groups substituted for one or more of the three hydrogen atoms in the R group, hence

    ethylcarbinol $H_3C\overset{H}{\underset{H}{C}}{-}\overset{H}{\underset{H}{C}}OH,$ or C_3H_7OH

3. IUPAC (International Union of Pure and Applied Chemistry). In the name of the longest carbon chain containing the OH group, the terminal 'e' is replaced by 'ol', and preceded by a number indicating the location of the OH group in the chain, the whole being preceded by names and locating numbers of other groups attached as side chains, hence

    2-propanol $H_3C{-}\overset{H}{\underset{OH}{C}}{-}CH_3,$ or C_3H_7OH

    3-methyl-2-butanol $H_3C{-}\overset{H}{\underset{OH}{C}}{-}\overset{CH_3}{\underset{H}{C}}{-}CH_3,$ or $C_5H_{11}OH$

When the carbon chain contains a double bond (an alkene group), the number indicating its location is written first, and the number indicating the location of the OH group is inserted just before the 'ol' suffix, hence

$$\text{2-buten-1-ol} \qquad \text{H}_3\text{C--C=C--C--OH,} \quad \text{or} \quad \text{C}_4\text{H}_7\text{OH}$$

Note that the carbon atoms are numbered from right to left to give the lowest value for the OH group location.

When the carbon chain incorporates an aromatic ring (for example, benzene C_6H_6), at least one carbon atom must be located between the ring and the OH group, otherwise the compound will be a phenol, hence

benzyl alcohol $\qquad$ C--OH, or C_7H_7OH

phenol $\qquad$ --OH, or C_6H_5OH

Alcohols are classified as primary, secondary or tertiary according to the number of other carbon atoms attached to the carbon atom bearing the OH group. Thus

Primary: RC—OH   Secondary: RC—OH   Tertiary: RC—OH

See table A1.1 for general properties.

Bibliography

Morrison, R. T., and Boyd, R. N., *Organic Chemistry*, 2nd edn, Allyn & Bacon, Boston, Mass. (1960).

Noller, C. R., *Textbook of Organic Chemistry*, Holt-Saunders, London (1966).

Weast, R. C. (ed), *Handbook of Chemistry and Physics*, 55th edn, The Chemical Rubber Co., Cleveland, Ohio (1974/5).

Table A1.1   Alkyl alcohols

Structural formula Condensed	Extended	Primary/ secondary/ tertiary	Names	General properties Rel d @ 20/4 °C (Water = 1)	bp (°C)	mp (°C)
CH₃OH	H₃C—OH	P*	methyl alcohol carbinol methanol	0.7915	64.8	−95.5
C₂H₅OH	H₃C—C—OH (H above, H below)	P	ethyl alcohol methylcarbinol ethanol	0.7894	78.4	−117.3
	H₃C—C—C—OH (H H above, H H below)	P	n-propyl alcohol ethylcarbinol 1-propanol	0.8036	97.3	−126.5
C₃H₇OH	H₃C—C—CH₃ (H above, OH below)	S	i-propyl alcohol dimethylcarbinol 2-propanol	0.7853	82.4	−89.5

	Structure	Class	Names	Density	b.p.	m.p.
	H H H H₃C–C–C–C–OH H H H	P	n-butyl alcohol n-propylcarbinol 1-butanol	0.8097	117.4	−89.8
	H H H₃C–C–C–CH₃ H OH	S	s-butyl alcohol methylethylcarbinol 2-butanol	0.8075	99.5	−114.7
C₄H₉OH	H H H₃C–C–C–OH CH₃ H	P	i-butyl alcohol i-propylcarbinol 2-methyl-1-propanol	0.8020	108.1	−108
	CH₃ H₃C–C–OH CH₃	T	t-butyl alcohol trimethylcarbinol 2-methyl-2-propanol	0.8070	99.5	25.5

* Generally classed as primary, but really unique with 1 C atom only.

203

Appendix 2 Use of Ternary System Diagrams

The following notes outline the ternary form of data plotting for a three-component mixture. An equilaterial triangle is constructed, and lines drawn parallel to each side, typically at spacings of 10 or 20 per cent. The three separate upper sketches in figure A2.1 show these lines for concentrations of components A, B and C independently, the arrow symbol in each case representing an increasing percentage towards the apex. When the diagrams are combined, as in the lower sketch, the numberings are frequently omitted

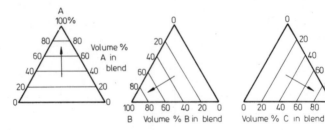

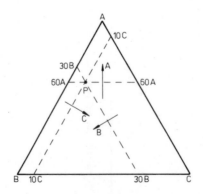

since they interfere with each other and, as shown for the point P, since the concentrations of the three components can be read off easily as A = 60 per cent, B = 30 per cent and C = 10 per cent. Any point within the triangle must give a unique mixture of three concentrations totalling 100 per cent. Iso-property curves can then be superimposed to show the variation of the property with the blending.

This type of diagram is used widely in chemical engineering to represent properties of three-component mixtures, but is equally useful in mechanical engineering with such blends as hydrazine—ammonia—water, hydrocarbon—alcohol—water, and so on, with superimposed curves representing either physical properties (for example, melting points), or combustion performance (for example, power output). Examples of the former are given in figures 8.5 and 8.6, and of the latter in reference 1. As suggested in reference 2, these diagrams can also be plotted on a three-dimensional basis.

References

1. M. S. Janota, J. R. Cooper, R. J. Crookes and M. A. A. Nazha, Performance and emissions of spark-ignition engines operating with alcohol—gasoline mixtures, Paper C 17/75, *Power Plants and Future Fuels*, Institution of Mechanical Engineers, London (1975) 105—18.
2. B. C. Dutton, Interchangeability prediction — the framework of a new approach, *J. Inst. Fuel*, LI (1978) 225—9.

Appendix 3 Fuel Property Measurement

Many individual property tests for fuel feedstocks and their products have been standardised by such bodies as the British Standards Institution, the Institute of Petroleum, the American Society for Testing and Materials, and the American Petroleum Institute. Such standardisation helps to achieve results with acceptable repeatability (same operator with same apparatus) and reproducibility (different operator with similar apparatus). The methods of test are considered here, together with any additional background philosophy, whereas typical tests results and their significance are covered in chapters 5, 6 and 8. Illustrations of the apparatus for most of these tests can be found in reference 1.

In most applications, particularly those with continuous-flow air-breathing combustion, the key property of an energy-storing fuel is the calorific value, but it has been found convenient here to consider first the relative density, and to adopt this as a general basis of comparison by using it as the abscissa against which can be plotted calorific value and all the other properties of interest. The following notes outline briefly the most commonly measured properties for identifying and assessing gaseous, liquid and solid fuels by type and quality.

A3.1 Relative Density (formerly Specfic Gravity)

For a gaseous fuel, the density may be found directly by weighing a sample in a Chancel flask of known volume. The relative density is customarily expressed with reference to air, both at some standard temperature and pressure, and may be determined by timing the flow of equal volumes of sample and air through a fixed orifice, using the relationships

$$\text{volume flow time} \propto (\text{gas density})^{\frac{1}{2}} \ .$$

hence

$$\text{relative density of sample} = \text{rel } d = \left(\frac{\text{sample flow time}}{\text{air flow time}} \right)^2$$

For a liquid fuel, density of the sample may be expressed either directly or relative to that of water, each at some standard temperature. Alternatively, this latter value may be inserted in the Tagliabue formula, as adopted by the American Petroleum Institute, to give

$$\text{degrees API} = \frac{141.5}{\text{rel } d \text{ @ } 60/60\ ^\circ\text{F}} - 131.5$$

Again, the most direct method involves measuring the mass of a sample contained in a density bottle of known volume, but a commonly used indirect method for the less viscous liquids is based on the buoyancy of a hydrometer floating in the sample. In the case of liquefied gases, the sample and hydrometer are contained in a sealed and protected glass cylinder.

When density can only be measured at a temperature other than standard, the temperature discrepancy must be allowed for by the use of a correcting factor appropriate to the measured level of density, as in method IP 59/72 for petroleum products (see figure 6.1). For industrial fluids, the corresponding information may be given in terms of either the density–temperature gradient at 20 °C, or as a density equation incorporating temperature, as for example

$$(\text{rel } d)/^\circ\text{C} = 0.94 \times 10^{-3}, \text{ for methane}$$

and

$$\text{density} = 1.0253\,(1 - 0.00085t)\ \text{g/cm}^3, \text{ for hydrogen with } t \text{ in } ^\circ\text{C}.$$

For solid fuels, the bulk density is determined by measurement of the mass of a given volume of fuel particles, and this varies mainly with particulate size and free water content. The lump density can be estimated by filling the voids with a measured volume of immiscible liquid of known density. This method can be extended using a liquid (for example, mercury) over a range of pressure in order to estimate the numbers of pores within different size ranges within the body of the solid. As with liquid fuels, the density of solid fuels is expressed relative to water.

A3.2 Calorific Value

When a body of fuel and oxidant burns completely in an adiabatic manner, all the combustion energy released is contained within the resulting products, and the temperature so reached is described as the adiabatic combustion, or flame, temperature. If energy is now transferred across the boundary of the products to an extent that the final temperature drops to that of the initial reactants, the reaction is isothermal overall. As outlined in section 5.3, this energy can transfer in the forms of work W and/or heat Q, but the work term can be eliminated in the two special cases of constant-pressure steady-flow, and constant-volume non-flow. Since the energy then transfers as heat only, it can be determined simply from the temperature rise of a known mass of cooling water, and the resulting calorific value is frequently described as 'heat of combustion', or 'heating value'. The temperature rise is arranged to be as small as practicable in order to approximate to the isothermal process.

As indicated in section 5.4, laboratory determination of calorific value is based on conditions of constant-pressure flow for the gaseous fuels, and constant-volume non-flow for the liquids and solids. In the flow tests, corrections are made for the energy remaining in the flue gases and for the expansion of the cooling water and, in the non-flow tests, for the heat contributions of the ignition wire and the gelatine capsule used for containing the more volatile samples. The gaseous fuels burn completely at åtmospheric pressure, but the liquids and solids require higher pressures. For an accurate comparison, therefore, a common condition of constant pressure should be used, together with a common quantity basis, mass or volume.

All the experimental results are gross values since the final temperature of the products is near ambient, the water content condensing to the liquid phase and adding its latent heat of vaporisation to the combustion energy.

For a gaseous fuel mixture, the conversion from the laboratory-determined gross value of energy density to the net value, at 1 atm and 25 °C, is as follows

$$Q_{net,p} = Q_{gr,p} - 0.01962 \left(d + \frac{ey}{2} \right) \quad MJ/m^3$$

where d = volume per cent hydrogen in fuel and e = volume per cent C_xH_y component in fuel, for the dry gas with its volume measured at 0 °C.[2]

For liquid and solid fuels at the reference temperature of 25 °C, the following expression is used for specific energy

$$Q_{net,v} = Q_{gr,v} - (0.2059H + 0.0230W) \quad MJ/kg$$

where H = mass per cent hydrogen in fuel and W = mass per cent water in fuel.[2]

For liquid petroleum fuels, an alternative expression is given by[3]

$$Q_{net,v} = Q_{gr,v} - 0.21219H \quad MJ/kg$$

Although liquid fuels are commonly used in non-flow combustion at near constant volume in the spark-ignition engine, a very wide use is made of steady-flow combustion at constant pressure in the furnace, gas turbine, ramjet, rocket and a variety of chemical and industrial processes. Consequently, the experimental values obtained for liquid and solid fuels are sometimes converted to net values at constant pressure, as follows

$$Q_{net,p} = Q_{gr,v} - (0.2121H + 0.0243W + 0.00080) \quad MJ/kg$$

where O = mass per cent oxygen in fuel.[2]

For coal tar fuels, the following approximations are frequently made

(CTFs 50 and 100) $Q_{net,v} = Q_{gr,v} - 1.63$ MJ/kg

(CTFs 200 to 400) $Q_{net,v} = Q_{gr,v} - 1.40$ MJ/kg

and for coals[4] $Q_{net,v} = Q_{gr,v} - 1.00$ MJ/kg

As indicated in section 5.4, certain empirical expressions are adopted to give results of normally acceptable accuracy without the need for precise calorimetry. Typical examples are shown below.

1. Aviation gasoline and kerosines, on sulphur-free basis

$$Q_{net,p} = k_1 + k_2(A \times G) \quad \text{MJ/kg}$$

where k_1 = constant for fuel type (from 41.6680 to 41.9557), k_2 = constant for fuel type (from 0.20543×10^{-3} to 0.25407×10^{-3}), A = aniline point ($^\circ$F), G = gravity in degrees API.[5]

2. Industrial kerosines to residual fuel oils

$$Q_{net,v} = (46.392 - 8.792d^2 + 3.187d)$$
$$[1 - (x + y + s)] + 9.420s - 2.449x \quad \text{MJ/kg}$$

where d = relative density at 15/15 $^\circ$C, x = mass proportion of water, y = mass proportion of ash and s = mass proportion of sulphur.[6]

3. Coals

$$Q_{gr} = 0.336C + 1.42H - 0.145O + 0.094S \quad \text{MJ/kg}$$

where C = mass per cent carbon in coal, H = mass per cent hydrogen in coal and O = mass per cent oxygen in coal, all on a dry mineral-matter free basis.[4]

A3.3 Distillation

In contrast to an individual elemental or compound material exhibiting a single boiling point, a blend of different materials, as in a commercial petroleum fuel, boils over a range of temperature. A broad indication of the type of blend, and of its components, can be gained by the simple ASTM batch distillation test in which a 100 ml sample is evaporated at a controlled rate by heating in a flask incorporating a side arm, condensed in an ice-cooled tube, and collected in a graduated cylinder. Corresponding readings of vapour temperature and condensate recovery are plotted as a distillation curve showing the boiling levels of the various components. The initial boiling point (ibp) is taken as the temperature observed at the fall of the first droplet of condensate, and the final boiling point (fbp) as the highest temperature reached during the test. With petroleum fuels, a maximum distillation temperature limit of 370 $^\circ$C is set in order to avoid cracking of the heavier hydrocarbon molecules. In automatic versions of the distillation apparatus, the mercury-in-glass thermometer is replaced by a thermocouple or resistance thermometer, and the rising meniscus of the distillate is followed by a photocell, the data being either printed out or traced on an $X-Y$ plotter. The air initially within the ullage space of the distillation flask is rapidly displaced by the freshly generated vapour, giving an air/fuel ratio of zero. The behaviour of the fuel over a range of air/fuel ratios at temperatures closer to ambient, as in a carburreted engine manifold, may be explored by a more fundamental laboratory approach, such as the equilibrium air distillation (EAD) test in which the fuel sample is introduced into a thermostatically controlled air stream, and then permitted to vaporise to an equilibrium extent determined by the prevailing test temperature. Measurement of the air and fuel flow rates, and of the unvaporised liquid at the outlet of the apparatus over a period of time, permits the construction of an EAD curve on the basis of temperature versus per cent volume vaporised. This is analogous to the conventional ASTM curve, and lies underneath it. A whole family of such curves can be drawn, with values of air/fuel mass ratio rising from zero for the ASTM curve to 50 or more at lower temperatures.[1] The points where these curves reach the 100 per cent vaporised ordinate are the dew points for the corresponding mixtures.

An alternative laboratory approach is to determine the vapour/liquid volume ratio with a temperature-controlled burette in which the pressure of the vapour/liquid mixture can be adjusted to atmospheric by means of mercury displacement. The volume of vapour (V) produced is compared with the original volume of unvaporised liquid (L), and plotted as a V/L ratio against temperature. In essence, the V/L curve explores a wide zone centred on the ibp with an accuracy much greater than that in the ASTM test. Since these more precise laboratory tests are somewhat time-consuming to complete, it is customary to use simplified equations or nomograms based on correlations of temperatures and curve gradients derived from the simpler conventional ASTM distillation test.

A3.4 Vapour Pressure

The absolute vapour pressure of a liquid may be defined as the pressure exerted by the vapour above the free surface of the liquid at the given temperature. If air is present with the vapour, the fuel vapour pressure represents the partial pressure of the vapour within the mixture, and its sum with the partial pressure of the air gives the total pressure of the vapour/air mixture, which is equal to 1 atm in the case of the container vented at sea level. The partial pressure of a component of mixed gases is that pressure applied by the component when it occupies the full volume of the container, the several components all being able to exist in this way since the molecules of one component occupy the intermolecular space of the others. If the components are imagined separated into individual regions within the container, the volume of each region is known as the partial volume of that particular component, and each component then experiences the total pressure.

Within a constant volume container, an increase in temperature will raise the pressure of the existing vapour in a near-linear manner, approximating to the ideal gas law of $P = (mR/V)T$, but will also add to the mass of vapour due to additional vaporisation, and so increase the vapour pressure further. Consequently, the overall vapour pressure rises with temperature in more of an exponential manner. A plot of log vapour pressure versus linear temperature usually shows a slight curving to the right, particularly above the boiling point where the vapour approaches more closely to an ideal gas with its linear P/T relationship. However, since interest is usually centred on vapour pressures below the boiling point, it is customary to adjust the temperature scale in order to eliminate the slight curvature and give a convenient straight-line presentation, as in figure 6.6.

The standard laboratory test for liquid fuels is conducted at a single temperature of 37.8 °C (100 °F), using a Reid apparatus consisting of a sealed bomb made up of a fuel chamber connected to an air chamber fitted with a pressure gauge, the chambers being immersed in a thermostatically controlled water bath. The pressure indicated by the gauge is corrected for ambient pressure, and for the rise in pressure of the air and water vapour present initially in the air chamber. The resulting pressure is an absolute value since atmospheric pressure is exerted both inside and outside the bomb when it is sealed at the start of the test. With liquefied gases, on the other hand, the bomb is first filled with sample, part of which is then removed and replaced by vapour only, consequently the resulting pressure is a gauge value. The standard test temperature in this case is 45 °C. A micro method of measuring vapour pressure has now been developed, requiring a sample of 1 ml only, using the evacuated bulb principle with a mercury manometer operating against a constant head.

A3.5 Flash Point

Every fuel is capable of burning over a range of fuel—oxidant proportions, the weak and rich limits of which are determined by the types of fuel and oxidant, and the physical conditions obtaining. These limiting mixture strengths are usually expressed in terms of per centage volume of fuel in the mixture and, in the case of methane—air mixtures at ambient temperatures, the weak and rich mixture limits are approximately 5 and 15 per cent respectively. For the paraffins, both limits tend to fall, and approach each other slightly, as the size of the molecule increases. For mixtures of conventional liquid petroleum fuels with air, the weak mixture limit is common at about 1 per cent, and the rich mixture limit falls slightly from about 6 per cent (gasoline) to 5 per cent (residual fuel oil).

By Avogadro's law, the partial pressure exerted by a component of a gaseous mixture is related directly to the partial volume of the component within the mixture, thus

$$\frac{\text{fuel partial (vapour) pressure}}{\text{mixture pressure}} = \frac{\text{fuel partial volume}}{\text{mixture volume}}$$

At the weak mixture limit of petroleum fuels, these ratios equal 0.01. As shown in the previous section, the fuel vapour pressure is, in turn, related directly to the temperature of the vapour, consequently, for a fuel–air mixture at atmospheric pressure

fuel vapour pressure at weak mixture limit = 0.01 (atmospheric pressure)

= 1.01325 kPa

It follows that when a bulk of liquid petroleum fuel is heated at atmospheric pressure, the vapour–air mixture above it will first become flammable when the fuel vapour pressure reaches this value. Although this vapour pressure is common for all the liquid petroleum fuels, the temperature at which it is achieved will vary widely, due to the differences in levels of vapour pressure, that is, of volatility between fuels. Thus the weak *mixture* limit is common, but the weak *temperature* limit is not. The latter is known as the *fire point*, since it is the temperature at which the mixture, on heating, can first support continuous combustion. In practice, it is found more convenient to measure the *flash point*, which is very slightly below the fire point, and is defined as the temperature at which the mixture will just flash, and then extinguish, on the application of a standard source of ignition. An upper flash point can be visualised immediately above the rich mixture limit of flammability, but this is not normally measured since it invariably occurs at about 30 °C above the conventional flash point. Flash point values for conventional and alternative fuels are included in the vapour pressure curves of figure 6.6, and shown in figures 8.1 and 8.2. Strictly, the mixture limits used should apply at the flash point temperature levels and not at ambient temperature where they are usually measured. Flammability ranges widen slightly with temperature increase (by about 1.3 per cent volume per 100 K), and allowances have been made for this effect in locating the relevant points on the vapour pressure curves.

Laboratory methods of determining flash point include the Abel, Pensky–Martens, Tag and Cleveland. All involve the controlled heating of the fuel sample in a standardised container, with the repeated introduction into the vapour space of a standard-sized test flame until the onset of flash. In most cases, a stirrer is incorporated in the vapour–air space, and a time sequence adopted for insertion of the test flame. Also in most test methods, the fuel cup remains closed during the heating period, and is opened only for introduction of the test flame, whereas in some versions the cup remains open throughout the test. Flash point results for a given fuel tend to be a few degrees higher in the open-cup test due to the loss of vapour during heating.

Modern tendencies are towards standardisation to two basic approaches. The first is the adoption of the miniaturised Setaflash portable instrument requiring a charge of 2 ml (cf. 80 ml for the Abel apparatus). The second is the adoption of *any* suitable closed-cup apparatus, but with the cup in direct contact with water in a heater bath. For additional speed in testing, a go/no-go procedure is recommended in which the sample is tested at a specified temperature to determine whether flash does or does not occur. In an automatic version of the Pensky–Martens flash tester, a control unit determines both the heating rate and the insertion of an electrically heated incandescent test bead. The temperature of the sample is recorded continuously, and locked when the pressure wave resulting from the flash operates a balanced-vane device. The 1972 Regulations[7] specify a highly flammable liquid as one giving off a flammable vapour at a temperature less than 32 °C using the Abel apparatus on a go/no-go basis.

A3.6 Spontaneous Ignition Temperature

Combustion may be initiated either by an intensive source of localised energy (spark, flame, pyrotechnic, etc.) as in the flash point test or, alternatively, by the overall application of energy by means of heat and/or pressure throughout the body of the mixture. In this latter case, the energy of the mixture reaches a level sufficient for ignition to take place spontaneously after a brief period of delay. The spontaneous ignition temperature of a fuel may therefore be defined as the minimum temperature to which the fuel must be heated in the presence of air to promote ignition, in the absence of any localised source within the mixture.

The standard test method involves an open, heated flask into which is injected a measured volume of sample by means of a hypodermic syringe. A stop-watch is started at the instant of injection, and stopped on the appearance of ignition. The temperature of the system is plotted against the reaction-delay period, and the test repeated at progressively reduced temperatures to determine the minimum level for ignition, which is termed the spontaneous ignition temperature (SIT). At atmospheric pressure, the delay periods are extensive, being of the order of several seconds, and are most probably occupied by complex chemical pre-reactions involving the rapid formation and decay of such species as aldehydes, peroxides, hydroperoxides, alcohols, and so on.

Spontaneous ignition is an important property in any situation in which a fuel and oxidant mixture can be raised to a temperature well above ambient in the absence of any concentrated source of ignition. In fuel storage, this situation can arise in a fuel system subjected to heat, as in supersonic flight. Spontaneous ignition also sets a limit of 'flash back' in combustion chambers using fuel pre-vaporisation. In piston-engine combustion chambers, unburnt charge can be stressed sufficiently for spontaneous ignition to occur, leading to spark knock. Alternatively, a spontaneous process may be relied upon to provide the main source of ignition, as in a compression-ignition engine. However, these latter two reactions differ from the laboratory spontaneous ignition test in that, in the engines, the pressures are high and the delay periods available very short, being less than a millisecond.

Spontaneous ignition is promoted by the breaking of bonds in molecules of fuel and oxidant, permitting atoms from the two types of molecule to combine in a process of combustion. Clearly, the smaller, more compact fuel molecule will be able to withstand thermal agitation more successfully than the larger, heavier fuel molecule which may contain numerous side chains and other complexities. Furthermore, higher levels of SIT would be expected with the more compact molecular structures of the ring chain and isomerised types, as shown for normal and iso-octane (2,2,4-trimethylpentane) in figure 6.10.

A3.7 Thermal Stability

At the SIT level and above, fuel oxidation reaction energy is sufficient to promote ignition, but more moderate oxidation reactions also take place during heat soakage below this level, and the resulting products can take the form of either complex gum-like matter or solid particulates, with attendant problems in fuel systems and burners. The significance of thermal stability became emphasised in recent years due largely to the kinetic heating involved in high-speed flight, particularly during descent with reduced fuel flow, and a fuel coker test was devised in which the sample is pumped at a specified rate along the outside of a resistance-heated aluminium tube, and then through a heated stainless-steel cloth filter. The sample is rated both on the rise in deposit-induced pressure drop across the filter in a given time, and on the colour of the film of deposit along each 1 in. length of the heater tube. The 'break point' of the fuel is taken as the maximum temperature reached by the heater tube without the formation of deposits, and lies in the region of about 270 °C for Avtur, representing a fuel temperature of about 205 °C. The original ASTM-CRC coker rig is now replaced by the Alcor jet-fuel thermal oxidation tester (JFTOT) working on the same principle but using a smaller quantity of sample.

A3.8 Viscosity

Weak electrostatic forces act between the molecules of a body of fluid which, if the molecules are relatively large and closely disposed, are sufficient to permit the fluid to exist in the liquid phase under ambient conditions. However, these same forces promote resistance to internal displacement and flow. This resistance is termed viscosity, and since liquid fuels expand on heating, the rise in intermolecular distances incurs a fall in viscosity.

The dynamic viscosity (symbol η) of a sample may be defined as the tangential force on unit area of either of two parallel planes at unit distance apart when the space between the planes is filled with the sample, and one of the planes moves with unit velocity in its own plane relative to the other. Hence it is the force per unit area to produce a unit velocity gradient. The units are given by

$$\frac{\text{force}}{\text{area x velocity/length}} = \frac{[M]\,[L]\,[T^{-2}]}{[L^2]\,[L]\,[T^{-1}]\,[L^{-1}]}$$

$$= [M]\,[L^{-1}]\,[T^{-1}]$$

In metric terms, the unit of dynamic viscosity is the g/cm s, or poise, P. Since this is inconveniently large in practice, the centipoise, cP, is widely used, where 1 cP = 0.01 P = 1 mN s/m^2. The viscosity of heavy fuels is determined on a dynamic basis from the resistance incurred by motor-driven rotation of one cylinder inside another when located in the sample.

The kinematic viscosity (symbol ν) may be defined as the quotient of the dynamic viscosity and the density of the sample (ρ). Hence, $\nu = \eta/\rho$, with units given by

$$\frac{[M]\,[L^{-1}]\,[T^{-1}]}{[M]\,[L^{-3}]} = [L^2]\,[T^{-1}]$$

In metric terms, the unit of kinematic viscosity is the cm^2/s, or stokes, St. Here again, it is more convenient to use the smaller unit, the centistokes, where 1 cSt = 0.01 St = 1 mm^2/s. Kinematic viscosity is of general interest in fuel technology in connection with the pumping and atomisation of liquid fuels.

Kinematic viscosity may be measured as a 'conventional' property, that is, dependent on the instrument and method used or, preferably, as an 'absolute' property of the fuel alone. Both approaches depend on the efflux time of a given volume of sample flowing under its own head through a restriction. This follows because the force resisting the laminar (low speed) flow of a fluid through a restriction is approximately proportional to the dynamic viscosity, whereas the force promoting the flow is that due to gravity, which is proportional to the density.

The simple conventional methods incorporate a short length of restriction and include the Redwood, Saybolt and Engler, but are becoming obsolete. The absolute determination of kinematic viscosity generally employs a glass U-tube viscometer with a capillary built into one leg. The instrument is suspended vertically in a thermostatically controlled water bath, and the time measured for a given volume of sample to flow through the capillary. This measured time is inserted into an equation to give a direct measure of the kinematic viscosity in centistokes

$$v = Ct - B/t \quad \text{cSt}$$

where C = instrument calibration constant, B = instrument type constant, depending upon the capillary bore, and t = efflux time in seconds. The operating range of efflux time is 120 to 1500 s, and five different sizes of instrument are available, together covering an overall range of viscosity from 0.5 to 1500 cSt.

Many of the above features are incorporated into a modern instrument[8] in which six of the nine tubes available are mounted semi-permanently in a thermostatically controlled oil bath. Each tube consists of a single vertical capillary limb with a horizontal section at the top to serve as a constant-head device, and a calibrated bulb near the bottom. A micro sample of 0.3 ml is introduced, and a timer operated manually as the leading meniscus passes calibration marks at each end of the bulb. The time interval is then recalled from a memory store, and multiplied by the tube constant to give a direct measure of the viscosity in centistokes. Finally, the viscometer tube is cleaned and dried *in situ* by means of a vacuum purging system. A computing model of this instrument incorporates fibre optics and operates automatically from injection of the sample to tube cleaning and drying.

Since the electrostatic forces between the fuel molecules vary with molecular spacing on an inverse square basis, the expansion with rise in temperature results in a similar relationship between viscosity and temperature. However, straight-line plotting of kinematic viscosity with temperature is achieved by modifying both scales to the following equation

$$\log \log (v + a) = n \log T + b$$

where a, n and b are constants as in the ASTM and 'Refutas' methods, shown plotted in figure 6.2.

A3.9 Melting, Freezing, Cloud and Pour Points

An individual element or compound material consisting of identical molecules will experience a change of phase from solid to liquid at a fixed level of melting temperature at any given pressure, and in the literature it is customary to denote such temperatures as the melting, rather than the freezing, points. When a material comprises a blend, on the other hand, melting will take place progressively, generally from the lighter to the heavier components, and solidification will proceed progressively in the reverse direction. With commercial hydrocarbon fuel blends, solidification of the heavier components results in a cloud of wax crystals within the body of the liquid, and the temperature at which these first appear is defined as the cloud point. The sample is contained in a glass test jar located in an air cavity within a metal cooling bath, the test jar being removed for inspection at each °C temperature drop. In the case of aviation fuels, however, both the test jar and the cooling bath consist of evacuated double-walled glass vessels, and the so-called freezing point of the sample is defined as the temperature at which the wax cloud disappears on subsequent warming, the sample being stirred in the process. Freezing points and cloud points are therefore very closely related.

With further cooling of a fuel blend sample, the wax crystals increase in size and number, and eventually coalesce to form a rigid structure which shows no movement on tilting the test jar to the horizontal for a period of 5 s. A temperature 3 °C above the test temperature is defined as the pour point. In fact, the lightest fractions of the blend are likely to be still liquid at the pour point, existing within the interstices of the wax crystals, and this can be demonstrated by the regaining of fluidity when the apparently frozen sample is stirred. Materials exhibiting this behaviour are described as thixotropic. In an automation version of the pour point apparatus,[9] a metal disc is partly immersed in the sample, and at set intervals is rotated slightly by means of a solenoid, so disrupting a beam of light directed on to a photocell. By means of thermoelectric elements fitted to the bath, the sample is first pre-heated under standardised conditions, and then progressively cooled. When the pour point is reached, the disc fails to rotate, so exposing the photocell to the light beam. The temperature indicator then locks, a warning bell rings, and the thermoelectric elements re-heat the bath ready for the next test. Both repeatability and reproducibility are improved, with much less demand on the operator's time.

Clearly, wax crystals or any other solid particulates within a liquid will create interference in the capillary tube of a viscometer, and give an apparent increase in viscosity over and above that due to the falling temperature. For this reason, the modified plot of viscosity versus temperature loses its linearity and curves upwards as the temperature falls from the cloud point to the pour point (see figure 6.2). Comparable behaviour can be expected with any alternative fuel based on a blend of components with differing melting points.

Tests conducted with distillate petroleum fuels in full-scale fuel tanks and pumps have shown minimum temperatures for pumpability to lie from 4 to 16 °C below the freezing points, and from 1 to 7 °C below the pour points. Neither of the standard laboratory tests is therefore a sufficiently representative or precise indicator of low-temperature limits on handling, and a need exists for improved correlation. This need may well be met by the 'Setapoint detector', under development by Stanhope-Seta Ltd., which employs a pulsating flow of cooled sample across a filter element until a temperature is reached where the flow ceases. A pumpability test is available for fuel oils in which the sample is subjected to a specified rate of shear between the two cylinders of a Ferranti portable motorised viscometer during a period of cooling. The handling and storage temperatures are defined at specified levels of dynamic viscosity. In an alternative laboratory test for residual fuel oils, a number of frozen samples are pre-heated to different temperatures, then poured into separate U-tubes and warmed. The fluidity temperature for each sample is recorded as the lowest temperature at which the sample will flow a given distance in a period of 1 min under an applied suction.

A3.10 Laboratory Combustion Tests

A group of tests exists for the investigation of the carbon properties of fuels used for illumination, heating, and work transfer in gas turbines. Illuminating kerosines refined for lighthouse and railway wick-lamps are tested in the actual units in which they are to be used, whereas kerosines for other types of lamp are given a 24-hour burning test in a standard design of flat-wick lamp adjusted to a standard flame size and shape. The mass of fuel consumed is measured, together with the mass of char produced on the wick end, the 'char value' being reported in units of mg per kg fuel. The 'bloom' effect on the lamp glass caused by the products of sulphur and other contaminants is eliminated by using a glass which has been 'aged' by previous use and acid treatment.

In testing fuels for pressure-vaporising appliances, the actual appliance is used for the test and, in general, sensitivity to fuel quality is restricted to the presence of corrosive sulphur contaminants. Kerosines for gas turbines are tested in the smoke point apparatus, based on the conventional design of circular wick illuminating lamp. The wick is adjusted vertically to find the maximum height for a non-smoking flame, measured against a polished scale located within the lamp. The lamp is designed to permit a certain rate of air flow into the combustion zone and, when the fuel concentration becomes excessive, cracking occurs with resultant carbon release in the form of smoke. An inclined mirror provides a plan view of the flame, with the tell-tale central dot in the presence of smoke.

A3.11 Anti-knock Rating

Spark knock occurs in the spark-ignition piston engine when the severity of the operating conditions is sufficient to permit the end-gas mixture to ignite spontaneously before being consumed by the advancing spark-ignited flame. One of the most effective controlling parameters of knock severity is compression ratio, and the CFR single-cylinder test engine is designed so that the cylinder body and head unit can be moved axially in order to change the compression ratio over the range 3/1 to 30/1 while the engine is running. Increase in compression ratio leads to the onset of spark knock, a standard intensity of which is adopted for test purposes. For motor gasolines, two methods of test apply, the Research method at 600 rev/min and a mild mixture temperature of about 32 °C, together with the Motor method at 900 rev/min and a comparatively severe mixture temperature of 150 °C. For a given fuel, the difference in the ratings by these two methods, known as the research appreciation, gives a measure of the temperature sensitivity of the fuel. In both tests, knock intensity is measured by an electronic knock meter based on the magnetostriction properties of the metal core of a solenoid detector fitted in the cylinder head, sensitive to the vibrations induced by knock.

To avoid variation in results with atmospheric conditions, rating is assessed against a fuel scale based on levels of zero for a poor anti-knock reference fuel, n-heptane, and 100 for a superior reference fuel, iso-octane (2,2,4-trimethylpentane). The octane number of a sample is defined as the volumetric per cent content of iso-octane in the reference fuel blend that just matches the knock behaviour of the sample under the specified conditions of test. For aviation gasolines, the weak-mixture method at 1200 rev/min uses the variable compression ratio technique, together with a thermal plug knockmeter sensitive to the high temperatures induced by knock, and is roughly equivalent to the flight cruise condition. The rich-mixture method at 1800 rev/min, on the other hand, uses variable boost pressure with a constant compression ratio of 7/1, relying on aural detection of trace knock, and simulates the take-off condition.

Over the years, the anti-knock quality of aviation gasolines improved, eventually equalling and then exceeding that of iso-octane itself, and a revised system of rating was derived, in terms of the performance number, based on the indicated mean effective pressure obtained with the sample, expressed as a percentage of the peak value for iso-octane, hence one standardised Avgas was given the grade-rating of 100/130, being 100 octane (or performance) number at weak-mixture (cruising) conditions, and 130 performance number at rich-mixture (take-off) conditions.

In contrast to spark knock in the spark-ignition engine, diesel knock occurs in the compression-ignition engine when the operating conditions are too mild, as in cold starting, and the spontaneous ignition required by the injected fuel charge is sluggish, accompanied by an excessive time delay. Since the fuel metering system continues to inject fuel throughout the delay period, the relatively large quantity of fuel present in the chamber when ignition eventually does occur leads to momentary uncontrolled explosive burning, with attendant rough running, vibration and smoke before the flame settles down to the control of the subsequent injection rate. In the CFR single-cylinder test engine, variable compression ratio from 7.5/1 to 40/1 is achieved by means of a pre-combustion chamber of adjustable length. An ignition delay equivalent to $13°$ crank angle is adopted as standard, and a fuel scale used, as before, using cetane (n-hexadecane, $C_{16}H_{34}$) and isocetane (2,2,4,4,6,8,8-heptamethylnonane, also $C_{16}H_{34}$) as reference fuels with ratings of 100 and 15 respectively. Slightly less accurate methods are also available for use in engines other than the CFR model, using either variable delay or throttling to misfire, since this obviates the need for special delay-indicating instrumentation. A rough guide to compression-ignition quality is also given by the diesel index, defined as

$$\text{diesel index} = 0.01 \text{ (aniline point, }^\circ\text{F) (API gravity)}$$

and by empirical expressions for the calculated cetane index, based on the 50 per cent distillation temperature and the API gravity.[10]

In view of the inverse spontaneous-ignition relationship between spark knock and diesel knock, a similar relationship is found between octane and cetane ratings for a given set of fuels. Hence, fuels suitable for use in high-performance spark-ignition engines behave poorly in compression-ignition engines, and vice versa. This poses a major problem in the development of multi-fuel engines, and these are frequently based on both spark-ignition and fuel injection designed to achieve a stratified charge.

These two groups of methods of rating the anti-knock qualities of conventional fuels apply generally also to alternative fuels, although in some instances (for example, the alcohols), operation is possible at mixtures which are so fuel-weak that the performance differs significantly from that under standard CFR test conditions, making the values of anti-knock rating some-what academic.

A3.12 Components, Contaminants and Additives

The components of a mixture of gaseous fuels may be identified and measured either by chemical or physical means. The former include the selective absorption in liquid reagents, using apparatus of the Orsat, Haldane, Gooderham or Bone and Wheeler types. Use may also be made of solid reagents, such as soda asbestos for carbon dioxide, and magnesium perchlorate for water, contained in U-tubes that are weighed before and after absorption, combined with small furnaces to oxidise different combustible components in turn. In the chromatographic method, a mixture sample is introduced into a carrier fluid, and the components separated physically owing to different rates of adsorption and desorption with a stationary (solid or liquid) bed material. As each component leaves the bed in turn, the relative proportions are determined by some detecting instrument such as a katharometer or a flame ionisation detector. The former depends on the change in thermal conductivity of the carrier fluid owing to the presence of the desorbed component, whereas the latter senses the substantial increase in ion concentration in a hydrogen—oxygen flame due to the presence of carbon compounds. The components can then be identified by comparing them with known samples.

Many other techniques are available for the determination of fuel components, based on the accurate assessment of such properties as infrared absorptivity, paramagnetism, sonic velocity, chemiluminescence and relative density.

Standard tests are available for determination of the components of liquid fuel blends. The paraffinic content of a hydrocarbon blend, for example, is assessed directly from the aniline point, which is the lowest temperature at which the sample is completely miscible with an equal volume of aniline. The fluids are stirred mechanically, and the temperature found at which they either become miscible, and thus transparent, on warming to ambient, or separate and become opaque on cooling to ambient. Aniline, being an aromatic compound, is miscible in aromatic but not paraffinic hydrocarbons, hence a high aniline point indicates a high paraffinic concentration.

The bromine number is the number of grams of bromine that react with 100 g of the sample, which is dissolved in a specified solvent and treated with standard bromide–bromate solution. Olefins are susceptible to addition reactions at the double bond, and the quantity of bromine reacted gives a direct indication of the olefin content. The combined olefin plus aromatic content of the lighter hydrocarbon fuels is determined by reactions of a mixture of the sample and phosphorus pentoxide in concentrated sulphuric acid. The mixture is shaken and centrifuged, and the volume of acid-absorbed material taken as the olefin plus aromatic content.

Concentrations of all three main hydrocarbon types may be assessed together by means of a chromatographic type adsorption method. A small (0.75 ml) sample is introduced into an adsorption column packed with activated silica gel containing a layer of fluorescent dyes. Desorption is achieved by the addition of alcohol, and the hydrocarbon types separate out with the dyes, so that the interface boundaries of the saturates, olefins and aromatics are identified by yellow, blue and reddish-brown fluorescence of the dyes under ultraviolet light. The relative lengths of the zones correspond to the volumetric concentrations of the three hydrocarbon types.

The carbon content of a liquid fuel can be determined in terms of the char value, described in section A3.10, whereas the carbonaceous deposits likely to arise from the heavy fuels can be assessed by the carbon residue test in which a weighed fuel sample is heated in a glass bulb with a capillary opening in order to drive off the volatile matter, and then to crack and coke the residue. The carbon residue is expressed in terms of the mass of residue as a percentage of the original sample. The concentration of hydrogen can be determined by low resolution nuclear magnetic resonance techniques in which the sample is subjected to a magnetic field together with a matched frequency of radiation, and measurement made of the net energy absorbed by the hydrogen nuclei in transferring between lower and higher levels of spin energy.

The analytical methods for coals and related solid fuels fall into two groups. The proximate analysis concerns the main compound components, and comprises drying to measure the water content, and high-temperature heating to determine the volatile matter, both tests being conducted in an oxygen-free atmosphere. The mass of fixed carbon is found by difference, allowing for ash. The ultimate analysis, on the other hand, concerns the elemental concentrations, and includes burning in a stream of oxygen to determine the content of carbon and hydrogen from the absorption of their oxide masses. The oxygen content is found by difference, allowing for the nitrogen and sulphur.

Untreated gaseous fuels invariably contain some contaminants which may be incombustible (for example, CO_2 and N_2), combustible but corrosive (for example, SO_2) or unacceptably malodorous (for example, H_2S). The contaminants of liquid petroleum fuels include high-boiling asphaltene hydrocarbons, resinous organic gums, weak organic and strong inorganic acids, finely divided solids promoting sediment, unsaturated sludge, inorganic ash, water, sodium, vanadium, sulphur in various forms, and sometimes fuel-bound nitrogen depending on the nature of the parent crude, the type of product, and its production history. Other inorganic contaminants likely to be present in trace quantities are chlorine, oxygen, potassium, calcium, nickel, arsenic and lead. Many of these contaminants, particularly ash, nitrogen and sulphur, are found in solid fuels also. The contaminant concentrations can be determined using a range of laboratory methods including filtration, solvent removal, evaporation to dryness, titration with alkali, burning, absorption and X-ray analysis.

Whereas commercial fuels are produced in blends of a number of selected components, each in a concentration of several per cent, additives are far more potent, being incorporated purposefully in trace concentrations only, up to about 0.2 per cent by volume, in order to improve, modify or suppress some property of a fuel or its components. If not naturally fuel-soluble, solubility is achieved by compounding the additive atoms to give molecules with external hydrocarbon radicals, as for example with lead in TEL, $Pb(C_2H_5)_4$. Additives assist in improving the handling characterisation of liquid fuels by tackling low-temperature oxidation (anti-oxidants and metal deactivators), icing (icing inhibitors and surface-active agents), corrosion (corrosion inhibitors), wax formation (pour point depressants), sludge formation (stabilising agents and dispersants), carburettor deposits (detergents), microbial growth (biostats and biocides), static charging (anti-static additives), spillages and bulk odours (essential oils) and sea-water emulsion formation (demulsifying agents). Additives also assist in dealing with such combustion problems as spark knock (anti-knock additives and scavengers), surface ignition (deposit-modifying additives), diesel knock (cetane improvers) and high-temperature fouling and corrosion (anti-slagging and corrosion inhibiting additives), together with smoke, exhaust odour and slow burning. Laboratory methods exist for checking the concentrations of additives in finished fuels, based on chemical analysis, X-ray spectrophotometry, atomic absorption and other physical techniques.

222

References

1. E. M. Goodger, *Hydrocarbon Fuels*, Macmillan, London and Basingstoke (1975).
2. BS 526:1961 Definitions of the calorific value of fuels.
3. IP 12/73, *Heat of Combustion of Liquid Hydrocarbon Fuels*, Institute of Petroleum, London.
4. I. G. C. Dryden (ed), *The Efficient Use of Energy*, IPC Science & Technology Press, Guildford (1975)
5. IP 193/73, *Estimation of Net Heat of Combustion of Aviation Fuels*, Institute of Petroleum, London.
6. BS 2869:1970 Specification for petroleum fuels for oil engines and burners.
7. *Highly Flammable Liquids and Liquefied Petroleum Gases. Guide to the Regulations, 1972*, Department of Employment, HMSO (1973).
8. *Technical Leaflet on Setavis*, Stanhope-Seta Ltd, Park Close, Englefield Green, Egham, Surrey TW20 OXD.
9. K Campbell and J. Steen, The automatic determination of pour point, *J. Inst. Petrol.*, **56** (1970) 243–53.
10. IP 219/67, *Calculated Cetane Index of Diesel Fuel*, Institute of Petroleum, London.

Appendix 4 Tabulated Properties of Fuels

The comparative property data given in the following seven tables augment the information presented in table 5.1 and figures 5.1, 5.2 and 6.1 to 6.12, and are derived from the same references. For convenience of access, the tables are presented in this last appendix rather than in the body of the text.

Table A4.1 *Hydrocarbon gaseous fuels*

Property		Methane	Propane	Butane	North Sea gas	Commercial propane	Commercial butane	Acetylene
Formula		CH_4	C_3H_8	C_4H_{10}				C_2H_2
H/C atomic ratio		4	2.67	2.5	3.87	2.64	2.49	1
Molar mass	g/mol	16.043	44.097	58.124	17.24			26.038
Density (l) 15 °C	kg/l	0.424*	0.582	0.602	0.44*	0.52	0.58	0.61
Rel d(g) 15 °C		0.554	1.522	2.006	0.60	1.52	2.01	0.899
Vap/liq vol 15 °C		624	273	236	600	280	236	554
bp	°C	−161.5	−42.1	−0.5		−41	−3	−75
mp	°C	−182.5	−187.7	−138.4		−186	−140	−82
t_{crit}	°C	−82.6	96.7	152.0		95	150	35.4
p_{crit}	MPa	4.62	4.25	3.8				6.14
ΔH_{vap}	kJ/kg	510	426	385		358	372	818
$c_p(1)$*	kJ/kg K	3.87	2.48	2.36		2.4	2.3	
$c_p(g)$ 25 °C	kJ/kg K	2.23	1.67	1.68		1.6	1.7	1.69
$Q_{gr}(g)$	MJ/m^3	37.67	93.91	121.77	39.0	92.6	121.5	54.98
$Q_{net}(g)$	MJ/m^3	33.95	86.47	112.46	35.3	85.7	112.2	53.13
$Wo_{net}(g)$	MJ/m^3	45.62	70.09	79.40	45.6	69.5	79.1	56.03
$Q_{gr}(g)$	MJ/kg	55.54	50.38	49.56	53.1	49.8	49.4	49.94
$Q_{net}(g)$	MJ/kg	50.05	46.39	45.77	48.0	46.1	45.6	48.26
$Q_{net}(l)$	MJ/l	21.22	27.00	27.55	21.1	24.0	26.4	29.44
Net MJ/m^3 stoic mix		3.23	3.49	3.52	3.27	3.57	3.62	4.12
Net MJ/kg stoic mix		2.75	2.79	2.79	2.76	2.86	2.87	3.41

225

* At boiling point

Table A4.2 *Manufactured gaseous fuels*

Property	COG	BWG	CWG	CPG	BFG	Carbon monoxide
Rel d (g) @ 15 °C	0.38	0.55	0.63	0.89	1.03	0.967
H/C atomic ratio	4.71	2.04	2.19	0.7	0.11	0
Composition % vol						
$\quad C_xH_y$	30.6	0.8	21.0	0.5	–	–
$\quad CO$	7.4	41.0	30.5	29.0	25.5	100
$\quad H_2$	54.0	49.0	37.0	11.0	2.2	–
$\quad CO_2$	2.0	4.7	5.6	5.0	14.3	–
$\quad N_2$	5.6	4.5	5.5	54.5	58.0	–
$\quad O_2$	0.4		0.4			–
c_p(g) @ 15 °C						
$\quad$ kJ/m^3 K	1.32	1.25	1.34	1.25	1.29	1.04
$(A/F)_s$ molar	4.57	2.22	4.27	1.00	0.63	2.38
$(a/f)_s$ mass	12.03	4.04	6.78	1.12	0.61	2.46
Q_{gr}(g) MJ/m^3	19.89	11.14	18.95	4.95	3.18 ⎫	11.97
Q_{net}(g) MJ/m^3	17.70	10.19	17.31	4.77	3.13 ⎭	
Wo_{net}(g) MJ/m^3	28.72	13.74	21.81	5.06	3.08	12.17
Q_{gr} MJ/kg	42.32	16.63	24.61	4.50	2.50 ⎫	10.10
Q_{net} MJ/kg	37.66	15.21	22.48	4.34	2.46 ⎭	
Net MJ/m^3 st. mix.	3.19	3.17	3.29	2.39	1.92	2.73
Net MJ/kg st. mix.	2.89	3.02	2.89	2.05	1.53	2.92
$T_{p\ ad}$ K	2220	2080			1768	2399

Table A4.3 *Hydrocarbon liquid fuels*

Property	Gasolines		Kerosine	Gas oil	Diesel fuel	RFO class F	RFO class G	CTF		Shelldyne $C_{12}H_{14}$	60/40 mass B/Avtur
	Avgas	Mogas						50	400		
H/C atomic	2.11	2.03	1.96	1.83	1.63	1.57	1.55	0.82	0.65	1.142	1.96
Rel d 20/4 °C	0.72	0.74	0.8	0.84	0.93	0.95	0.97	1.00	1.25	1.092	1.32
bp °C	50–150	30–200	150–300	185–360	200+	–	–	–	–	258	–
Pour pt °C	– 60	– 60	– 50	0 summer – .7 winter	3	18				– 24	–
Flash pt °C	– 45	– 45	50	70	85	93	116	82	120	59	
SIT °C	470	312	255	245	240	235	230				
ΔH_{vap} kJ/kg 37.8 °C	310	310	300	285	270	260	250				
$c_p(l)$ kJ/kg K mid bp	2.3	2.3	2.1	2.0	1.9	1.9	1.8				
$Q_{gr}(l)$ MJ/kg	46.00	45.80	46.30	45.30	43.10	42.40	42.10	39.50	37.30	43.51	53.20
$Q_{net}(l)$ MJ/kg	44.00	43.80	43.30	42.50	40.60	39.90	39.70	37.87	35.90	41.60	52.00
$Q_{net}(l)$ MJ/l	31.68	32.41	34.64	35.70	37.80	37.90	38.50	37.87	44.88	45.60	68.64
Net MJ/kg stoic mix	2.72	2.71	2.76	2.74	2.73	2.71	2.70	2.91	2.65	2.86	4.12
$(a/f)_s$ mass	15.15	15.15	14.71	14.49	13.89	13.70	13.70	12.05	12.50	13.53	11.61

Table A4.4   Solid fuels

Property	Wood	Peat	Lignite (Brown coal)	High-volume coal	Medium-volume coal	Low-volume coal	Anthracite	Coke	C(gr)	B(c)
H/C atomic ratio	1.43	1.14	0.85	0.74	0.73	0.56	0.4	0.06	0	0
Rel d range	0.55–1.1	0.5–1.1	1.25–1.3	1.26–1.4	1.27–1.45	1.3–1.5	1.4–1.7	1.75–2	2.17	2.34
Rel d mean	0.75	0.88	1.28	1.33	1.36	1.4	1.55	1.88	2.17	2.34
% mass dmmf										
C	50	57.5	70	85	89.9	91.8	93	96.5	100	0
H	6	5.5	5	5.3	5	4.4	3.5	0.5	0	0
N + S	1	2	2	2.6	2.2	2.1	1.9	2	0	0
VM	85	68	53	35	27	16	7	1	0	0
O_2	43	32	21	16	8	5	4		0	0
Ash	0.6	5	5	5	5	4	3	7	0	0
Q_{gr} MJ/kg	19.2	21.5	26.8	34.9	36.6	36.7	36.0	33.7	32.8	57.8
Q_{net} MJ/kg	18.0	20.2	25.7	33.9	35.6	35.7	35.0	33.6	32.8	57.8
Q_{net} MJ/l	13.5	24.2	32.9	45.1	48.4	50.0	54.3	63.2	71.2	135.3
MJ/kg stoic mix	2.95	3.17	3.96	3.33	3.21	3.19	3.18	3.17	2.63	5.47
$(a/f)_s$ mass	5.10	5.38	5.49	9.17	10.10	10.20	10.00	9.62	11.48	9.56

Table A4.5 *Alternative fuels*

Property		Hydrogen	Methanol	Ethanol	1-Propanol	1-Butanol	Nitromethane	Ammonia	Hydrazine	UDMH	Diborane	Pentaborane	Triethyl-borane
Formula		H_2	CH_3OH	C_2H_5OH	C_3H_7OH	C_4H_9OH	CH_3NO_2	NH_3	N_2H_4	$(CH_3)_2N_2H_2$	B_2H_6	B_5H_9	$(C_2H_5)_3B$
H/C atomic ratio		–	4	3	2.67	2.5	3	–	–	4	–	–	2.5
Molar mass	g/mol	2.016	32.042	46.068	60.094	74.124	61.041	17.031	32.046	60.102	27.668	63.122	97.996
Rel d(l) 20/4 °C		0.071*	0.7915	0.7894	0.8036	0.8097	1.14	0.61	1.01	0.79	0.43	0.63	0.68
Rel d(g) 15 °C		0.070	1.106	1.591	2.075	2.560	2.108	0.588	1.107	2.075	0.955	2.180	3.384
bp	°C	–253	64.8	78.4	97.3	117.7	101	–33.4	113.5	63.1	–92.5	58.4	95
mp	°C	–259	–95.5	–117.3	–126.5	–89.0	–17	–77.7	2	–57.2	–165.5	–46.6	–134
t_{crit}	°C	–239.9	239.4	243.1	263.6	289.8	315	132.4	380	250	16.7	224	
p_{crit}	MPa	1.297	7.971	6.396	5.168	4.418	6.309	11.301	14.720	5.421	4.006		
ΔH_{vap}	kJ/kg	448	1089	858	670	607	563	1370	1397	583	517	580	370
c_p(l)	kJ/kg K	8.68	2.30	2.40	2.47	2.59	1.77	4.60	3.08	2.73	9	2.37	
c_p(g)	25 °C	14.31	1.36	1.42	1.44	1.46	1.17				2.04	1.26	2.42
Q_{net}(g)	MJ/m³	10.29						13.40			85.44		
Q_{gr}(l)	MJ/kg	141.9	22.68	29.77	33.66	36.07	12.02	22.48	19.43	32.99	77.78	70.88	50.40
Q_{net}(l)	MJ/kg	120.0	19.93	26.75	30.70	33.10	10.94	18.61	16.68	30.07	73.03	67.75	47.05
Q_{net}(l)	MJ/l	8.5	15.77	21.12	24.67	26.84	12.47	10.52	16.85	23.76	31.40	42.68	31.99
	MJ/kg stoic mix	3.38	2.67	2.69	2.71	2.73	4.06	2.63	3.15	2.95	4.58	4.81	2.98

* At boiling point

229

The levels of octane quality reported in the literature vary over the ranges shown, no doubt due to differences in purity of the samples tested.

Table A4.6   Octane quality

Fuel	Research octane No.	Motor octane No.
Representative natural gas	131	128
Methanol	104 to 112	87.4 to 98
Ethanol	106 to 110	89 to 99
Ammonia	111 to 130+	—
Hydrazine	110	—

For the alternative fuels generally, these values are somewhat academic due to the possibility of operating at mixture strengths far weaker than those used in the octane rating, and normal operation, of conventional fuels.

Table A4.7 Oxidants

Property	Air	Oxygen	Hydrogen peroxide	Nitric acid	Nitrogen tetroxide	Fluorine	Chlorine trifluoride	Oxygen difluoride
Formula	–	O_2	H_2O_2	HNO_3	N_2O_4	F_2	ClF_3	OF_2
Oxidant % mass	23.2	100	94.1	76	69.6	100	61.7	100
% vol	21.0	100	50	60	67.7	100	75	100
Molar mass g/mol	28.96	31.999	34.016	63.013	92.016	37.997	92.448	53.996
Density(g) kg/m^3	1.225	1.353	1.439	2.665	3.892	1.607	3.911	1.864
Rel d(g) 15 °C	1	1.105	1.175	2.175	3.177	1.312	3.193	1.522
Density(l) kg/m^3 15 °C	–	1.14*	1.45	1.56	1.45	1.66*	1.85*	1.53*
bp °C	–	– 182	150	86	21.2	– 188	11.8	– 146
mp °C	–	– 219	– 0.3	– 42	–11.6	– 220	– 83	– 223
ΔH_{vap} kJ/kg	–	213.53	1448.6	481.48	414.03	171.66		205.15

* At boiling point

231

Index

237